Technical Papers in Hyd

A contribution to the
International Hydrological
Programme

Study of the relationship between water quality and sediment transport

A guide for the collection
and interpretation of
sediment quality data

Prepared by:
H. L. Golterman
P. G. Sly
R. L. Thomas

Unesco

The designations employed and the presentation of the material
do not imply the expression of any opinion whatsoever on the
part of Unesco concerning the legal status of any country or
territory, or of its authorities, or concerning the frontiers of
any country or territory.

Published in 1983 by the
United Nations Educational, Scientific and Cultural
Organization
7, place de Fontenoy, 75700 Paris
Printed by Imprimerie de la Manutention, Mayenne

ISBN 92-3-102109-5

Preface

Although the total amount of water on earth is generally assumed to have remained virtually constant, the rapid growth of population, together with the extension of irrigated agriculture and industrial development, are stressing the quantity and quality aspects of the natural system. Because of the increasing problems, man has begun to realize that he can no longer follow a "use and discard" philosophy—either with water resources or any other natural resource. As a result, the need for a consistent policy of rational management of water resources has become evident.

Rational water management, however, should be founded upon a thorough understanding of water availability and movement. Thus, as a contribution to the solution of the world's water problems, Unesco, in 1965, began the first world-wide programme of studies of the hydrological cycle—the International Hydrological Decade (IHD). The research programme was complemented by a major effort in the field of hydrological education and training. The activities undertaken during the Decade proved to be of great interest and value to Member States. By the end of that period, a majority of Unesco's Member States had formed IHD National Committees to carry out relevant national activities and to participate in regional and international co-operation within the IHD programme. The knowledge of the world's water resources had substantially improved. Hydrology became widely recognized as an independent professional option and facilities for the training of hydrologists had been developed.

Conscious of the need to expand upon the efforts initiated during the International Hydrological Decade and, following the recommendations of Member States, Unesco, in 1975, launched a new long-term intergovernmental programme, the International Hydrological Programme (IHP), to follow the Decade.

Although the IHP is basically a scientific and educational programme, Unesco has been aware from the beginning of a need to direct its activities toward the practical solutions of the world's very real water resources problems. Accordingly, and in line with the recommendations of the 1977 United Nations Water Conference, the objectives of the International Hydrological Programme have been gradually expanded in order to cover not only hydrological processes considered in interrelationship with the environment and human activities, but also the scientific aspects of multi-purpose utilization and conservation of water resources to meet the needs of economic and social development. Thus, while maintaining IHP's scientific concept, the objectives have shifted perceptibly towards a multidisciplinary approach to the assessment, planning, and rational management of water resources.

As part of Unesco's contribution to the objectives of the IHP, two publication series are issued: "Studies and Reports in Hydrology" and "Technical Papers in Hydrology". In addition to these publications, and in order to expedite exchange of information in the areas in which it is most needed, works of a preliminary nature are issued in the form of Technical Documents.

The "Technical Papers in hydrology" series, to which this volume belongs, is intended to provide a means for the exchange of information on hydrological techniques and for the coordination of research and data collection. Unesco uses this series as a means of bringing together and making known the experience accumulated by hydrologists throughout the world.

Acknowledgements

The authors wish to express their appreciation to all of the participants of the September Workshop which followed the 1976 Sediment/Freshwater Symposium in Amsterdam, who contributed to much of the beginnings of this work.

In particular, we wish to acknowledge the efforts of Mr. H.F. Nicholson for all proof corrections and organization for the camera ready copy.

The authors have drawn heavily on both the published and unpublished works of a number of scientists and colleagues, particularly in the preparation of Chapters VI-X, and wish to extend special thanks in acknowledgement of the works and contributions by P. Cranwell, V. Damiani, U. Förstner, R. Frank, C.G. Gunnerson, M. Holdrinet, I. Jonnasson, R.A. Jones, S. Krishnaswami, D. Lal, G.F. Lee, N.C. Morgan and A.B. Viner.

The authors have received valuable technical support from a number of staff during the final preparation of this publication, and are particularly indebted to W.M. Finn, B. Marshall, J. Leatherdale and M. Stevens for their invaluable assistance.

The authors gratefully acknowledge the continued financial assistance of both the Canadian Federal Government and Unesco, without whose continuing support it would not have been possible to complete this guidebook.

Contents

List of tables

List of figures

Foreword

This publication may be considered as a companion volume to the UNESCO-WHO Report 'Water Quality Surveys' (Studies and Reports in Hydrology, No. 23) which was published in 1978.

The Water Quality Surveys Report was prepared by the International Hydrological Decade (IHD) Working Group on the Quality of Water, in coordination with the World Health Organization (WHO), following a 1968 proposal to develop a guidebook on Water Quality Surveys and its approval by the Coordinating Council of the IHD in 1969. The Working Group was established in 1970 and the text was completed in 1976.

Although the guidebook was not published until 1978, its outline, structure, and philosophy were known to the Intergovernmental Council of the International Hydrological Program (IHP) when it launched the IHP projects on, or related to, water quality. The IHP project 3.8.5, on the relationship between water quality and sediment transport, was in effect at this time and a rapporteur was appointed to compile a technical report on the subject.

In September 1976, a symposium on sediment-freshwater interactions was held in Amsterdam, under the joint sponsorship of the Societas Internationalis Limnologiae (SIL) and UNESCO. Immediately following this successful symposium, a workshop was held to prepare an outline of a manuscript on sediments as indicators of water quality. This proposal was accepted in 1977 and the Intergovernmental Council of the IHP appointed Dr. H.L. Golterman (Netherlands) as rapporteur for this project.

Subsequently, sections were prepared by individual contributors and largely recompiled at joint meetings of the authors in October 1979 and April 1980. Further changes and revisions were made in 1980 and a final draft was prepared and submitted to UNESCO in 1981.

Mr. W.H. Gilbrich from the IHP Secretariat assisted in the compilation of the publication.

This publication has been prepared in the form of a guidebook; it explains how sediments may influence water quality or, in turn, how the composition of sediments may be influenced by water quality. It shows how to evaluate the importance of sediments in aquatic systems (such as rivers, lakes, and estuaries) and it explains how sediment analyses may be used together with, or as an alternative to, water quality data as indicators of environmental conditions. It also explains the special value of sediment data in providing both a historical record and a register of transient events, as well as a means of providing a source of naturally-integrated environmental data. Sediments may also provide a means of concentrating certain contaminants, thereby allowing the use of less sensitive measuring techniques than might otherwise be necessary for the characterization of water quality at low concentrations.

This guidebook has been prepared to assist in the design, sampling, analysis, and interpretation of sediment studies in rivers, streams, lakes, ponds, and estuaries, particularly where such studies are being initiated for the first time or where the work is being undertaken by water quality staff not previously experienced in sediment studies.

The authors have tried to provide a simple text, to use only essential text references, and to provide a useful and additional bibliography of general publications which are most widely available.

The style of this publication is similar to that of the UNESCO-WHO publication, 'Water Quality Surveys', and cross-referencing has been used to aid the reader in understanding how sediment studies may be related to water quality monitoring, surveillance, and surveys.

The publication has been designed as a guidebook to sediment sampling. It leads the reader through a series of steps which begin with a description of the nature and properties of sediments; this is then followed by an explanation of how to plan a sediment sampling program, and what equipment to use. Later chapters discuss analytical methods and data processing. The chapter on the interpretation of results, provides a particularly important insight into the value of sediment sampling, and the limitations and uncertainties which must be placed upon the use of such data.

Both case histories and actual data have been used where possible, to substantiate discussion points and to illustrate important examples.

The guidebook is intended for use in the study of aquatic environments on a worldwide basis, and references are made to technologies which are most widely available.

Requests for advice and information concerning problems dealt with in this book may be sent to H.L. Golterman.

H.L. Golterman,
Station Biologique de la tour du valat,
Le Sambuc 13200,
Arles,
FRANCE.

P.G. Sly,
Department of the Environment,
National Water Research Institute,
Canada Centre for Inland Waters,
867 Lakeshore Road, P.O. Box 5050,
Burlington, Ontario,
CANADA. L7R 4A6

R.L. Thomas,
Department of Fisheries and Oceans,
Great Lakes Fisheries Research Branch
Canada Centre for Inland Waters,
867 Lakeshore Road, P.O. Box 5050,
Burlington, Ontario,
CANADA. L7R 4A6.

I Overview

I.1   Introduction

The importance of water quality in regard to both human health and the production of food supplies has become widely recognized in recent years; and, to some extent, the importance of water quality in the maintenance of healthy and desirable aquatic populations has also gained appreciation. However, the influence of sediments on water quality, the influence of water quality on sediments, and the use of sediments as environmental indicators, are not widely understood; as yet, only limited use of sediment data has been made in most environmental and water quality studies.

The aquatic environment should not be managed for its waters alone. Management practices should incorporate a clear appreciation of the roles and necessity of biological components (not addressed in this publication), and of the geological and surface soil components in the surrounding watershed and of suspended and bed materials in the water-bodies themselves.

This publication is intended to emphasize the value of sediment-related information in studies of the aquatic environment, to help in making decisions about when and where it will be useful to collect sediment data, and how to use the information. Sediment characteristics may vary slightly under different climatic conditions but may be used on a worldwide basis, either together with water quality information, or alone. Although attention is mostly directed to the use of sediment data in the study of river and lake systems, similar concepts may be used to study the role of sediments in other aqueous systems such as estuaries, wetlands, and marshes.

At the present time, standard analytical techniques are available to meet most sampling and analytical requirements for water quality studies, but the same is not true for sediment studies. Sediment sampling and analysis require the use of different techniques and equipment. The areal distribution of the samples is not the same and they are generally taken less frequently in time than for water samples. Sediment analyses are often based upon modified procedures of water quality analyses, or upon methods developed either in soil science or for purposes of mineral exploration. Some methodologies are unique to sediment studies. Difficulties in comparing data sets, caused by the use of different sampling and analytical procedures, may well arise and the use of standards and the comparison of test procedures is, therefore, of particular importance to sediment analyses.

Since it is the intention of this publication to present the role and techniques of sediment studies in a relatively simple form, no attempt has been made to present an exhaustive review of analytical procedures. Instead, the text provides a collation of the more useful and generally applicable tests which can be undertaken without the need for very advanced laboratory support. More specific and complex procedures may be found in the bibliography of supplementary references at the end of each chapter. As a further aid to understanding the relationships between water and sediment sampling and analytical techniques, the reader is referred to the UNESCO-WHO publication, Studies and Reports in Hydrology, No. 23, 'Water Quality Surveys'.

Because the significance of sediments in aqueous environmental studies is not widely understood, this contribution begins with a description of the nature and properties of sediments and their role in aquatic systems; this is further discussed in relation to the presence of contaminants.

TABLE I.1   The significance of sediment in aquatic systems and major concerns (shaded area) related to water quality

		MINERALS & ROCK FRAGS.	CLAY MINERALS	PRECIPITATES & COATINGS	ORGANICS
NON-WATER QUALITY CONCERNS	Food source for scavenging biota				x
	Substrate for micro biota (in suspension)	x	x		x
	Substrate for macro fauna (bottom habitat)	x			x
	Episodic burial of substrate	x	x	?	x
	Long-term erosion and sediment starvation	x	x		
	Rapid accumulation due to sediment excess	x	x		x
	Episodic channel instability	x	x		
	Abrasion	x			
WATER QUALITY CONCERNS OF GENERALLY INCREASING PRIORITY	Potential carcinogenic effects	x	?	?	x
	Adverse influence on respiration (aquatic fauna)	x	?		
	Restricted light penetration	x	x	?	x
	Clogging of water intakes	x		?	x
	Energy source for micro biota				x
	COD BOD O_2 depletion in overlying waters			x	x
	Conversion, methylation, degradation products	?	x	x	x
	Release of toxic substances and/or nutrients	?	x	x	x
	Scavenging of toxic substances and/or nutrients		x	x	?
	Transportation of toxic substances and/or nutrients		x	x	x
	Sink/Fixation of toxic substances and/or nutrients	?	x	x	x

Most waters contain substances such as nutrient elements, heavy metals, and metal compounds which, when present in excessive amounts, are regarded as potential contaminants. Persistant organics and biocides, and other miscellaneous materials are also considered to be contaminants. These potential contaminants may endanger the health of both human and aquatic organisms. They are often present in a dissolved state and large quantities may also be bound on to the bottom sediments or on to suspended matter by which they can be physically transported. In addition, the association with sediment provides a microbiological substrate which, in turn, may encourage a more rapid and complete transformation of certain contaminants.

Aquatic ecosystems are sustained by the availability of the dissolved forms of a number of nutrient elements, the most important of which include carbon, nitrogen, phosphorus, and silicon. The presence of suspended material is an important component in the cycling of these nutrients.

The availability of nutrients for metabolic processes and the extent of toxicity of poisonous substances are closely related to their chemical species in both solution and particulate form. The source of materials may significantly affect their distribution between solid and liquid phases. A substantial amount of both nutrient and toxic materials may be present as soluble species, and it is largely the influence of sediments upon the increase or decrease of such soluble forms which makes particulate matter so important in aqueous systems. C, N, P, and Si are present in sediments in several forms.

Particulate carbon is present as organic matter and as mineral carbonate.

Particulate nitrogen is also present in organic matter, and may be associated with clay minerals where ammonium-N is incorporated within the lattice structure or is adsorbed.

Phosphorus is present in organic material, in flocculates and coatings (as a result of sorption reactions with iron and aluminium), and in mineral form.

Silicon is present in diatomaceous organic debris (typically, as silicate, in skeletal form) and in mineral form (most frequently as quartz grains in sand, and with clay minerals in fine silt or clay-sized materials).

Toxic substances are present in a variety of natural and man-made (cultural) forms.

Toxic trace metals, for example, may occur as particulates in the form of precipitates, mineral and rock fragments, and other inorganic material.

Biocides (including pesticides, insecticides, fungicides, and herbicides) are usually found in association with clay minerals and organic matter.

Oils and greases typically occur in the form of particulate coatings.

The presence of certain fibrous minerals of the asbestos group, in high number counts and of very fine particle-size (clay-size and less), may be carcinogenic and pose a human health problem if present in potable water supplies.

A summary of some of the reasons which establish the importance of sediments in aqueous systems is provided in Table I.1. This table also emphasizes the principal concerns in relation to water quality.

I.3   Sampling Objectives and Program

Water-related studies have been described as MONITORING, SURVEILLANCE, and SURVEY activities in the UNESCO-WHO publication on Water Quality Surveys (see Table I.2). The definitions of monitoring and surveillance as used in this report are as follows:

MONITORING   - Continuous standard measurements or observations which are NOT specifically related to regulation or enforcement.

SURVEILLANCE - Specific observations and measurements (which may or may not be continuous) which directly relate to enforcement of regulations and controls.

In the planning of any sampling program the objectives must be considered first. The approaches to sampling differ considerably depending upon the type of study required. Examples of such studies are the characterization of unknown resources, the establishment of some form of reference by measurement of selected environmental indicators (similar to a list of water quality parameters), and the definition of the occurrence of anomalies.

A long-term program of sediment studies will normally consist of a series of objectives of increasing complexity, each drawing part of its information from the preceding data base; a typical sequence of objectives (of increasing complexity) may be illustrated as follows, though not all may be required to complete a program:

a) <u>Preliminary site characterization</u> - Low density sampling with limited analytical requirements, to provide a general characterization of an area for which little or no previous information exists.

b) <u>Identify anomalies</u> - More detailed sampling and analyses, designed to establish the presence and extent of anomalies.

c) <u>Establish references</u> - To create reference points, in the form of some measured parameters, for future comparison.

d) Identify time changes - To show trends and variations of sediment data over time, by use of sediment cores or other repeated sediment samplings.

Calculations of mass balance - To account for the addition and subtraction of sediment-related components within an aquatic environment (a complex study), by means of accurate and representative sampling analysis.

f) <u>Process studies</u> - Specialized sampling to improve state of knowledge about aquatic systems, through research.

TABLE I.2 Sampling objectives and activities - principal relationships

Sediments may be used as Indicators of Water Quality, to:	Summary of GEMS (Global Environmental Monitoring System) (GEMS, Operational Guide, WHO, Geneva; 1978)	Water Quality Surveys (UNESCO-WHO Report #23, Water Quality Surveys)	
- OBJECTIVES -		- TYPE OF ACTIVITY -	
Establish reference point(s) *Identify time changes (trends and history of loadings)	Cultural impact on water quality and suitability of water quality for future use	MONITOR	- Continuous standard measurement and observation of environment
Trace sources (spatial)	Observe sources and pathways of specified hazardous substances	SURVEILLANCE	- Continuous specific observation and measurement of environment relative to control and management
Characterize resources Identify anomalies Calculate mass balances Study processes	Determine quality of natural waters	SURVEY	- Series of finite duration, intensive programs to measure and observe environment in more detail for specific purposes

*Note: Because sediment time-series data, based upon core samples, represent a highly condensed time-series, it may be appropriate to include this sampling objective under SURVEY type activities, due to the relatively long period between such samplings; suspended sediment time-series data would be considered as a MONITOR SURVEILLANCE activity.

Program objectives largely control the type, density, and frequency of sediment sampling (and associated analyses); whereas the type of environment (rivers, lakes, and streams, etc.) largely controls the locations and logistics of sampling. As a general rule, logistics should be kept as simple as possible.

The types of equipment and accuracy of positioning required for sediment sampling are directly related to the accuracy of measurement required, and this, in turn, is again related to the program objectives. In general, studies for resource characterization can be completed with simple equipment and with less accuracy of positioning than process-related studies.

As with water quality samples, it is important to provide for careful preservation, transportation, storage, and subsampling of sediment. Care must be taken, also, to avoid loss or mix-up of sediment samples.

I.4   Sites and Collection

Sediments are eroded, transported, and selectively sorted into deposits. They have different textural properties which are caused by various combinations of wave action, current motion, and water density separation. While, therefore, sediments may be considered as integrators of many environmental processes, the characteristics of different depositional sites can be considered largely unique.

Sample sites which are chosen to be representative of sedimentary conditions take advantage of the properties of sediments as environmental integrators, and may be used to characterize the dispersal of point source inputs, to demonstrate changes in loadings with time, or to differentiate those components whose dispersal corresponds most closely to a diffuse origin.

Spatial distributions are normally defined by using grab samplers to recover material from the top few centimetres of a lake or river bed; trends in time-series data are usually based on the analysis of core samples, recovered from the top one to two metres of bed material. Mass balance studies, typically, require both types of sample data. Echo-sounding and side-scan sonar techniques may be used as an additional aid, both in the selection of sample sites, and by providing a fill-in guide to sediment homogeneity (and bed features) between sample sites.

The concentration of contaminants in bottom sediments is influenced by a number of factors, such as solubility/mobility, loadings, dilution (by sediments), textural effects, and in situ mixing (physical mixing and bioturbation). It is, therefore, important to maintain a consistent approach to both sampling and analysis in order to limit further complications which may be introduced during sample recovery and processing.

Suspended sediment samples may be recovered by means of sediment traps, sample bottles, or pumping. Pumping and filtration is most useful where analytical techniques require a moderately large quantity of sample, or where depth integration is required. Suspended load samples, also, must be representative of the hydraulic conditions and must take into account whether or not the water column is well mixed, the presence of entrained flows, buoyant (density) separation or the movement of nepheloid layers (very close to the bed). In rivers and river/lake systems particularly, sampling should be timed to coincide with flow conditions.

For all studies (except a preliminary investigation), it is advisable to have sufficient samples so that results can be subjected to some simple form of statistical analysis, as a means of validating distribution trends and anomalies. Likewise, sample positions should be known with sufficient accuracy so as to allow subsequent resampling of essentially the same material (allowing for time variable effects).

A log or report of field activities, sampling procedures, and sample description provides information additional to each sample analysis and is essential for the proper interpretation of sample data.

I.5   Analyses

Sediment samples may be taken from suspended material in the water column and from bed materials in lakes, rivers, and other aquatic systems. The samples may consist of live or dead materials, mineral grains or rock fragments, adsorbed inorganic components, and dissolved organic or inorganic compounds in interstitial waters.

Particle size and density are an important guide to the hydraulic behaviour of sediments, and the water content of the finer sediments can be seen to influence erodability of the bed. Water content is also related to the character of the interstitial waters. A variety of physical properties can be measured using standard geotechnical soil science methods; for example, the size of sand and gravel materials is frequently measured by sieving, and silts and clays can be determined by hydrometer or pipette techniques.

The mineralogical composition of gravels and sands may be identified by visual examination and, for fine sand/coarse silts, by the use of a petrographic microscope. The visual identification of mineral species in the fine silt- and clay-size ranges becomes increasingly more difficult with decreasing particle size and is replaced by DTA (Differential Thermal Analysis), x-ray diffraction or electron microscopy.

Characteristics such as colour, laminations, the presence of bottom fauna, and bedform add further important information for the analysis of bottom sediments, and should be recorded.

Techniques for the chemical analysis of elements in solution require that sediment samples undergo some form of preparation. For example, sediments may be digested in hot acid, in mixed acids at high temperature and pressure, or fused with caustic alkali; the choice of method(s) depends very much upon the elements chosen for analysis. Once in solution, there are many methods for determining the concentration of trace metals; these include titration, colorimetry, polarography, and atomic absorption spectrophotometry. Additionally, concentration by solvent extraction, or by ion-exchange techniques, may be carried out where natural concentrations are below the range of instrument detectability.

There are few simple techniques available for the differential analysis of organic compounds in sediments which, in general, represent only a few percent by weight of such samples. The identification of man-made organic compounds, and their degradation products (often at extremely low levels of concentration), requires the use of very sophisticated methods of sample preparation and chemical analysis.

Simple analytical procedures include: analysis of organic carbon and nitrogen by combustion or digestion, solvent extraction of wax fraction, alkali treatment of residuals for extraction of humic acids, and the use of acid treatments on original samples and analysis of filtrates by colorimetry for hydrolyzable amino-N and sugars.

More sophisticated techniques can provide total element analysis of C, H, and N, based on the use of CHN analyzers. Thin-layer chromatography, liquid and gas chromatography, and gas chromatography mass spectroscopy, provide highly sophisticated techniques for the separation of organic compounds into their various functional groups; natural groups include, for example, hydrocarbons, aromatic hydrocarbons, ketones, and fatty acids, while other groups of compounds including aliphatic hydrocarbons, polycyclic aromatic hydrocarbons, and organohalogen compounds result from man's activities.

A more detailed approach is required for the identification of the residues of persistent organochlorines and the less persistent pesticides and herbicides, e.g., organophosphates and phenoxyherbicides.

The analysis of organic compounds is complex and requires the use of advanced equipment, high quality reagents, and very high standards in laboratory procedures and cleanliness.

Samples of bottom sediments frequently contain a variety of living bottom fauna and flora, and it is possible to separate them from the sediments and to treat them as another subsample component. This separation can be useful since contaminants may be concentrated in the biota, at levels several hundreds/thousands of times greater than in sediments. Such analyses are useful mostly as an indicator of contamination since the uptake of contaminants by benthic populations is not consistent; concentrations depend upon a number of factors such as: exposure, feeding habits, life cycle stage/age, species variability, local population tolerance/rejection, etc.

Although most chemical analyses can be made upon sediment core and grab sample materials, it is particularly difficult to measure oxygen demand because of the rapid changes which take place as soon as the sediments are disturbed or removed from the bed. The use of bells (placed over the bed), to measure oxygen uptake or to measure the in situ production of gas (e.g., methane, or H_2S) under anoxic conditions, provides an alternative approach but which is often not satisfactory.

I.6   Data Handling and Processing

Sediment-related data can be generated in many different ways, and may be presented in many different forms.

Normally, after being used for interpretation of sample analyses, field notes, plotting charts, and photographic records will be placed in archive storage. Field and laboratory measurements (primary data) should be transferred to manual reference files and/or encoded for machine processing and storage (on cards, tape, or disc). The secondary data (such as that derived after statistical processing) can be subsequently added to the primary data file. All data transferred to file (manual or machine) should be rigorously checked before being accepted for either interpretive use or long-term storage.

Sample materials, also, may be considered as suitable for information storage; in such cases representative subsamples (from selected samples) are prepared, catalogued, and placed in sample collections for long-term storage. Such sub-samples are then available for subsequent comparison with later samples (from the same/similar sites) or to extend the range of original analyses.

A simplified scheme of data handling procedures is shown in Figure I.1.

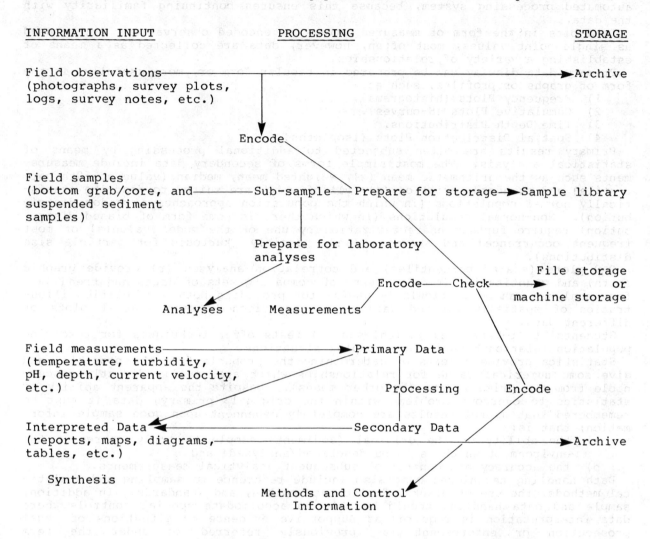

INFORMATION INPUT   PROCESSING   STORAGE

Field observations
(photographs, survey plots,
logs, survey notes, etc.)

Encode

Field samples
(bottom grab/core, and — Sub-sample — Prepare for storage → Sample library
suspended sediment
samples)

Prepare for laboratory
analyses

Analyses   Measurements   Encode — Check → File storage or machine storage

Field measurements
(temperature, turbidity,
pH, depth, current velocity,
etc.)

Primary Data

Processing   Encode

Interpreted Data
(reports, maps, diagrams, — Secondary Data → Archive
tables, etc.)

Synthesis

Methods and Control
Information

→ Archive

FIGURE I.1 Data handling procedures

SI units should be used to record results and, to avoid confusion, concentrations (element or compound) should be expressed as weight per unit dry weight and/or weight per volume; loadings should be expressed as dry weight per unit area; and loading rates should be expressed as dry weight per unit time, per volume or area.

All data should be cross-referenced to location/time/date as a minimum requirement. The name of the person collecting the information (and project number) should be filed with all archive material.

If possible, sediment-related data files should be designed to interlock with water quality and quantity survey files to allow ease of access and rapid interrogation of related data sets, e.g., water discharge vs. water quality vs. sediment characteristics.

Data storage systems should be designed to be as simple as possible and should not carry redundant or duplicate information. The format of data sets should assist rapid visual scanning (to check for errors or anomalies).

In most situations, manual data handling will be preferred over a completely automated processing system, because this ensures continuing familiarity with the data.

Data storage systems should be designed to be as simple as possible and should not carry redundant or duplicate information. The format of data sets should assist rapid visual scanning (to check for errors or anomalies).

In most situations, manual data handling will be preferred over a completely automated processing system, because this ensures continuing familiarity with the data.

Data bits in the form of measured values or encoded observations can be used as single-point values; most often, however, data are collected as a means of establishing a variety of relationships.

Primary data display can be prepared in tabular form or, more usefully, in the form of graphs or profiles, such as:
1) Frequency Plots (histograms).
2) Cumulative Plots (S-curves).
3) Time/Depth Distributions.
4) Spatial Distribution Plots (isopleths).

Primary results are often subjected to additional processing by means of statistical analysis. The most simple forms of secondary data include measurements such as the arithmetic mean (x), weighted mean, median (value at 50th percentile) and standard deviation (s); all of which are suited to describe statistically normal populations (in which the population approaches a random distribution). Non-normal populations (in which there is some form of biased distribution) require further characterization by use of the mode (value(s) of most frequent occurrence) and skewness (and, possibly, kurtosis for particle size distibutions).

Q-Q plots (shared percentiles) and correlation analyses (r) provide graphic (both) and quantitative (r only) means of comparing sets of data, and trend surface analyses can be particularly useful for providing both a simplified illustration of spatially plotted data or a comparison between spatial plots of different data.

Students' t (t-Test) and χ^2 (chi-square) tests offer techniques for resolving population relationships in more complex situations.

Statistics provide a means of determining the probable from the possible, and give some numerical value for relationships which are usually directly discernible from the primary data (by other means). Despite the apparent ability of statistics to overcome problems within the original (primary) data it must be remembered that useful results are completely dependent upon good sample information; that is:
   a) the ability of the original (sediment) sample to truly represent the environment which is to be described/analyzed; and
   b) the accuracy and control of subsequent analytical measurements.

Data handling techniques must also include reference to sampling and analytical methods, the use of blanks, duplicates, spikes, and standards. In addition, sample and data handling should be able to accommodate special controls where data interpretation is required as supportive evidence in situations of legal prosecution or enforcement (as previously referred to under the term SURVEILLANCE).

I.7   Interpretation

The interpretation of sediment data is designed to provide a means of differentiating natural conditions from man-made influences. These differences may be expressed as a change in relative composition of the same set of components (either by increase or reduction), or as the introduction of something entirely new.

The response to such changes will be expressed differently in each type of environment; i.e., certain contaminants, because of their rapid transport, may have little impact on a river system but may have a major impact on receiving lakes or reservoirs.

A few impacts may cause little significant change or may be otherwise termed acceptable; for example, increased sediment loading caused by changes in land use practices (which might be expected to occur over a five to ten-year period) will increase turbidity. However, this change may have little effect on local water use and, for the next 100 years or so, the deposited sediment may infill only dead space in a receiving reservoir.

It is possible that some impacts may cause changes which are considered desirable in their effects; for example, increased nutrient loadings into a few nutrient-poor lakes can be seen as a means of increasing biomass and fish productivity.

Many impacts, however, lead to undesirable changes of either a sublethal or lethal nature. Excessive nutrient loadings may result in changes in the plankton population and a shift in fish species (towards less desirable types). The presence of contaminants may result in the wide destruction of biomass, deformities, or loss of reproductive success.

Though such impacts are first felt by the biota indigenous to the aquatic system, these same changes illustrate the subsequent change from 'nuisance' to 'hazard' in terms of human use of the same aquatic environment (for food supplies, drinking water, and other contact activities).

The interpretation of sediment data can be used to:

1) demonstrate and identify many of the changes which take place in an aquatic system;
2) help trace contaminant sources;
3) help to understand the cause(s) of change and to explore the extent to which further change(s) may take place; and
4) provide guidance in the use of remedial measures.

In stating the uses of this type of information, it is clear that it remains largely a qualitative tool, but it can be used to provide strong guidance in the interpretation of contaminant influences on water quality and biota. This limitation is real and, for most natural and artificial compounds, the modelling of interactive processes at the sediment/water interface remains very much at the stage of exploratory research.

Although set water quality standards for certain water use requirements have been developed (for the concentration of total elements, specific compounds, and other characteristics), there are no generally accepted standards which may be used to characterize sediment quality on a similar basis.

Some empirical relationships have been derived from the disposal/recovery of dredged material (U.S. Corps Engineers, Vicksburg, Miss. - Dredged Material Research Program). Techniques, such as elutriate tests, have been developed to test for potential exchange across the sediment/water interface; however, these approaches are not yet widely accepted for general application.

Despite such limitations, sediments offer many advantages over water quality data for certain specific requirements. For example:

- Sediment core data can be used to show the frequency of events such as forest fires, droughts, floods, or to reconstruct approximate loading rates prior to the availability of documented observations.
- Sediments can provide information (at least partly) integrated over both time and space, characterizing the average conditions which would be definable only after more extensive water quality sampling.
- Sediments can act as natural concentrators of certain contaminants, allowing their detection by less sensitive analytical methods than would be required for water quality samples.

In the interpretation of sediment data, it is important to realize that nutrient availability and toxicity of contaminants are much influenced by its chemical speciation, and that biological utilization is strongly influenced by exposure. The environmental significance must thus be determined for both total loadings and concentrations.

Although some of the more obvious meanings of sediment data can be derived through the interpretation of results by relatively unskilled personnel, the full value of sediment studies can be developed only by experienced staff. For such studies it is more important to have well qualified and experienced people than the availability of highly sophisticated equipment (which, indeed, may not be in a fully operational condition ... or may remain without the availability of essential standards of high purity gases or reagents).

The authors recognize, in many cases, that investigators may wish to compare their own study areas with other study sites where investigations have been carried out and, perhaps, already published. This is a valuable approach during the initial stages of planning, and particularly so for the comparison of analytical techniques and resulting data for use in the later interpretive stages.

Figures I.2 and I.3 are included in this text as guides to choosing such sites. These figures show the global distribution of rainfall and major geological groupings. Together with latitude as a crude indicator of temperature regime, they may be used to show areas of probable similar environmental conditions (on a broad regional scale) in which natural sediment/freshwater

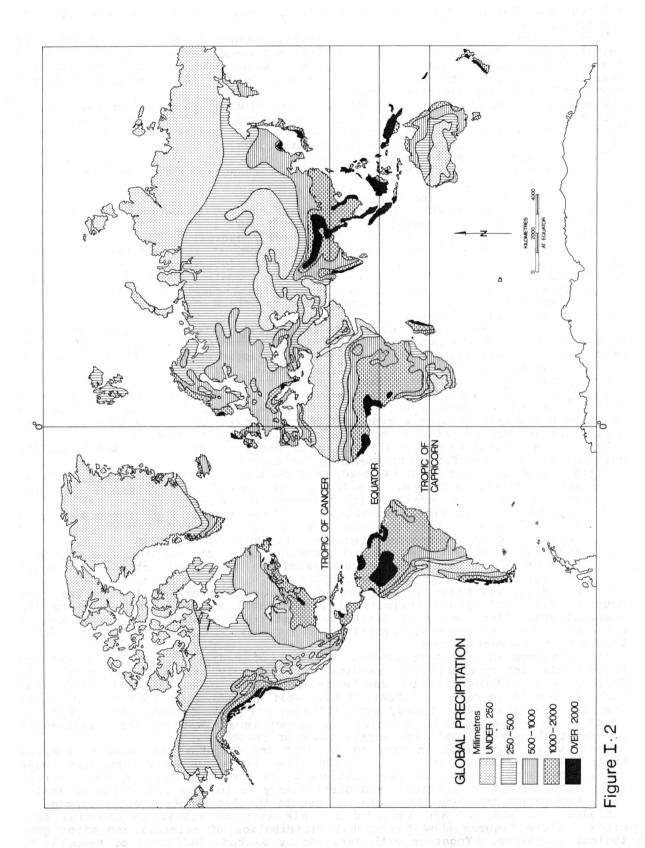

GLOBAL PRECIPITATION

Millimetres
UNDER 250
250 – 500
500 – 1000
1000 – 2000
OVER 2000

TROPIC OF CANCER

EQUATOR

TROPIC OF CAPRICORN

KILOMETRES
0   2000   4000
AT EQUATOR

N

Figure I·2

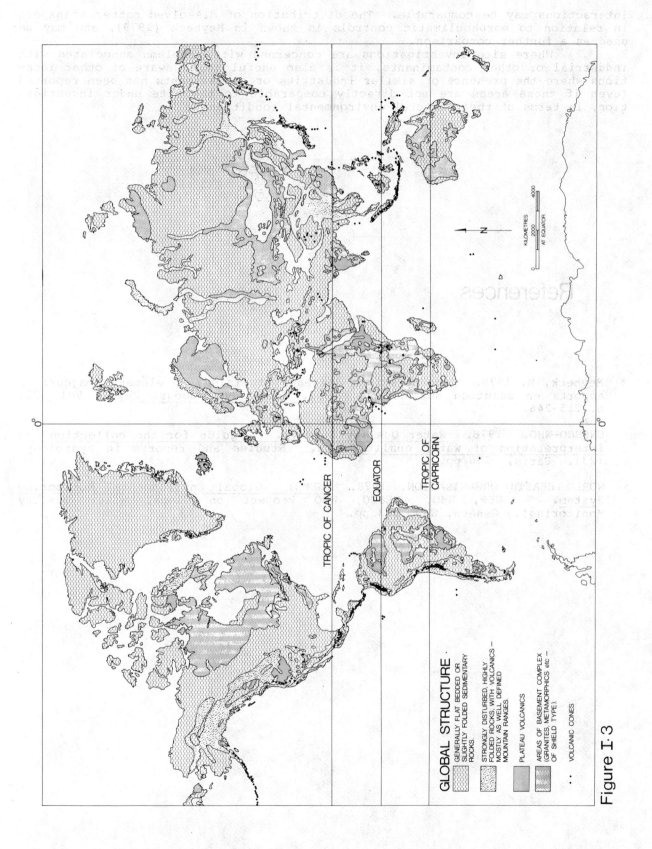

GLOBAL STRUCTURE.

GENERALLY FLAT BEDDED OR
SLIGHTLY FOLDED SEDIMENTARY
ROCKS.

STRONGLY DISTURBED, HIGHLY
FOLDED ROCKS, WITH VOLCANICS –
MOSTLY AS WELL DEFINED
MOUNTAIN RANGES.

PLATEAU VOLCANICS

AREAS OF BASEMENT COMPLEX
(GRANITES, METAMORPHICS etc –
OF SHIELD TYPE).

∴∴ VOLCANIC CONES

KILOMETRES

0   2000   4000
AT EQUATOR

TROPIC OF CANCER

EQUATOR

TROPIC OF CAPRICORN

Figure I·3

interactions may be comparable. The distribution of dissolved matter transport in relation to morphoclimatic controls is shown in Meybeck (1979), and may be used as a further comparison.

Where site investigations are concerned with problems associated with industrial or other contaminants, it is also useful to be aware of other locations where the presence of similar industries or contaminants has been reported (even if these areas are not directly comparable to the site under investigation, in terms of their natural environmental conditions).

References

*   Meybeck, M. 1979. Concentrations des eaux fluviales, en éléments majeurs et apports en solution aux océans. Rev. Géol. dyn. Géogr. Phys., Vol. 21: p. 215-246.

UNESCO-WHO. 1978. Water Quality Surveys. A guide for the collection and interpretation of water quality data. Studies and reports in hydrology, (23). Paris, 350 pp.

WORLD HEALTH ORGANIZATION. 1978. GEMS: Global Environmental Monitoring System. (UNEP, WHO, UNESCO, WMO Project on Global Water Quality Monitoring). Geneva, WHO, 313 pp.

*   Suggested text for further reading.

II   Nature and properties of sediments

II.1   Nature of Sediments

II.1.1   Introduction

Sediment is a general term which is used to describe both suspended and deposited material.   All natural waters contain varying amounts of suspended sediment.   In aquatic systems, sediment includes all particulate material which are washed or blown into a lake or river (allochthonous), or are formed in the water-body itself (autochthonous).   Alterations (diagenesis) which occur in the sediments produce new compounds (authigenic).   Diagenetic processes also cause changes in the chemical composition of pore fluids.

Sediments consist of inorganic and organic compounds, both of which come from sources outside or within the river or lake.   The organic matter consists of micro-organisms (phytoplankton, zooplankton, and bacteria), the remains of macrophytes and other large-sized organisms, together with the detritus derived from decaying material.   The inorganic matter consists of erosion products from rocks in the watershed (rock particles and clays), together with compounds such as $FeOOH$ (or $Fe(OH)_3$), SiO_2, and $CaCO_3$ which may be brought into the water, or formed within it, from soluble products or compounds.

Natural sediments are a mixture of different compositional types:
  a)   minerals and small pieces of rock derived from the fragmentation of source material;
  b)   clay minerals;
  c)   precipitates and coatings;
  d)   organic materials.

In addition, man-made debris may result in the production of sediments having characteristics similar to those of natural origin.   Sediment composition is largely controlled by the composition of the source rock from which it is derived by erosion and weathering; it is, additionally, influenced by climatic regime (weathering and hydrologic conditions), land form, land use, and time in transit.

II.1.2   Quantitative aspects

Sediments affect and influence water use and availability in many ways.   Quantitatively, wide variations in the particle size, such as gravel, sand, and silt, and amount of material, may cause channel instability or excessive erosion or deposition in both river/stream and lake systems.   High sediment loads may also cause problems associated with abrasion (e.g., turbine failures in hydro plants), and clogging of screens and intake filters at treatment plants.

Some rough estimates about total transport of particulate material can be given.   The total amount of particulate material transported by all rivers has been estimated to be about 15×10^9 metric tons per year (Sundborg, 1973) and, with an estimated river flow of slightly more than $30,000 \text{ km}^3$, this gives a world average of about 500 g m^{-3}.   A considerable portion of the total amount is

TABLE II.1 Hydrological river and sediment data (Turekian, 1971; Meybeck, 1976 and 1977; Livingstone, 1963; Leifeste, 1974; Curtis et al., 1973)

	Catchment Area in 10³ km²	Runoff in 10³ km³ year⁻¹	Average Conc. Dissolved Load g m⁻³	Flux Dissolved Load 10⁹ metric tons year⁻¹	Average Conc. Suspended Load g m⁻³	Flux Suspended Load 10⁹ metric tons year⁻¹	Ratio Suspended to Dissolved Load
Colorado River	637	0.021	760		13,930	–	–
Pacific Slopes, California	303	0.072	167		970	–	–
Western Gulf	829	0.049	770		1,880	–	–
Mississippi River	3240	0.555	248	0.137	510	0.30	2
South Atlantic and Eastern Gulf	735	0.291	171		131	–	–
North Atlantic	383	0.188	128		156	–	–
Columbia	679	0.250	85	0.021	56	0.014	0.67
U.S. totals and weighted means	6807	1.500	153	0.321	295	0.442	1.90
North America total		4.555– 6.43	142– 89	0.646 0.572			
Rhine	220	0.070	200–250(2) 600–900(3)	0.015(2) 0.068(3)	57–67	0.003–0.004	0.20
Rhône	100	0.053					
Europe total		2.500– 3.00	182–101	0.455 0.303			
Asia		11.050–12.25	142–111	1.570 1.360			
Nile	3000	0.090					
Africa total		5.900– 6.00	121– 96	0.715 0.581			
Australia		0.320– 0.61	59–176	0.019 0.107			
Amazon	6300–7000	5.500	52.9(1)	0.292	100	0.529	1.50
Rio de la Plata	3200	0.725	114	0.070		0.129	1.85
South America total		8.000– 8.10	69– 71	0.0552 0.575			
World total		32.300–36.45	120– 88	4.000 3.500			

(1) Earlier data 60 to 70 g m⁻³.
(2) Before 1900.
(3) Present time.

transported by a few large rivers; thus, the Amazon is estimated to carry about 0.5×10^9 metric tons per year or about three percent of the world total.

There is some evidence (Table II.1) that the proportion of suspended matter seems to be about 1.5 to 2 times that of the dissolved load. Only in hardwater rivers, like the Rhine, does the dissolved components appear to be relatively more important (Table II.1)

The annual variation in quantities of suspended load is, of course, considerable: thus the Rhine, having an average of 57 g m^{-3}, spans a range of 50 to 500 g m^{-3}. Certain rivers have very high values during severe flood and some examples are given in Chapter III. Also, the year to year variation is considerable; the Rhine, for example, has ranged between 2 and 4×10^6 metric tons per year between 1930 and the present (Golterman, 1975a).

Meybeck (1976 and 1977) related total erosion in watersheds to their surface size, and he arrived at the following relationships:
1) 500 metric tons per km^2 for small alpine rivers;
2) 200 metric tons per km^2 for middle-sized basins (Area = about 100,000 km^2); and
3) 140 metric tons per km^2 for large basins (Area > 400,000 km^2).

His estimate for a world figure is 20×10^9 metric tons per year, or five times the dissolved load; this estimate is somewhat higher than those made previously. A global mean denudation of 75 to 100 metric tons per year per km^2 can be calculated, for comparison, from Schuiling's (1977) data.

The erosion or denudation of rocks and soil in a watershed depends basically upon four factors:
a) Size of basin, which has a damping effect on differences caused by local effects and events.
b) Gradient, or relief in the watershed, which influences both rainfall and stream velocity and, therefore, the quantity and size of material transported and eroded.
c) Source material, which controls character and availability of material for erosion.
d) Climate (quantities and distribution of rain and temperature), and vegetation, which strongly influence weathering.

In aqueous systems the total quantity of eroded material in sediment budgets should be equal to the sum of the dissolved and particulate fractions of water-transported material (including bed and suspended loads).

When studying specific watersheds it is, therefore, important to measure the ratio of dissolved to particulate material.

Some estimates of the total quantities being eroded can be obtained on a local scale. In an example cited by Wyldman and Poliquin (1973), who were studying the effects of oilfield development on soil erosion in the Swan Hills watershed of Alberta (western Canada), a good relationship could be established between rainfall and soil loss using ground plots of only 160 ft^2 or about 15 m^2 in size (Figure II.1).

Using a different approach, Lal and Banerji (1977) were able to estimate the amount of silt entering Indian reservoirs, as opposed to soil loss in a watershed. In their example, based on Indian data, they described an equation in which:

$$S = 1/100 \ (C/I)^{0.22} (I/W)^2$$

Where   S = siltation index ($m^3 \ km^{-2} \ y^{-1}$)
         C/I = capacity to inflow ratio (where C is the original capacity and I is the average annual inflow)
         I/W = inflow per unit watershed area ($10^3 m^3 \ km^{-2}$)

The coefficients of (C/I) and of (I/W), of course, depend upon geology, climate, and land use, and may have to be measured separately for different regions.

Other methods are also available for calculating sediment accumulation (Canada Department of the Environment, 1973), many of which allow the separation of sediment (redistributed within a basin by internal erosion) from the accumulation of externally derived materials (from the watershed).

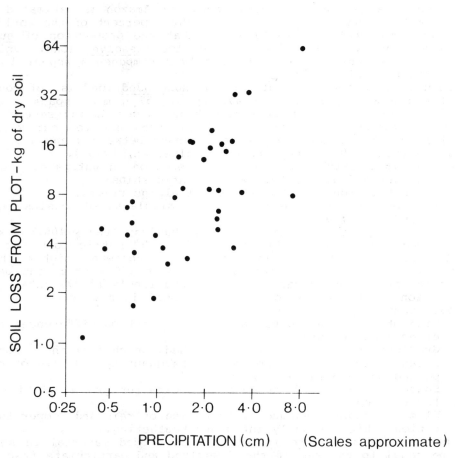

FIGURE II.1 Precipitation vs soil loss.
Storm events over 0.25 cm (1967-1969).
(Modified after Wyldman and Poliquin, 1973)

II.2   Size of Sediment Particles

Sediments in mid-latitude rivers and streams or lakes are often typified by a
bulk composition in which mineral and rock fragments > clay > organics > preci-
pitates/coatings (except for hard waters, such as in some Swiss lakes and marl
lakes, where $CaCO_3$ usually forms the bulk of the material). In contrast, in
regions where sediment transport is limited and evaporation is high (some low
latitude areas), typical composition may be precipitates/coatings > clay >
mineral and rock fragments > organics. Organic material may be predominant in
marshes or wetlands. (See Figure II.2.)
    The size of individual particles varies greatly; the coarsest materials in-
clude boulders, cobbles, gravel, and sand; the finest materials include silt and
clay (mud being an undefined mixture of silt and clay), and colloids which do
not settle.
    Several of the different components may be recognized by their size. Coarse
gravels and sands usually form much of the bed load of rivers and streams, and
form the bottom deposits in the shallow nearshore environment of lake systems.
In these environments, strong currents or wave action are required to provide
the turbulent motion necessary to raise coarse materials above the bed and,
because of this, they rarely enter suspension. Finer silts and clays (muddy
material) are frequently in suspension and only settle permanently to the river
or lake bed under calm water conditions.
    There is no satisfactory definition of the boundary between the size fractions
of silt and clay. Some authors consider that all particulate matter in rivers
is silt, while others define silt as being all particles with a grain size smaller than 16 μm or even 50 μm.

Before further discussing size fractionation, it must be noted that the use of sizing has developed as much in response to the availability of techniques (i.e., size classification) as to the identification of precise property boundaries. In addition, there is the unresolved problem of defining exactly what one is measuring at small particle sizes, after treatment by dispersants. Although technical difficulties remain, size fractionation is essential, not only because of the need to differentiate physical characteristics but also because chemical properties, such as adsorption capacity, depend strongly on the particle size.

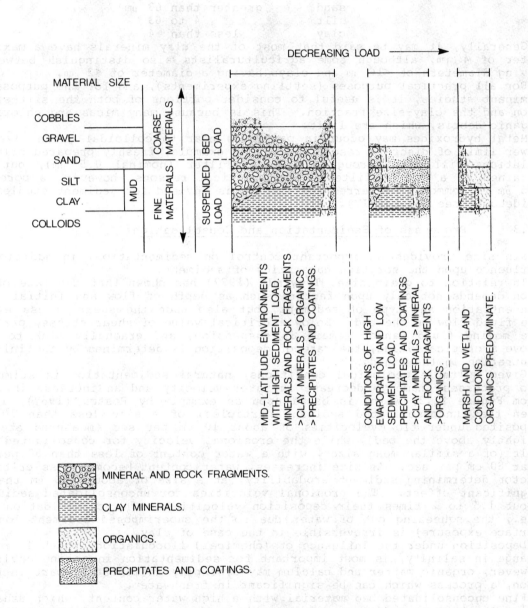

MINERAL AND ROCK FRAGMENTS.

CLAY MINERALS.

ORGANICS.

PRECIPITATES AND COATINGS.

NOTE: These distributions represent the more extreme ranges of sediment composition and are not based upon actual case examples.

FIGURE II.2   Sediment particle size-composition relationships in different river/lake environments

There are several different systems of classification. The United States Department of Agriculture has used the following, limiting diameters in microns, or, as now denoted, micro meters (μm):

fine gravel	1000 to 2000	μm
coarse sand	100 to 1000	
medium sand	25 to 500	
fine sand	50 to 100	
silt	5 to 50	
clay	less than 15	

Geochemists have been using the following limits (based largely upon the Wentworth classification):

sand	greater than 63 μm
silt	4 to 63
clay	less than 4

Generally, it may be said that most of the clay minerals have a maximum diameter of 4 μm, although some agriculturalists also distinguish between clays having diameters of $\leq$16 μm and clays having a diameter of $\leq$2 μm.

For all practical purposes (settling experiments), and for the purpose of contaminant studies, it is useful to consider portions of both the silt-size fraction and the clay-size fraction. This is because many micas and chlorites, and organic debris, which are limit.

Metal hydroxides may occur in particles near to colloidal grain size, at the lower limit of discrete resolution; as an example, freshly prepared diluted Fe^{3+} solutions will pass through a 0.45 μm filter (nominal 0.5 μm), but will be retained on a 0.1 μm filter. For practical reasons, however, a pore size of 0.5 μm is commonly preferred and its use is advised for sediment studies in this guidebook (see Chapter IV).

II.3   Processes of Sedimentation and Consolidation

Grain size provides an important control on sedimentation, in addition to its influence upon the sorption capacities of sediment.

In relation to grain size, Terwindt (1977) has shown that the rate of deposition depends not only upon factors such as depth of flow and initial suspended concentration and type of sediment, but also upon the shear stress exerted by the fluid flow on the bed. Below a critical value of shear stress, particles in the moving fluid cannot remain in suspension, and gradually sink to the bed. Above a critical value, the rate of deposition is determined by the initial concentration in the fluid.

Given suitable geological conditions, natural sedimentation is stimulated by two processes, namely, decrease in water velocity and an increase in salinity. From Figure II.3, which is based upon an example by Postma (1967), it can be seen that unconsolidated sediment particles, of a size less than 10 μm, are deposited under flow velocities of about 10 cm per sec (measured at a height slightly above the bed), while the erosional velocity for consolidated clay and silt (of a similar mean size), with a water content of less than 50 percent, is near 80 cm per sec. As size increases, water content becomes less critical as a factor determining sediment erodability; at a size of about 100 μm there is no significant effect. The erosional velocities for unconsolidated sediments are about 1.5 to 2 times their deposition velocities. The consolidation process, i.e., the squeezing out of water due to the superimposed sediment load (or by surface exposure) is irreversible in the case of clay.

Deposition under the influence of (chemical) flocculation, which is related to change in salinity, is most important for sedimentation in marine environments. However, organic matter and calcium may also play an important part in flocculation, a process which can be significant in freshwater.

Fine unconsolidated bed material with a high water content, which usually contains the highest pollutant concentrations, is re-eroded before material having a low water content, such as sub-aerially dried mud of a river bank. Because of this, the greatest transport of particulate contaminants will occur during conditions of high water flow (such as experienced in severe flooding). Substantiation of this may be found in the work of Lazlo (cited in Förstner, 1977b) who found that mercury concentrations in the Sajo River had been reduced to one-quarter of the preflood values three months after a major flood. The complexity of the relationship between sediment concentrations and discharge is demonstrated in Figure II.4 (see also Chapter III).

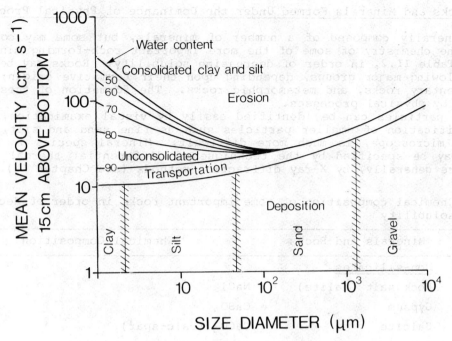

FIGURE II.3   Settling curves for sediment of differing
texture as function of mean water velocity.
Modified, after Postma (1967)

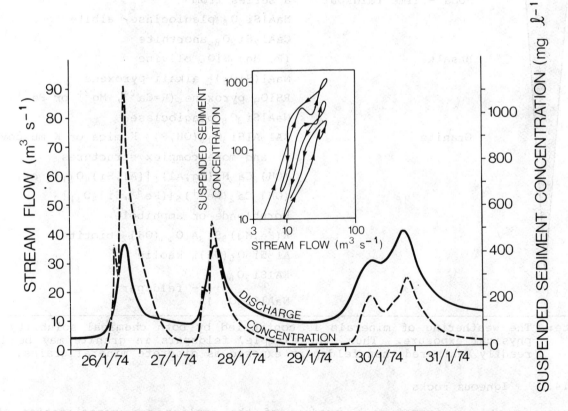

FIGURE II.4   Suspended sediment concentration to stream flow during a series
of storm runoff events on the River Dart, Devon, England.
After Walling (1977)

<u>Rocks and Minerals Formed Under the Dominance of Physical Processes</u>

Rocks are generally composed of a number of minerals, but some may consist of only one. The chemistry of some of the more important rock-forming minerals is outlined in Table II.2, in order of decreasing solubility. Rocks may be divided into the following major groups, depending upon their formative origin; igneous rocks, sedimentary rocks, and metamorphic rocks. The formation of these groups is dominated by physical processes.

Large rock particles can be identified easily by visual examination, but the visual identification of smaller particles such as fine sand and silt, even by petrographic microscope, is much more difficult. Mineral species in the clay size range may be specified by the technique of differential thermal analysis (DTA) or, more generally, by X-ray diffraction methods (see Chapter IV).

TABLE II.2 Chemical composition of some important rocks in order of decreasing solubility

Solubility	Minerals and Rocks	Chemical Composition
	Non-silicates	
	Rock salt (halite)	$NaCl$
	Gypsum	$CaSO_4$
	Calcite	$CaCO_3$ (calc-spar)
	Dolomite	$MgCO_3 \cdot CaCO_3$ (pearl-spar)
	Silicates	
	Feldspar	$KAlSi_3O_8$ orthoclase
	Soda – lime feldspar	a series from
		$NaAlSi_3O_8$ plagioclase, albite to
		$CaAl_2Si_2O_8$ anorthite
	Basalt	$(Fe,Mg)_2SiO_4$ olivine
		$NaAl(SiO_3)_2$ alkali-pyroxene
		$RSiO_3$ pyroxene ($R=Ca^{2+}$, Mg^{2+} or Fe^{2+})
		$NaAlSi_3O_8$ plagioclase
	Granite	$KAl_2AlSi_3O_{10}(OH,F)_2$ K mica or K muscovite
		and more complex structures
		$(OH)_2Ca_2Na(Mg,Al)_5[(Al,Si)_4O_{11}]_2$ or
		$(OH)_2Ca_2(Fe^{2+})_5[(Fe^{3+},Si)_4O_{11}]_2$
		hornblende or amphibole
		$K(Fe,Mg)_3Si_3AlO_{10}(OH)_2$ biotite
		$Al_2Si_2O_5(OH)_4$ kaolin
		$KAlSi_3O_8$)
		) – feldspar
		$NaAlSi_3O_8$)

Note: The weathering of minerals is controlled by both chemical solubiity and physical exposure. Thus, for example, feldspars in granite may be less readily weathered than feldspars exposed as discrete mineral grains.

II.4.1   Igneous rocks

Igneous rocks are formed as a product of the cooling and consolidation of a magma. Their major constituents are silicates (mainly of aluminium or magnesium) or silica.

The composition of igneous rocks can be expressed by chemical or mineralogical composition. The chemical composition is usually expressed as the norm, in percentage of the oxides of all elements present (Table II.3). Often the individual significance of each oxide may be interpreted in several different ways (Milner, 1962), e.g.:

1) SiO_2 present in quartz, chert, flint, silicate minerals, and clay.
2) Al_2O_3 present in feldspar, mica, silicate, and clay minerals.
3) Fe_2O_3 present in ferromagnesium silicates and sedimentary iron ores.
4) FeO present in various silicates and sedimentary iron ores.
5) MgO present in ferromagnesium silicates, in dolomitic limestone, and as magnesite replacing dolomite and limestone.
6) Cl present in rock salt and chlorapatite.

TABLE II.3 The chemical composition of some igneous rocks. Norm (or normative) analyses of two selected igneous rocks with high and low SiO_2 content (as oxides), and crustal average. Data from Dapples, 1959.

	Granite	Olivine gabbro	Average of 16 km crust
SiO_2	70.18	46.49	59.08
TiO_2	0.39	1.17	1.03
Al_2O_3	14.47	17.73	15.23
Fe_2O_3	1.57	3.66	3.10
FeO	1.78	6.17	3.72
MgO	0.88	8.86	3.45
CaO	1.99	11.48	5.10
Na_2O	3.48	2.16	3.71
K_2O	4.11	0.78	3.11
H_2O	0.84	1.04	1.30

Common minerals include quartz, and the feldspar, mica, olivine, pyroxene, and amphibole groups (see Tables II.2 and II.4).

During the cooling process of a large magma reservoir, a differentiation takes place. This usually results in the formation of rocks having successively different chemical composition; typically, changing from basic (silica poor) to acidic (silica rich) composition.

Firstly, heavy dark minerals are formed; these include the olivines with a low SiO_2 content, and a ratio of 1 SiO_2 to 2 (Mg,Fe)O. These sink to the bottom of the magma reservoir and, as they contain less silica than the average magma, the remaining magma will be relatively enriched in silica and some other elements. Progressively, rocks with a higher content of silica solidify. These later-stage rocks still contain some dark minerals, such as pyroxenes (SiO_2:(Ca,Mg,Fe)O = 1:1), amphiboles, micas (glimmers), and, in smaller quantities, even some olivine, but they also contain increasing amounts of light minerals. The light minerals include feldspars (plagioclase, orthoclase, and microcline) and finally quartz, which fills the interstitial spaces between the earlier-formed minerals. Variations occur due to the presence of iron or aluminium in the melt. An example of the normative chemical composition (expressed as oxides) is given in Table II.3 and the mineralogical composition is outlined in Table II.5.

II.4.2   Metamorphic rocks

Metamorphic rocks may be derived by the alteration of either igneous rocks or sedimentary rocks, which have been subjected to high temperature and/or intense pressure. They may be of different metamorphic grade, depending on formative pressure and temperature (such as the sequence: slates, schists, gneiss). Thus changes occur in the texture, appearance, and mineralogical composition of the original rock type. The new rocks may contain such minerals as amphiboles, chlorites, and micas, in addition to feldspar and quartz. High grade rocks may be formed containing new metamorphic minerals, such as garnet and kyanite. These rocks often have a layered or schistose structure and are called schists.

TABLE II.4 Mineralogy, composition (average mineral composition on a percent basis) and density of some igneous rocks (modified from Strahler and Strahler, 1973)

| | SILICATE MINERALS | | IGNEOUS ROCKS | | | | |
| | | | GRANITIC | | BASALTIC | | |
Mineral	Composition	Density (g cm^{-3})	Granite Rhyolite	Diorite Andesite	Gabbro Basalt	Peridotite	Dunite
	(Density, g cm^{-3})		2.7	2.8	3.0	3.3	3.3
Quartz (FELSIC, light colour)	SiO_2	2.6	27%	2%			
Potash feldspar	$KAlSi_3O_8$	2.6	40%	1%			
Plagioclase Na-rich — feldspar intermediate	$NaAlSi_3O_8$ (Na 100% / Ca 0%)	2.6	15%	61%			
Ca-rich	$CaAl_2Si_2O_8$ (Na 0% / Ca 100%)	2.8			43% (18%)*		
Biotite (mica group) (MAFIC, dark colour)	Complex aluminosilicates with K,Mg,Fe and water	2.9	12%	2%			
Amphibole group (hornblende)	Complex aluminosilicates with Ca,Mg,Fe	3.2	6%	17%			
Pyroxene group (augite)	Complex aluminosilicates with Ca,Mg,Fe	3.3		18%	57% (64%)*	40%	ultra mafic
Olivine	$(Mg,Fe)_2SiO_4$	3.3			0% (18%)*	60%	100%

ALUMINOSILICATES (Biotite, Amphibole, Pyroxene)

* Olivine-rich gabbro and basalt.

44

Under conditions of severe folding and thrusting, some of the earth's crust may be subjected to intense temperature and pressure, in which sediments depressed into the deeper parts of the folds become permeated by the underlying magma and form gneisses. Gneiss differs from schist by having a coarser and larger-scale banding of light and dark minerals. Limestone rocks which undergo metamorphism become marbles; quartz sand or sandstones (devoid of dark minerals) are altered into quartzites. Minerals produced by intense metamorphism are generally resistant to weathering. Thus, water-bodies in such areas usually contain little suspended matter, and they are also characterized by a small capacity for chemical reactions such as adsorption.

TABLE II.5 Magmatic differentiation of igneous rock. (Modified from Dapples, 1959)

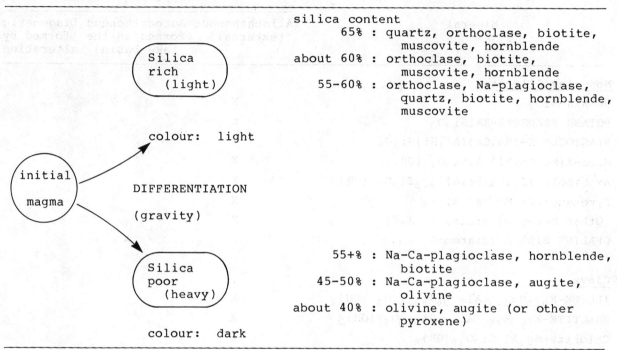

silica content

Silica rich (light)

65% : quartz, orthoclase, biotite, muscovite, hornblende
about 60% : orthoclase, biotite, muscovite, hornblende
55-60% : orthoclase, Na-plagioclase, quartz, biotite, hornblende, muscovite

colour: light

initial magma

DIFFERENTIATION

(gravity)

Silica poor (heavy)

55+% : Na-Ca-plagioclase, hornblende, biotite
45-50% : Na-Ca-plagioclase, augite, olivine
about 40% : olivine, augite (or other pyroxene)

colour: dark

II.4.3 Sedimentary rocks

Sedimentary rocks are formed by weathering, in which some of the components of igneous and metamorphic and previously formed sedimentary rocks are set free. The largely unaltered rock fragments and mineral particles are known as clastics and, after erosion and re-deposition, the clastics may form a wide range of new sedimentary rocks such as breccias and conglomerates (of very coarse rock fragment material), pebble beds, sandstones (in which quartz often dominates the mineral assemblage), and mud and clay stones.

In temperate regions chemical weathering may produce various forms of hydrous aluminium silicate (clay material II.6.1) and under tropical conditions aluminium and iron may remain in the form of hydroxides, during so-called lateritic weathering.

Components that are released include the alkaline elements sodium and potassium which are easily dissolved and ultimately appear in the hydrosphere (although some potassium is also adsorbed on to clay). Calcium will also go into solution and may later form carbonate rocks with the CO_2 of the atmosphere, through the $CO_2/HCO_3^-/CO_3^{2-}$ system. Despite chemical weathering, clastic carbonates are a frequent form of sedimentary deposit.

Englund et al. (1977), described the weathering of late Precambrian and Cambro-Silurian sedimentary rocks in the watershed of Lake Mjøsa (Norway) which is dominated by sandstones, shales, and limestone; the authors found a clear correlation between the regional distribution of different rock types and the chemical composition of the water. The Cambro-Silurian calcareous rocks produced the highest concentrations of minerals in the water, while the lowest values were obtained for rivers draining sandstone areas and Precambrian gneisses and granites.

Table II.6 provides a summary of the mineralogical composition of sediments which have been deposited in typical freshwater environments, and distinguishes those derived from allochthonous and autochthonous sources and formed by diagenetic processes.

TABLE II.6 Minerals reported from freshwater lake sediments* (modified from Jones and Bowser, 1978)

Mineral	Type of Source		
	Allochthonous (external)	Autochthonous (formed in the lake basin)	Diagenetic (formed by alteration
Non-clay Silicates			
QUARTZ-SiO_2	X		
POTASH FELDSPAR-$KAlSi_3O_8$	X		
PLAGIOCLASE-$(Na,Ca)(Al,Si)Si_2O_8$	X		
Mica-$K(Mg,Fe,Al)_3AlSi_3O_{10}(OH)_2$	X		
Amphibole-$(Ca,Mg,Fe,Al)_{3.5}Si_4O_{11}(OH)$	X		
Pyroxene-$(Ca,Mg,Fe)_2Si_2O_6$	X		
(Other heavy minerals, ρ 3.0)	X		
OPALINE SILICA (diatoms)		X	
Clays			
ILLITE-$K_{0.8}Mg_{0.35}Al_{2.26}Si_{3.43}O_{10}(OH)_2$	X		
SMECTITE-$X_{0.3}Mg_{0.2}Al_{1.9}Si_{3.9}O_{10}(OH)_2$	X		
Chlorite-$Mg_5Al_2Si_3O_{10}(OH)_8$	X		
kaolinite-$Al_2Si_2O_5(OH)_4$	X		
mixed-layer clays, vermiculite-intermediate	X		?
palygorskite-$(Ca,Mg,Al)_{2.5}(Si_4O_{10}(OH)\cdot4H_2O$	X		?
nontronite-$X_{0.5}Fe_2Al_{0.5}Si_{3.5}O_{10}(OH)_2$			X
Carbonates			
CALCITE-$CaCO_3$	X	X	x
DOLOMITE-$Ca,Mg(CO_3)_2$	X		?
Aragonite-$CaCO_3$	x	X	
Mg-Calcite-intermediate		x	X
rhodochrosite-$MnCO_3$			X
monohydrocalcite-$CaCO_3\cdot H_2O$		X	?
siderite-$FeCO_3$	?		?

* Print size is varied to illustrate frequency of occurrence.   Cont'd..../

TABLE II.6 (Cont'd)   Minerals reported from freshwater lake sediments* (modified from Jones and Bowser, 1978)

Mineral	Type of Source		
	Allochthonous (external)	Autochthonous (formed in the lake basin)	Diagenetic (formed by alteration)
Fe-Mn Oxides			
GOETHITE, Lepidocrocite-FeO(OH)	X	x	X
MAGNETITE-Fe_3O_4	X		
Hematite, Maghemite-Fe_2O_3	X		?
birnessite-$(Na,Ca)Mn_7O_{14} \cdot 3H_2O$		?	X
todorokite-$(Na,Ca,K,Ba,Mn)_2Mn_5O_{12} \cdot 3H_2O$		?	X
psilomelane-$(Ba,K)(MnO_2)_{2.5} \cdot H_2O$			X
ilmenite-$FeTiO_3$	X		
Phosphates			
APATITE-$Ca_5(PO_4)_3(OH,F)$	X		x
Vivianite-$Fe_3(PO_4)_2 \cdot 8H_2O$			X
ludlamite-$(Fe,Mn,Mg)_3(PO_4)_2 \cdot 4H_2O$			X
(?) lipscombite-$Fe_3(PO_4)_2(OH)_2$			X
(?) phosphoferrite-$(Mn,Fe)_3(PO_4)_2 \cdot 3H_2O$			X
(?) anapaite-$Ca_3Fe(PO_4)_2 \cdot 4H_2O$			X
Sulfides			
MACKINAWITE-$FeS_{0.9}$		x	X
pyrite-FeS_2	X		x
greigite-Fe_3S_4			X
sphalerite-ZnS		x	
Fluoride			
fluorite-CaF_2			X

* Print size is varied to illustrate frequency of occurrence.

II.5   Rocks and Minerals Formed Under the Dominance of Chemical Processes

Sedimentary rocks, in which chemical processes dominate formation, include non-clastic carbonates, evaporites and hydrolysates. After burial under heavy layers of sediment a certain degree of recrystallization may occur, which further consolidates the deposit.

II.5.1   Carbonates

These are typically formed by reaction between atmospheric CO_2 and calcium (II.4.3) and magnesium, and biogenic activity is particularly important in their formation. Algal and coral limestones form a substantial part of this rock type.

II.5.2   Evaporites

Occasionally, salt deposits are formed by evaporation in closed sea or lake basins. The most important deposits include rocksalt, halite ($NaCl$), gypsum ($CaSO_4$), and calcite ($CaCO_3$). Ideally, the order of crystallization of salts in a lake or sea is as follows: calcite ($CaCO_3$), anhydrite ($CaSO_4$) or gypsum ($CaSO_4 \cdot 2H_2O$), $NaCl$, Na_2SO_4, $Na_2SO_4 \cdot 10H_2O$, followed by the double sulphates of Na, K, and Mg. The last salts to be formed are generally those of KCl and $MgCl_2$, providing the evaporite sequence is completed.

II.5.3   Precipitates and coatings

Hydrous metal (Fe, Mn, Al) oxides can be formed from a variety of sources, but are formed mainly by the weathering of various minerals. They enter water-bodies from both ground and surface waters. They occur both in the dissolved and in the particulate state, but in the former case, only in the reduced oxidation state ($Fe^{2+} + Mn^{2+}$). Upon contact with water containing oxygen and in alkaline to slightly acid pH range, Fe^{2+} is rapidly oxidized to Fe^{3+}, which will then rapidly hydrolyze to the insoluble $Fe(OH)_3 \cdot xH_2O$ precipitate.

A relatively higher pH for equivalent rates of oxidation is needed in the case of Mn^{2+}. Due to adsorption of Mn^{2+} on the formed hydroxides, MnO_2 is seldom found; it probably occurs only under high pH or redox values.

In anoxic sediments, both Fe^{2+} and Mn^{2+} migrate through the interstitial waters until they come in contact with O_2, where precipitation of $Fe(OH)_3 \cdot xH_2O$ and $Mn(OH)_{3-4}$ then occurs. In lake waters, considerable amounts of Fe^{2+} and Mn^{2+} are often found in anoxic hypolimnia. Due to upward migration of the metals and downward migration of O_2 (diffusion and sinking of the thermocline) a contact zone will be established and precipitation of iron and manganese hydroxides will occur. These precipitates may, under the right conditions, nucleate and form freshwater ferro-manganese concretions (Damiani et al., 1977). In the same way, particles of other substances, e.g., $CaCO_3$, may be coated by thin layers of these hydroxides. (For further reading, see Stumm and Morgan, 1970.)

II.6   Fine Particulate Materials

II.6.1   Clay particles

The term clay refers both to a series of minerals in which the lattice is characterized by sheet structures, and to a group of particles whose size is less than four microns (see Section II.5). It is usual to specify clay minerals when referring to their physio-chemical composition; otherwise, the term clay is assumed to refer to particles of a certain size in which the clay minerals constitute a large portion of the material. Compositionally, quartz and feldspars may dominate particles in the 1 to 4 μm range and, in general, the clay minerals dominate the <1 μm range.

Clay minerals, formed from rock material by erosion and weathering, are essentially aluminium silicates, but of various specific mineral forms. The weathering process schematized in Table II.7 is represented by arrows whose function is not to symbolize distinct chemical reactions, but rather to represent the general trend of a mixture of chemical reactions whose details are incompletely understood. No general scheme of weathering is yet available which would allow prediction of the type of clay mineral in a given river or lake. As an example, Englund et al. (1977) found a high content of illite and chlorite in the sediments of Lake Mjøsa. In this study, the immaturity of these sediments was demonstrated by their close relationship to the source tills and underlying rocks, which were also rich in illite and chlorite.

Weathering is basically a hydrolysis of primary and secondary minerals. The extent of the hydrolysis depends on the type of rock, climate, and relief.

The most important stage of the weathering process, in diagenesis of clay, is the conversion of a primary into a secondary mineral (a disproportionate or incongruent dissolution of aluminium silicate). An atmospheric influence is necessary for this dissolution to occur, since it provides H_2O (rainfall is an important factor in the weathering process), in the presence of such gases as CO_2, H_2S, SO_2 (or even HCl from volcanic action).

In some areas, kaolinite may be formed directly in igneous rocks by late-stage geothermal effects during magmatic cooling (kaolinization).

TABLE II.7 Schematic representation of the weathering process

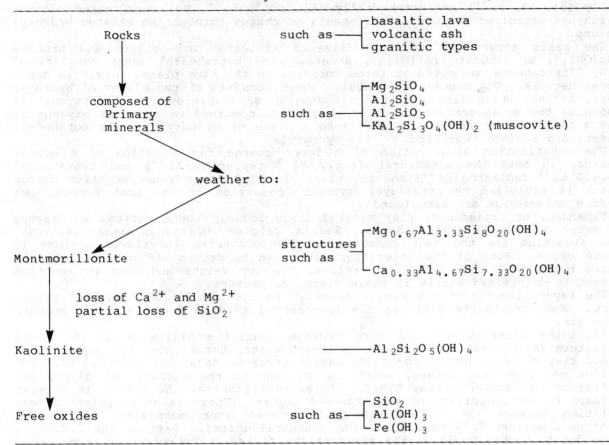

The breakdown process is accompanied by a release of both cations and silica. The water becomes alkaline due to the reaction of H_2CO_3 as proton donor. The solid residue becomes, therefore, more acidic than the aluminium silicate. The $O_{10}(OH)_2$ unit is typical of structures formed during this process. In this way, feldspars produce kaolinites, montmorillonites, and micas, all of which will be transported by the rivers as solids, in addition to the soluble products. Weathering can be simplified as follows:

Primary Mineral   Secondary Mineral
orthoclase
$6KAlSi_3O_8 + 4CO_2 + 28H_2O --- 4K^+ + 4HCO_3^- + KH_2Al_3Si_3O_{12} + 12Si(OH)_4$
                                                          (muscovite)

$6KAlSi_3O_8 + 6CO_2 + 33H_2O --- 6K^+ + 6HCO_3^- + 3Al_2Si_2O_5(OH)_4 + 12Si(OH)_4$
                                                          (kaolinite)

$6KAlSi_3O_8 + 6CO_2 + 48H_2O --- 6K^+ + 6HCO_3^- + 6Al(OH)_3 + 18Si(OH)_4$
                                                          (gibbsite)

The $Si(OH)_4$ will be removed largely in soluble form. Clays are formed in the solid phase in temperate zones. $Al(OH)_3$, $Mn(OH)_{2-4}$, $Fe(OH)_3$, $(FeOOH)$, and quartz, are formed by lateritic weathering in tropical zones.

Clays have significant absorption capacity through which they can bond and transport several compounds including many pollutants.

Clay minerals occur in almost all types of sediments and sedimentary rocks, in which they are often the most abundant mineral, perhaps as much as 40 percent by composition. Fifty percent or more of the clay minerals in the earth's crust are of illite. This is followed, in order of relative abundance, by montmorillonite and mixed layer illite-montmorillonite, chlorite and mixed layer chlorite-montmorillonite, and kaolinite. All clays are built up of tetrahedrally (Si, Al, Fe^{3+}) and octahedrally (Al, Fe^{3+}, Fe^{2+}, Mg) coordinated cations which are organized to form either sheets or chains through the related hydroxyl anions.

The basic structural units in layered silicates are silica and brucite ($Mg(OH)_2$), or gibbsite ($Al(OH)_3$), sheets. The tetrahedral sheet consists of SiO_4^{2-} tetrahedra connected at three corners, in the same plane, forming a hexagonal network. The brucite or gibbsite sheet consists of two planes of hydroxyl ions, between which lies a plane of magnesium or aluminium ions. This unit is known as the octahedral sheet. The sheets are combined so that the oxygens at the tips of the tetrahedra project into a plane of hydroxyls in the octahedral sheet, and replace two-thirds of the hydroxyls.

The substitution of a cation of a lower charge for a cation of a higher charge, in both the octahedral (e.g., Mg^{2+} replacing Al^{3+}) and tetrahedral (e.g., Al^{3+} replacing Si^{4+}) sheets, gives the clay layer a net negative charge which is satisfied by interlayer cations (potassium is the most common, but sodium and calcium are also found).

Expanded, or expandable, clay minerals have loosely bound cations and layers of water between the silica sheets. Sodium, calcium, hydrogen, magnesium, iron, and aluminium are the most common naturally occurring interlayer cations in these cases. Much of the interlayer water can be driven off only at temperatures between 120 and 200°C. Therefore, the dry weight and loss on ignition cannot be determined easily if these clays are present.

The layer electric charge ranges from 0.3 to 1.0 per $O_{10}(OH)_2$ unit of structure. Montmorillonite falls in the low-charged (0.3 to 0.6) group of expanded minerals.

Kaolinite minerals are all pure hydrous aluminium silicates of the basic structure $2Al(OH)_3 \cdot 2Si(OH)_4$ which, on losing water, turns into $Al_2Si_2O_5(OH)_4$.

All clay minerals have a so-called cation exchange capacity, (C.E.C.) but iron oxides and aluminium oxides, which are present on the surfaces of clays, may influence the measured clay C.E.C. In montmorillonite, the C.E.C. is closely related to the proportion of the expanded layers. There is an excellent linear relation between the C.E.C. and surface area (one monovalent cation per 0.67 nm^2, against 0.75 to 1.0 nm^2 for montmorillonite). Part of the C.E.C. is also due to broken bonds at the edges of the flakes. The charge is reversible, being negative in a basic environment and positive in an acidic environment.

Negative ions may be adsorbed, but the mechanism is complicated, as will be discussed further in Section II.7.

II.6.2 Organic matter

Sediments and suspended matter contain small amounts of organic compounds, either derived from the land by water or wind erosion, or produced in the water itself. These fluxes include, besides the so-called natural products, variable loads of pollutants and their degradation products. Often these compounds are linked with inorganic materials such as clay or $CaCO_3$. Compounds which are slowly degraded are called refractory; sorption on to sediment particles may greatly influence the extent and the rate of degradation.

The organic compounds are mainly bitumens, lipids (including fatty acids), and humic substances, which offer extensive sites for both physical and chemical sorption. The humic compounds, either in dissolved or particulate form, will form stable complexes (so-called chelates) with most cations. These include bivalent or higher charged ions, such as calcium and iron (as natural ions), and pollutants such as copper and mercury. The humic compounds, therefore, greatly influence the chemical state of these metals.

It is difficult to draw a sharp distinction between natural and man-made compounds. Eglington et al. (1975) pointed out that, for example, a fluorocarbon or chlorocarbon may originate not only naturally but also as a pollutant. Aromatic hydrocarbons such as perylene are believed to be formed naturally. Turpentines, natural oil seeps, and plant waxes may also contaminate the environment with compounds that are, more often, considered to be man-made pollutants.

The organic matter in sediments can be used to differentiate between allochthonous and autochthonous materials. Cranwell (1977) used an organic fraction, soluble in an organic solvent, and compared this with corresponding extracts from soils and aquatic detritus. Separation of the extract gave several classes, differing in functional group, in which the abundance and percentage composition of each class may be related to the source of the organic matter. Sediments from two lakes, differing in trophic state, illustrated the influence of source material on the composition of the organic fraction.

The downward transport of organic matter with sediments, mostly in the form of humic compounds, is not a one-way transport; considerable release may occur. Stabel and Munster (1977) found that, due to different pH values (and calcium concentrations, for example) in interstitial waters, considerable concentrations of humic matter were found in the interstitial (or pore) waters, from where they could diffuse into the lake water. The determination of the molecular weight fractions of these compounds, although not a very simple technique, can be used to follow these processes.

II.7   The Bonding Process

Sediments may provide a means of transport and/or sink for both nutrient and toxic contaminants by means of chemical processes such as adsorption, (ion) exchange, co-precipitation or complexation, and chelation. Not all reactions are possible, however, in all sediments (see Table II.8). Several of these reactions are pH dependent and, since pH conditions change, natural sediments may release the contaminants and thus act as a source of nutrients and toxic contaminants. Some compounds, also, may be released under reducing conditions (mercury, iron bound compounds, etc.). There are two forms of bonding defined as physical and chemical sorption. They may be described as:

$$clay^- + X^+ \longrightarrow clay\ X$$
$$clay^-H^+ + X^+ \longrightarrow clay\ X + H^+$$

Normally they are not identified separately.

II.7.1   Physical sorption

Clay minerals, and the intergrown metal-hydroxides, have reversible adsorption properties determined by their structure and surface, and by the chemical composition of the solution in which the mineral is suspended. The residual charge of a clay mineral particle is usually negative and it therefore attracts cations, in competition with the charge of the hydrating ions. The C.E.C. is thus measured at pH = 7 (see Chapter IV). Montmorillonite, smectite, and vermiculite have large C.E.C.'s (100 to 150 mmol per 100 g clay mineral, further called unit); kaolinite has 3 to 18 units. Intermediate values, 10 to 40 units, have been measured for illites and chlorites. However, there is some concern about the purity of these minerals, and whether or not the C.E.C. is more influenced by metal coatings. The interpretation of C.E.C. for pollution studies is conjectural.

The mutual exchangeability of cations depends upon their charge density and upon their relative concentrations in solution. Usually, Rb from clay is exchanged less readily than K, and K less than Na because the charge density of Na is greatest. A high charge density causes a stronger binding of a cation to its hydration-shell complex in solution. In order for an ion to be adsorbed on to a clay-mineral surface, part of the water molecule forming its hydration shell must be stripped off. In calcareous clays, Ca^{2+} is the most abundant exchangeable cation; in lime-free clays, the H^+ ion replaces it.

In natural waters, adsorption equilibria are attained between suspended particles and a few of the dissolved components. These equilibria depend on temperature, pH, and the kind of clay present, and control the trace element content of the water. If, for example, Zn is released into a river to increase concentrations to greater than 1 ppm, the Zn will return again to the normal concentration range of between 10 and 100 µg per litre at a distance of some 10 km downstream. In a simulation experiment, a suspension containing 0.01 percent of illite in H_2O (a value frequently observed in river water) extracts about 80 percent of the Cu content from a solution with 0.3 ppm of Cu at pH = 6.8. In a natural river the dissolved Cu concentration will be decreased further, due to the presence of metal-hydroxides (and biota).

TABLE II.8 Carrier substances and mechanisms of heavy metal bonding (from Förstner, 1977a)

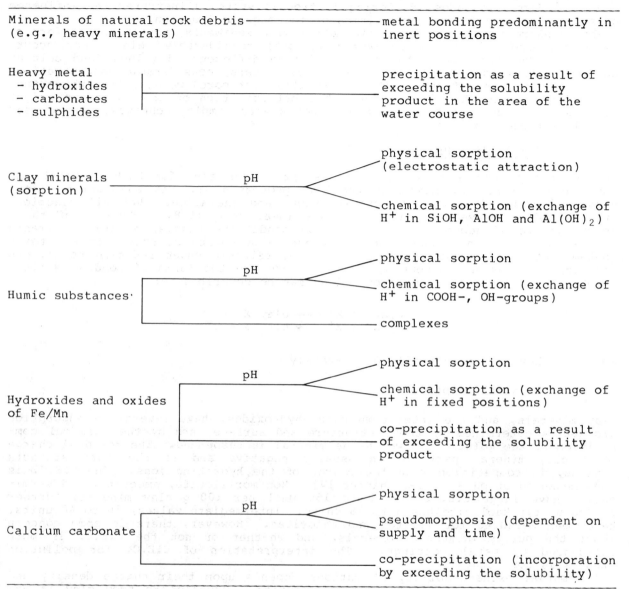

| Minerals of natural rock debris (e.g., heavy minerals) | metal bonding predominantly in inert positions |

Heavy metal
 – hydroxides
 – carbonates
 – sulphides

precipitation as a result of exceeding the solubility product in the area of the water course

Clay minerals (sorption) —— pH

physical sorption (electrostatic attraction)

chemical sorption (exchange of H^+ in SiOH, AlOH and Al(OH)$_2$)

Humic substances· —— pH

physical sorption

chemical sorption (exchange of H^+ in COOH-, OH-groups)

complexes

Hydroxides and oxides of Fe/Mn —— pH

physical sorption

chemical sorption (exchange of H^+ in fixed positions)

co-precipitation as a result of exceeding the solubility product

Calcium carbonate —— pH

physical sorption

pseudomorphosis (dependent on supply and time)

co-precipitation (incorporation by exceeding the solubility)

II.7.2   Chemical sorption

In this process, the cations are exchanged for the H^+ of Si(OH), Al(OH), Al(OH)$_2$, and FeO(OH) groups of clay minerals and metalhydroxides, and the –COOH and –OH groups of organic compounds such as humic substances. The reaction may be simplified as follows:

$$2 \ FeO(OH) + Cu^{2+} \longrightarrow 2H^+ + (FeOO)_2Cu$$

Apparently the process is pH dependent because it also influences the solubility of the FeO(OH).

The chelating process represents a special case of H^+ exchange in which the metal exchanged for the H^+ also forms a binding with N atoms of the complex. EDTA and NTA are strong chelating agents while glycine is a weak agent. Naturally-occurring humic substances are a moderate chelating agent, but it must be realized that different values are found for the different metals.

Sorption and cation exchange take place on fine-grained substances with large areas, and a generalized sequence of the capacity of solids to sorb heavy metals is as follows: MnO_2 > humic acids > hydrous iron-oxide > clay, but, here again, specific differences in value are found. It appears, for example; that while metals such as nickel, cobalt, and chromium show a strong association with MnO_2, the metals zinc, copper, lead, and mercury are widely associated with humic substances and hydrous iron-oxides and clay. For further reading about humic substances, see Povoledo and Golterman (1975).

The ability of biocides to ionize determines whether or not these substances will have an ionic charge in water. Cationic herbicides (such as cyperquat, difenzoquat, and paraquat) are readily adsorbed by the negatively charged colloidal particles of mixed clay and organic composition, and become fixed within the internal layering of expanding clay minerals. Nonionic biocides may be physically adsorbed on to sediments, but their association with such particles depends on the lipophilic nature of the sediment; low solubility pesticides (such as aldrin, BHC, lindane, trifluralin, DDT, dieldrin, endrin, and oryzalin) are not adsorbed by the strongly hydrophylic clay particles. Pesticides which incorporate complexing agents such as phosphate (demeton, disuftenon, glyphosate, parathion, and phorate) or arsenic (DSMA, MAMA, and MSMA) readily complex with clay materials. For further information see Weber (1977) from whom Table II.9 is quoted.

Phosphates may become incorporated in sediments by precipitation or co-precipitation ($CaCO_3/Ca_5(PO_4)_3OH$, or organics) or through adsorption processes (iron hydroxide or clay). The removal of soluble phosphates by hydrous iron oxides is a typical result of sorption reactions and plays a major role in limiting nutrient availability

$$\begin{array}{c} {>}Fe\text{-}OH \\ + \quad H_2PO_4^- \\ {>}Fe\text{-}OH \end{array} \qquad \begin{array}{c} Fe\text{-}O \quad\quad O \\ \diagdown \ \diagup \\ P \\ \diagup \ \diagdown \\ Fe\text{-}O \quad\quad OH \end{array} \qquad + \quad H_2O \quad + \quad OH^-$$

Phosphate adsorption on clays is a rather more complex set of reactions. In the first place, charged sites, caused by substitution of Al or Mg for Si, may fix phosphate anions (Van Wazer, 1961, pp. 1663 and 1676). Another form of (loosely) bound phosphate may occur according to the equilibria:

$$R\text{-}OH_2^+Cl^- \quad + \quad H_2PO_4^- \quad \rightleftharpoons \quad R\text{-}OH_2^+ \cdot H_2PO_4^- + Cl^-$$

or:

$$2R\text{-}OH_2^+ \cdot OH^- \quad + \quad HPO_4^{2-} \quad \rightleftharpoons \quad (R\text{-}OH_2^+)_2\ HPO_4^{2-} \quad + \quad 2OH^-$$

in which the OH^- originates from broken bonds or from hydrous oxides of Al and Fe.

These two processes are pH dependent. The phosphate is reversibly adsorbed, depending on the phosphate concentration. Furthermore, phosphate ions may substitute for lattice hydroxyl-ions and, thereby, become a more immobile part of the clay structure. Although this kind of phosphate is bound more firmly than that previously mentioned, it can be displaced by strong alkali, due to the similarity of the hydroxyl- and phosphate-ion. This type of binding takes place above the iso-electric point (which also provides a means by which to distinguish between these fractions). In clay, the sorption of phosphates exceeds the anion exchange capacity for ions such as Cl^-, NO_3^-, and SO_4^{2-}; at lower pH values phosphate remains bound, as is shown in Table II.10.

The total capacity of anion-exchange, again, is a function of the degree of weathering. Phosphate adsorption on particulate matter in the River Rhine, where it plays a major role, will be discussed in Chapter VI.

II.8   Processes of Precipitation and Co-precipitation

Under the slightly alkaline conditions of normal surface waters, precipitates and coatings may be formed when the solubility product of a certain compound is exceeded. It must be noted that this may happen irrespective of whether or not the components are derived from the same or different sources; e.g., apatite, where the calcium is present naturally, and the phosphate is derived from some 'cultural' or otherwise external source.

TABLE II.9 Classification of selected pesticides based on overall characteristics ionizability, water solubility, presence of complexing elements, and vapourizability (from Weber, 1977)

IONIC PESTICIDES

Cationic Pesticides	Basic Pesticides	Acidic Pesticides
cyperquat	ametryn	dalapon
difenzoquat	atrazine	dicamba
diquat	prometon	picloram
paraquat	prometryn	2,4-D

NONIONIC PESTICIDES

High Water Solubility		Moderate Water Solubility		Low Water Solubility	
Volatile	Non Volatile	Volatile	Non Volatile	Volatile	Non Volatile
aldicarb	carbetamide	CDEC	butachlor	aldrin	DDT
CDAA	fenuron	EPTC	diuron	BHC	dieldrin
dimethoate	methomyl	pebulate	fluometuron	lindane	endrin
molinate	propoxur	vernolate	monuron	trifluralin	oryzalin

With Complexing Element	
Volatile	Non Volatile
demeton	DSMA
disulfoton	glyphosate
parathion	MAMA
phorate	MSMA

TABLE II.10 Amounts of phosphate, sulphate and chloride adsorbed on a kaolinite clay (NIPE) and on a montmorillonite clay (SHARKEY) as a function of pH (from Golterman, 1973)

NIPE				SHARKEY		
	m-equiv. sorbed per 100 g colloid				m-equiv. sorbed per 100 g colloid	
pH	Cl	SO_4	PO_4	pH	Cl	PO_4
7.2	0.0	0.0	31.2	6.8	0.00	22.00
6.7	0.3	2.0	41.2	5.6	0.00	36.50
6.1	1.1	5.5	46.5	4.0	0.05	47.40
5.8	2.4	7.1	50.8	3.2	0.10	64.00
5.0	4.4	10.5	66.1	3.0	0.10	73.50
4.0	6.0	-	88.2	2.8	0.40	100.00

The associated co-precipitation of various heavy metals with hydroxides and carbonates is of particular importance to water quality in many areas. The removal of heavy metals such as cadmium, zinc, and copper by co-precipitation with iron hydroxide is a significant process.

Calcium carbonate has been found to remove most metal carbonates from solutions that have a low solubility, e.g., cadium and lead. However, it seems to be less competitive for heavy metals than iron hydroxides, and the co-precipitated concentrations of cadmium, copper, zinc, and cobalt appear to be much lower in the carbonate deposits than in iron hydroxide rich sediments. Co-precipitation of copper appears to take place under a wide range of competing conditions, but zinc and cadmium may be less effectively co-precipitated in the presence of strong complexing agents.

Co-precipitation of apatite with calcium carbonate is a significant process controlling phosphate concentrations in hard, eutrophic, waters. It may be an important sink for phosphate in deep lakes such as the Swiss Alpine lakes where, due to great water depth, apatite sedimentation is an irreversible process. In shallower lakes, the removal may be reversible due to pH changes and the availability of very small particles to algae, under conditions of limited external supply (see also Section II.11).

II.9   Properties Related to the Organic Matter

The organic composition of particles can be distinguished as easily biodegradable (especially in polluted rivers) or as refractory, although the limits between the two groups are vague because the breakdown of organic matter is closely related to the rate of microbial activity. Under conditions of cold and fast flowing water (such as in Alpine mountain areas) little degradation takes place. In warmer water, and under less turbulent conditions (such as in lakes), degradation is more rapid; much of this takes place during the sedimentation of particles to the bottom, especially in lakes deeper than 10 to 25 m.

In many shallow lakes, therefore, sediments may provide an important substrate and a food source for microbial populations, as well as a source of heavy metals which can be released as toxic substances following biochemical conversions, e.g., methyl mercury, lead, and arsenic.

Phosphate can be released from organic compounds although, due to high concentrations in the interstitial water, it may be re-bound into calcium or iron compounds before a complete transfer can take place into the overlying lake or river waters.

The presence of sediments may have a significant influence on biological communities such as plankton, benthic organisms, and fish. High concentrations of suspended matter may result in low primary production because of restricted light penetration. The availability of dissolved oxygen may be limited by high sediment oxygen demand, either by COD or BOD. The presence of high suspended sediment concentrations may adversely affect respiration and may also result in the burial of existing substrates.

In deeper lakes, refractory material will reach the bottom; e.g., organic matter at the surface of sediments in Lakes Erie and Ontario has a content of about 30 percent fulvic and humic acids and 60 percent humins. Fulvic and humic acids, and humins (together called humic substances) form complex organic materials of heterogeneous mixed polymer systems. Fulvic acids (comprising hydrophylic and polyhydroxide aliphatic and aromatic acids) are the most soluble material and provide an important mechanism for the transport of metal ions in solution. Humic acids are mostly insoluble and immobilize heavy metals; they are partly soluble under high pH conditions but these rarely occur in nature. Humins have the highest molecular weight, are highly polymerized, and they are insoluble.

Fulvic and humic acids behave as negatively charged species in solutions and the neutralization of this charge by interaction with metal ions, metaloxide colloids, or adsorption on to clays, results in flocculation and further co-precipitation. A strong correlation between metals and organic carbon may exist where metals and organics interact in solution, and subsequently become attached to clay particles by adsorption (Table II.8).

Under some conditions, however, there may be competition for adsorption sites between metal ions and organics.

The following sequence has been generally established to characterize the binding strength of selected heavy metals with fulvic and humic acids:

$$UO_2^{2+} > Hg^{2+} > Cu^{2+} > \begin{matrix} Pb^{2+} \\ || \\ Ca^{2+} \end{matrix} > Zn^{2+} > Ni^{2+} > Co^{2+}$$

Experimental evidence suggests that the presence of alkali and alkali-earth cations, which are generally in much greater abundance, significantly modify base metal interactions with organics, by competing for adsorption sites.

Field studies show that, although dispersion of naturally occurring iron and lead may be associated with organic complexing, copper is associated with sorption on to organic-rich sediments, and nickel is controlled by interference reactions with carbonates and hydroxides at alkaline pH.

Competition for dissolved metal ions may also exist between organic ligands and sulphide ions. Inorganic sulphur, present as mono or polymeric hydro-sulphides, is an effective complexing agent. Field studies show that copper is strongly held by sulphide precipitation but that iron and zinc are held by organic complexing. If solubility data for metal sulphides are used for prediction, it may be anticipated that cadmium will behave like zinc, and that arsenic and mercury will be largely fixed as sulphide or organic-sulphide complexes.

Interactions between metals and organics, in aqueous systems, are complex and remain only partly understood; it is evident, however, that pH and Eh effects have a significant influence upon the binding strengths and order of metal-organic stabilities. The alkali solubility of soil organic matter is largely dependent upon the metal ions present. For further reading see Jonasson (1977) from which Table II.11 is taken.

II.10   Transport of Contaminants

The transport of contaminants in aqueous systems may be accomplished (a) by movement in solution, frequently in association with colloidal materials; (b) in association with particulate matter; and (c) in association with biota.

a) The movement of materials in solution follows the diffusion and dispersal patterns which characterize each separate water-body and/or water mass within it. The ratio of heavy metals distributed between aqueous and solid phases undergoes a change in equilibria towards the solid phase, thus the total amount of heavy metals in solution (and some other contaminants) generally diminish in a downstream direction, under normal flow conditions. The average ratio between dissolved and solid species for, for example, boron, zinc, and cadmium is between 2:1 and 1:1; for copper, mercury, chromium, and lead the ratio is about 0.5:1 or 0.25:1; iron, aluminium, and manganese are almost totally transported as solids under normal Eh conditions (Table II.12). Alkali and alkali-earth metals are predominantly present in dissolved form.

TABLE II.11 Generalized metal-organic-solid reaction scheme as proposed by
Curtis (1966), after Jonasson (1977). CP = clay particles,
ORG = organic matter.

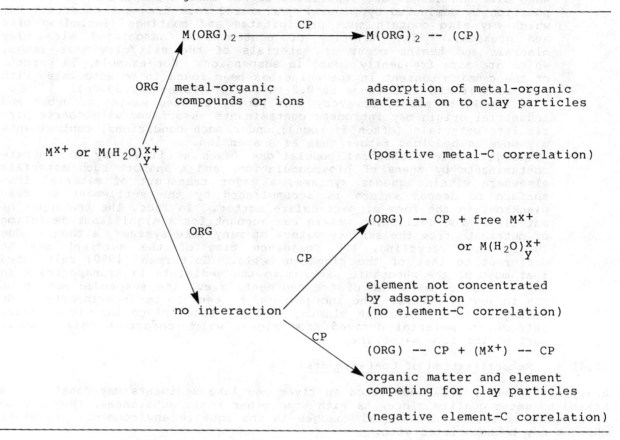

TABLE II.12 Metal transport in rivers (from Förstner, 1977b)

| Metal (example) | Percentage Particulate-Associated Metals of Total Metal Discharge (solid + aqueous) | | |
	U.S. Rivers	*F.R.G. Rivers	Rhine (Netherlands)
Sodium	–	0.5	–
Calcium	–	2.5	–
Strontium	21	–	–
Boron	30	–	–
Cadmium	–	30	45
Zinc	40	45	37
Copper	63	55	64
Mercury	–	59	56
Chromium	76	72	70
Lead	84	79	73
Aluminium	98	98	98
Iron	98	98	98

* Federal Republic of Germany.

b) The movement of the contaminants with particulates is largely influenced by the size and form of the host material. Generally, particulates of sand size and larger are restricted to bed load transport in which composition is dominated by mineral grains and rock fragment materials but which may also contain some precipitates and coatings (including oils and greases). The majority of contaminants associated with clay minerals and humins occur in materials of the silt/clay size range, which are more frequently found in suspension. For example, 98 percent of the cadmium content in the Rhine has been found to be associated with particles in the size range of 0.2 to 0.6 μm (Förstner, 1977b).

It should be noted, however, that poorly treated wastes of urban and industrial origin may introduce contaminants associated with coarse particulate materials (often fibrous); under such conditions, contaminants may move as bed load rather than as suspension.

c) Although mobile biological populations (such as fish) may concentrate contaminants by means of bioaccumulation, and transport such materials elsewhere within aqueous systems, a major transport of material from surface to deeper waters is accomplished by the settlement of dead plankton, in the form of particulate matter. In fact, the transport of materials from epilimnion waters can account for a significant depletion of nutrients from the surface waters of many lake systems, although, due to internal recycling, the residence time of the nutrient may be different to that of the plankton cells. Golterman (1980) calculated that most of the phosphate sinking to the sediments is transported with the inorganic component of the sediment, i.e., the suspended matter of the inflowing rivers. The inorganic sink seems to be less important for nitrogen because nitrogen sinking probably takes place largely as dead, refractory, material derived from algae, which comprises only a small part of the live material.

II.11   Remobilization of Contaminants

Heavy metals which are immobilized in river and lake sediments may constitute a hazard to water quality since, as with some other toxic substances, they may be released as a result of chemical changes in the aquatic environment. Chemical changes may be associated with:

Increasing salinity.
Lowering of pH, and leaching by organic acids.
Changes in Eh and/or oxygen deficit.
Microbial transformation - e.g., methylation.
The presence of synthetic complexing agents (e.g., NTA).
Physical disturbance of bed materials.

II.11.1   Salinity

Increasing salinity in water-bodies, such as occur in estuaries or under conditions of high evaporation, leads to competition between dissolved cations and adsorbed heavy metal ions, and results in the partial replacement of some heavy metals. Downstream of the freshwater tidal interface, a pronounced remobilization of mercury, zinc, chromium, lead, copper, and arsenic (carried as industrial contaminants by river sediments) has been noted at the mouth of the Rhine (Chapter VI). In the Rhine, it is assumed that oxygenation and increased salinity have resulted in rapid decomposition of organic materials which are associated with the heavy metals. Since the order of remobilization appears to be approximately the reverse of the solubility product of the sulphides of these metals, it is likely that the greater complexing affinities of, for example, mercury and copper, towards soluble organic matter, are more important (kinetically) than their sulphide solubilities. Thus, the formation of soluble metal-organic complexes may offer an important mechanism for remobilizing contaminants from sediment materials.

In estuarine systems, the decrease of heavy metal content in sediment may be also accounted for by the diluting effect of clean sediment which is frequently transported inshore from the marine environment.

Increased sedimentation in estuarine conditions, due to flocculation of (colloidal) particles, provides a mechanism which works against the partial replacement of heavy metals. This flocculation may be caused by the NaCl concentration but also, probably by the higher Ca-concentrations in seawater; both may influence heavy metal adsorption. The relative importance of all these mechanisms has yet to be finally established.

II.11.2   pH and leaching

A lowering of pH leads to the dissolution of carbonate and hydroxide minerals and also, as a result of hydrogen ion competition, to an increased desorption of metal cations. Severe pH changes as a result of industrial impacts, particularly in waters poor in bicarbonate ions, may cause intense dissolution of a wide range of metals. The high concentrations of dissolved iron, manganese, nickel, cobalt, copper, and zinc, for example, are typical of the drainage from many mines.

The presence of dissolved organic acids in water also significantly contributes to the leaching and dissolution of mineral materials, especially those particulates entrapped within organic sediments. Prolonged attack by fulvic and humic acids can result in the extraction of a variety of elements, including many metals. Humic acid, for example, rapidly decomposes many common sulphide minerals (chalcopyrite, $CuFeS_2$; chalcocite, CuS_2; sphalerite, ZnS; galena, PbS; and pyrite FeS_2) and oxides (pyrolusite, MnO_2; and goethite, $FeOOH$) and carbonates (such as calcite, dolomite, and malachite $Cu_2(OH)_2CO_3$). Decreasing pH will release phosphates from iron and calcium complexes. Increasing pH may release phosphate from iron but not from calcium complexes. In Figure II.5, it can be seen that the solubility of PO_4-P (orthophosphate), at concentrations above 1 mg l^{-1} and pH ≤ 6.5, can be controlled by precipitation with $FeOOH$. At the same concentrations but with pH ≥ 7, calcium will control solubility. PO_4-P concentrations of about 0.1 mg l^{-1} are unaffected by precipitation with $FeOOH$ but Ca will continue to control solubility at pH ≥ 7.

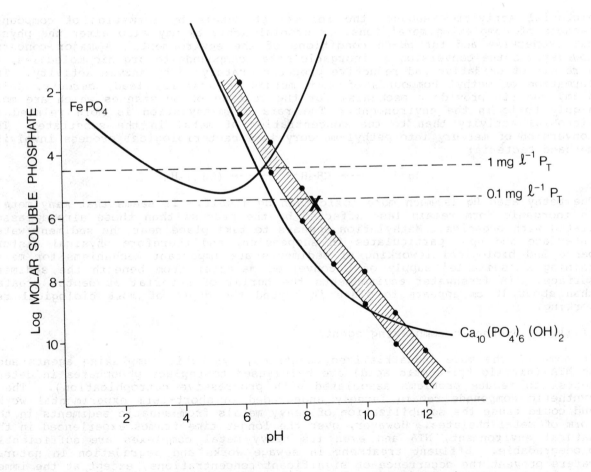

FIGURE II.5 Solubility diagram for phosphate phases

The shaded band is calculated with a range of solubility product for $(Ca)_{10}(PO_4)_6(OH)_2$ between 10^{-100} and 10^{-106}; Ca^{2+} is kept constant at 1×10^{-3} Ml^{-1} (using appropriate acid dissociation constants).

The line plots for $FePO_4$ and $Ca_{10}(PO_4)_6(OH)_2$ are taken from Stumm and Baccini (1970).

Note: Due to $CaCO_3$ precipitation, Ca^{2+} will tend to be less than 1 mM. The point X, indicated at 8.4, has 0.8 mM. Because of precipitation, the real solubility line will be slightly above the shaded area.

II.11.3   Eh and oxygen deficit

A decrease of redox potential (Eh) is caused by microbial activity, associated with increased concentrations of organic material which, under oxic conditions, would have been completely oxidized to CO_2. Organic matter, in solution, may reduce $Fe(OH)_3$ from sediments to soluble Fe^{2+}. Any co-precipitates with metallic coatings may become partly remobilized and release co-precipitated toxins, e.g., heavy metals. Organic matter may also act as a reducing agent where the presence of humic material can affect the stabilization of ferrous iron, in oxygenated solutions, by complexation with organic acids. In particular, the formation of polynuclear species of iron and manganese oxides (initial dissolution of hydrated manganese oxide, followed by analogous iron compounds) play an important role in the remobilization of iron and manganese from reduced sediments.
   In the release of copper, zinc, and cadmium from anoxic sediments it seems that the processes may be controlled more by microbiological activity and subsequent formations of complexes than by ion migration alone.

II.11.4   Microbial activity, transformations

Microbial activities enhance the release of metals by formation of compounds capable of complexing metal ions. Microbial activity may also alter the physical properties and the pH-Eh conditions of the environment. A major concern, however, is the conversion of inorganic metal compounds to organic molecules, as a result of oxidative and reductive processes catalyzed by enzyme activity. The formation of methyl compounds of such metals as arsenic, lead, mercury, selenium, and tin provide a mechanism for the release of substances which are more highly toxic in the environment. The rate of methylation is more related to microbial activity than to the concentration of metal in the substrate. The conversion of mercury into methyl-mercury is a bacteriological process involving methane bacteria:

$$Hg^{2+} \longrightarrow CH_3Hg^+ \longrightarrow (CH_3)_2Hg$$

The methylated Hg is much more toxic than Hg itself. It seems that many metals in inorganic form remain less affected by the process than those already associated with organics. Methylation appears to take place near the sediment/water interface and upon particulates in suspension, and therefore physical disturbance and biological reworking of sediments are important mechanisms for maintaining a 'suitable' supply of unconverted material from beneath the sediment surface. In freshwater environments the burial of material at depths greater than about 10 cm appears to place it beyond the depth of most biological reworking.

II.11.5   Synthetic complexing agents

In some of the more industrialized countries, synthetic complexing agents such as NTA (nitrilo tri-acetic acid) are being used to replace phosphates in detergents (to reduce problems associated with progressive eutrophication). These synthetic compounds remain largely undegraded in short-term experimental work, and could cause the solubilization of heavy metals from aquatic sediments in the form of metal chelates. However, over the longer time frames experienced in the natural environment, NTA and even its heavy metal complexes are sufficiently biodegradable. Effluent treatment in sewage works and degradation in natural waters prevent the occurrence of significant concentrations, except at the immediate outlet of some sewage plants.

II.11.6 Physical disturbance

The physical disturbance of bottom sediments by natural means, such as wave and current activity, or by bottom fauna, or by man-induced changes such as realignment of water courses and ship movement and dredging, provides a further mechanism for the release of contaminant materials.

Typically, contaminants may be released by the dispersion of soluble species held in concentrated pore waters (in addition to the mechanisms discussed earlier). However, contaminant release, following physical disturbance of bottom sediments, may vary considerably at different times of year, since the chemical regime of the overlying waters is changeable and depends upon climatic and other seasonal conditions.

II.12 The Significance of Biological Exposure

II.12.1 Biological exposure and the significance of bioturbation

Although there is no doubt that the effects of contaminants on biota are very closely related to both the toxicity of substances and their concentration, there are additional factors associated with the type and duration of exposure. These are of particular importance to systems involving sediment/water interaction.

Biological populations which are sedentary, or of limited mobility, tend to be exposed to contaminants for a greater length of time than those whose mobility or seasonal migration allows them to follow avoidance reactions or to make temporary egress at contaminated sites. Conversely, biological populations which are mobile may be more subject to shock effects, when passing through a stressed system and without an opportunity to acclimatize.

At present, there is no clear understanding and little published information which can be used to quantify the significance of exposure under existing natural conditions. This is particularly true for situations in which exposure to contaminants may give rise to sub-lethal effects or delayed reactions (such as fish carcenomas or tissue degeneration). However, an estimate of the effect of more lethal contaminants on select biota can be simulated, to some extent, by laboratory experiments and the typical lethal dose (LD_{50}) or lethal concentration (LC_{50}) tests of bio-assay experiments may be taken as a coarse guide to contaminant impact upon natural biological systems.

Few impact studies have been able to explore either the complexities of combined dose and exposure problems, or to evaluate the combined effects of multiple contaminants (such as may be produced when receiving areas are subject to a mixture of industrial contaminants and biocides applied for agricultural purposes).

Generally, the more labile substances have greater impact on the biota in terms of shock loading rather than in terms of exposure time. On the other hand, more stable compounds (such as DDT and its degradation products, or PCBs) which can be ingested through the food web, can be bio-magnified in orders of thousands or even millions of times and have a cumulative effect which is very definitely related to exposure, as well as concentration.

Under some conditions, where natural biological communities have been exposed to contaminants for a relatively long time, it is possible for local populations to show genetic adaptation (or resistance) which allows certain species to persist under otherwise contaminanted conditions.

Generally speaking, this kind of adaptation is most characteristic of very long-term biological exposure to contaminants (such as heavy metals) which are of consistent composition; concentrations, for example, may be naturally high because of some local geological or soil conditions or, perhaps, the long-term exposure of old mine waste materials. Biological populations subject for lesser periods to cultural contaminants (which may be of varying composition) are, therefore, much affected by exposure.

Biological populations can be affected by the intake of contaminants during respiration or ingestion and, therefore, contaminants associated with suspended particles as well as bottom sediments may be important. Biological populations (such as various species of worms, insect larvae, gastropods and lamellibranchs) which inhabit the bottom sediments may be almost continuously exposed to contaminants and, by the process of bioturbation (biological reworking of the sediment during the process of feeding and relocation), new layers of contaminant may be re-exposed at the sediment/water interface for many years after contaminant input has ceased.

II.12.2 Nutrient availability from sediments

Just as the biota may be exposed to toxic contaminants which are present in suspended and bottom sediments so, too, various forms of nutrient may be biologically available. This can be shown in simple experiments in which natural wet sediments are mixed with algal cultures that are devoid of phosphate, iron and nitrogen salts; nearly all sediments will support algal cultures.

Due to the overwhelming influence of phosphate on the trophic status of lakes, especially in temperate waters, much research has been carried out recently on the availability of phosphate from sediments for algal growth. Based on most lake sediment studies, it so far appears that between 20 and 100 percent of the sediment phosphate is biologically available.

Golterman (1977a) showed that, although phosphate bound into the clay lattice (natural clay phosphate) is not available, phosphate freshly adsorbed on to clays is available to Scenedesmus cultures; all of the new-bound phosphate appeared to be available to the cultures. Apatite phosphate is partially available, depending upon the grain size; iron phosphate is completely available.

Williams et al. (1980) showed that between 38 and 83 percent of the non-apatite inorganic phosphate (NAI-P fraction) derived from eroding bluff materials, suspended solids in streams, and bottom sediments from Lakes Ontario and Erie, was available for Scenedesmus cultures.

It should be noted that, in such experiments, it is important that the algae are mixed with the sediment particles without separation by some form of physical barrier, such as a dialysis tube. Some sediments so strongly adsorb K^+ that this must be added, in addition, especially if K_2HPO_4 is used as the only source of P; it should be replaced by KCl.

Sediments can often supply some nitrogen, but the quantities of this nutrient are much less than the phosphate (in terms of algal demand).

In most sediments, there is sufficient iron to support good algal growth. However, this is not always the case and eroding sandy bluff materials and glacial silts may be quite impoverished.

Whether or not the potential availability of nutrients can be used to characterize the actual availability in a natural lake system is largely dependent upon the hydrodynamics of the lake. To ensure a high degree of availability in the epilimnion waters for as long as possible, the finest silty-clay size particles must remain exposed and suspended; the fine suspended load from inflowing streams must not pass through the lake as an entrained flow, but must disperse and remain in suspension. In shallow lakes the resuspension of bottom sediments (in response to disturbance of the lake bed by wind-wave action) may further contribute to the re-suspension and exposure of fine particulates with their freshly adsorbed phosphate, making it available to algal populations. In very shallow lakes (less than a few meters) re-suspension may not even be necessary because of the proximity of the photic zone and the sediments.

References

CANADA DEPARTMENT OF THE ENVIRONMENT. 1973. Fluvial processes and sedimentation. Proc. Hydrol. Symp. Univ. Alberta, Edmonton. Inland Wat. Direct., Ottawa. 759 pp.

Cranwell, P. 1977. Organic compounds as indicators of allochthonous and autochthonous input to lake sediments. In: Golterman, H.L. (ed.), Interactions between sediments and fresh water, p. 133-141. Junk/Pudoc, The Hague.

Curtis, C.D. 1966. The incorporation of soluble organic matter into sediments and its effect on trace element assemblages. In: Hobson, G.D.; Louis, M.C. (eds.), Advances in organic geochemistry, p. 1-13. Pergamon Press, Oxford.

Curtis, W.F.; Culbertson, J.K.; Chase, E.B. 1973. Fluvial-sediment discharge to the oceans from the conterminous United States. U.S. Geol. Surv., Circ., 670.

Damiani, V.; Ferrario, A.; Gavelli, G.; Thomas, R.L. 1977. Trace metal composition and fractionation of Mn, Fe, S, P, Ba and Si in the Bay of Quinte freshwater ferromanganese concretions, Lake Ontario. In: Golterman, H.L. (ed.), Interactions between sediments and fresh water, p. 83-93. Junk/Pudoc, The Hague.

* Dapples, E.C. 1959. Basic geology. John Wiley & Sons, New York. 609 pp.

Eglington, G. 1975. Environmental chemistry. Chem. Soc., London. 199 pp.

Eglington, G.; Simoneit, B.R.T.; Zoro, J.A. 1975. The recognition of organic pollutants in aquatic sediments. Proc. Roy. Soc. London, Sect. B, 189, p. 415-442.

Englund, J.O.; Jørgensen, P.; Roaldset, E.; Aagaard, P. 1977. Composition of water and sediments in Lake Mjøsa, South Norway, in relation to weathering process. In: Golterman, H.L. (ed.), Interactions between sediments and fresh water, p. 125-133. Junk/Pudoc, The Hague.

Förstner, U. 1977a. Metal concentrations in freshwater - natural background and cultural effects. In: Golterman, H.L. (ed.), Interactions between sediments and fresh water, p. 94-104. Junk/Pudoc, The Hague.

Förstner, U. 1977b. Trace metals. In: Shear, H.; Watson, A.E.P. (eds.), The fluvial transport of sediment-associated nutrients and contaminants, p. 219-233. Internat. Joint Commiss., Great Lakes Regional Off., Windsor, Ontario.

Gibbs, R.J. 1973. Mechanisms of trace metal transport in rivers. Science, 180, p. 71-73.

Golterman, H.L. 1973. Natural phosphate sources in relation to phosphate budgets. Wat. Res., 7, p. 3-17.

Golterman, H.L. 1975a. Chemistry. In: Whitton, B.A. (ed.), River Ecology, p. 39-80. Blackwell Sci. Publ., Oxford. 725 pp.

* Golterman, H.L. 1975b. Physiological limnology; an approach to the physiology of lake ecosystems. Elsevier, Amsterdam. 489 pp.

Golterman, H.L. (ed.). 1977a. Interactions between sediments and fresh water. Junk/Pudoc, The Hague. 473 pp.

Golterman, H.L. 1977b. Nutrients – P. (Abstract). In: Shear, H.; Watson, A.E.P. (eds.), The fluvial transport of sediment-associated nutrients and contaminants, p. 157-159. Internat. Joint Commiss., Great Lakes Regional Off., Windsor, Ontario.

Golterman, H.L. 1980. Phosphate models – a gap to bridge. Hydrobiologia, 72, p. 61-71.

Hutzinger, O.; Van Lelyveld, L.H.; Zoeteman, B.C.J. (eds.). 1978. Aquatic pollutants; transformation and biological effects. Pergamon Press, Oxford. 519 pp.

Jonasson, I. 1977. Geochemistry of sediment/water interactions; metals. In: Shear, H.; Watson, A.E.P. (eds.) The fluvial transport of sediment-associated nutrients and contaminants, p. 255-271. Internat. Joint Commiss., Great Lakes Regional Off., Windsor, Ontario.

Jones, B.F.; Bowser, C.J. 1978. The mineralogy and related chemistry of lake sediments. In: Lerman, A. (ed.), Lakes; chemistry, geology, physics, p. 179-235. Springer-Verlag, New York/Heidelberg.

Lal, V.B.; Banerji, S. 1977. A multivariate prediction equation for rate of sedimentation in North Indian reservoirs. In: Golterman, H.L. (ed.), Interactions between sediments and fresh water, p. 183-188. Junk/Pudoc, The Hague.

Leifeste, D.K. 1974. Dissolved-solids discharge to the oceans from the conterminous United States. U.S. Geol. Surv., Circ., 685.

* Lerman, A. (ed.). 1978. Lakes; chemistry, geology, physics. Springer-Verlag, New York/Heidelberg. 363 pp.

Livingstone, D.A. 1963. Chemical composition of rivers and lakes. U.S. Geol. Surv., Profess. Pap. 440G, p. 1-64.

Meybeck, M. 1976. Total mineral dissolved transport by world major rivers. Hydrolog. Sci., Bull. Sci. Hydrolog., XXI, 2/6, p. 265-284.

Meybeck, M. 1977. Dissolved and suspended matter carried by rivers: composition, time and space variations, and world balance. In: Golterman, H.L. (ed.), Interactions between sediments and fresh water, p. 25-32. Junk/Pudoc, The Hague.

Milner, N.B. 1962. Sedimentary petrography. 2 vols. George Allen and Unwin Ltd., London. 1358 pp.

* Neff, J.M. 1978. Polycyclic aromatic hydrocarbons in the aquatic environment. Sources, fates and biological effects. Applied Science Publishers Ltd., Essex, England. 262 pp.

Postma, H. 1967. Sediment transport and sedimentation in the estuarine environment. In: Lauff, G.H. (ed.), Estuaries, Publ. Amer. Assoc. Adv. Sci., 83, p. 158-179.

* Povoledo, M.; Golterman, H.L. (eds.). 1975. Humic substances. Centre for Agricultural Publication and Documentation, Wageningen. 360 pp.

Schuiling, R.D. 1977. Source and composition of lake sediments. In: Golterman, H.L. (ed.), Interactions between sediments and fresh water, p. 12-19. Junk/Pudoc, The Hague.

Shear, H.; Watson, A.E.P. (eds.). 1977. The fluvial transport of sediment-associated nutrients and contaminants. Internat. Joint Commiss., Great Lakes Regional Off., Windsor, Ontario.

Stabel, H.H.; Münster, U. 1977. On the structure of soluble organic substances in sediments of Lake Plussee. In: Golterman, H.L. (ed.), Interactions between sediments and fresh water, p. 156-161. Junk/Pudoc, The Hague.

Strahler, A.N.; Strahler, A.H. 1973. Environmental geoscience. Hamilton Publ. Co., Indianapolis. 511 pp.

Stumm, W.; Baccini, P. 1978. Man-made chemical perturbation of lakes. In: Lerman, A. (ed.), Lakes; chemistry, geology, physics, p. 91-126. Springer-Verlag, New York/Heidelberg.

* Stumm, W.; Morgan, J.J. 1970. Aquatic chemistry. Wiley Interscience, New York, London, Toronto. 583 pp.

Sunborg, A. 1973. Significance of fluvial processes and sedimentation. In: Fluvial processes and sedimentation, p. 1-10. Proc. Hydrol. Symp. Univ. Alberta, Edmonton. Can. Dept. Environ., Inland Wat. Direct., Ottawa.

Terwindt, J.H.J. 1977. Deposition, transportation and erosion of mud. In: Golterman, H.L. (ed.), Interactions between sediments and fresh water, p. 19-25. Junk/Pudoc, The Hague.

Turekian, K.K. 1971. Rivers, tributaries and estuaries. In: Hood, D.W. (ed.), Impingement of man on the oceans, p. 9-73. Wylie Interscience, New York, London, Toronto.

Van Wazer, J.R. (ed.). 1961. Phosphorus and its compounds. Vol. 2. Technology, biological functions and applications. Wiley Interscience, New York. 1091 pp.

Walling, D.E. 1977. Natural sheet and channel erosion of unconsolidated source material. In: Shear, H.; Watson, A.E.P. (eds.), The fluvial transport of sediment-associated nutrients and contaminants, p. 11-33. Internat. Joint Commiss., Great Lakes Regional Off., Windsor, Ontario.

Weber, J.B. 1977. Geochemistry of sediment/water interactions; pesticides. In: Shear, H.; Watson, A.E.P. (eds.), The fluvial transport of sediment-associated nutrients and contaminants, p. 245-253. Internat. Joint Commiss., Great Lakes Regional Off., Windsor, Ontario.

* Wetzel, B. 1975. Limnology. Saunders, Philadelphia, London, Toronto. 743 pp.

Williams, J.D.H.; Shear, H.; Thomas, R.L. 1980. Availability to Scenedesmus quadricauda of different forms of phosphorus in sedimentary materials from the Great Lakes. Limnol. Oceanogr., 25, p. 1-11.

Wyldman, E.C.; Poliquin, W.H. 1973. Effects of oilfield development on sedimentation in the Swan Hills, Alberta. In: Fluvial processes and sedimentation, p. 192-207. Proc. Hydrol. Symp. Univ. Alberta, Edmonton. Can. Dept. Environ., Inland Wat. Direct., Ottawa.

* Suggested textbooks for further reading, not necessarily mentioned in the text.

III Sediment sampling programs

III.1 Program Objectives

The results of analyses on bed and suspended sediment samples may be used to define and understand many processes, and to solve many problems occurring in both lacustrine and fluvial systems; but clear resolution of the objective is an essential and basic requirement before adequate design of a sampling strategy can be carried out. Also, failure to obtain the necessary number and quality of samples can nullify the expenditure of effort and money on analyses and data synthesis (see also Chapter V).

The relationship between study design and objective is, however, complicated by logistical factors, which include such concerns as:
- local availability of sampling platform or vessel
- time available
- access to sampling region
- suitability of survey system to locate sample positions and run survey lines
- availability of trained personnel and support staff
- availability of equipment
- storage and security
- transport systems
- follow-up capability

The recent and accelerating interest by environmental and associated agencies in adopting sediment analysis as an integral component of their programs, substantiates the fact that the application of sediment research to environmental problems has achieved considerable success. Based on published research, it is possible to outline several useful objectives for sediment sampling programs, and to present comments about some of their limitations. The limitations are generally a function of incomplete knowledge or technique. Some objectives to which sediment analyses may be directed are summarized below.

III.1.1 Fundamental studies of sedimentary and geochemical processes

A sampling program may be designed, specifically, to study the sediment system as an entity of its own. Such studies are usually undertaken by geo-specialists (e.g., sedimentologists or geochemists) as a means of furthering existing knowledge and as a means of meeting the specialized interests of the investigator. These types of investigation may be holistic or highly specialized but, because their applications largely lie outside the interests of this guidebook, they are not discussed here in further detail. These types of study do, however, provide the pool of existing and growing knowledge upon which applied environmental studies are dependent and they will be used to provide examples of the use of sediments as indicators of existing water quality and of water quality trends in time.

III.1.2   Preliminary studies of bottom sediments

This type of study is based upon a limited survey of the distribution of bottom
sediment types, together with an analysis of sediment texture. The sorting of
sediment by waves and currents results in a graduation of sediment type and texture which, in the simplest sense, provides an integration of the physical conditions which control these characteristics.

The characteristics of bottom sediments, within an aqueous system, are largely
unique for specific locations and water depths, and are conditioned by regional
and local basin forms, sources, and supply, and by climate and weather (see also
VI.2).

An understanding of the sediment distribution within an aqueous system is an
essential prerequisite of sampling for specific environmental purposes.   It
would be, for example, foolish to sample an ancient clay or an erosional lag
deposit, if one is examining a sediment sequence for the occurrence of an
organic contaminant. Sampling for contaminants must be carried out in an area
of the water-body where active accumulation of sediment is taking place. The
intent of a preliminary study is, therefore, to define suitable sampling locations and to provide background information for use in later data interpretation.

III.1.3   Determining the occurrence of specific components

This type of sampling is designed to answer a relatively simple question which
relates to the presence or absence of a specific component; generally, a contaminant of either local or regional concern. Such a question might be, 'Are
there PCBs in this area?' For this purpose, a single sediment sample can be
taken from a depositional area near the centre of a lake and analyzed for PCBs.
The answer, 'yes' or 'no', is soon known and the investigator may then wish to
obtain other information with more resolution as, for example, the source of
such a contaminant, the extent of its dispersal, the temporal variation in
loading to the system, and levels in the biotic compartments which will reveal
the extent of bio-accumulation and bio-magnification (through all trophic levels
within the aqueous system). The use of sediment samples as an efficient means
of carrying out preliminary studies is, therefore, of particular importance.

The reason for selecting a sediment sample, in the case of the PCB example
cited above, is based upon the ability of fine sediment to rapidly adsorb and
concentrate poorly soluble compounds from water. This results in increased concentrations which are orders of magnitude greater than those found in the water.

With this type of compound, even higher concentrations may be found at the top
of the food chain. However, sediment samples are usually preferred because bed
materials are less prone to show variability after deposition, and are not as
much subjected to the influences of seasonal migration or morphological changes
which affect many biological forms during their life cycle.

Soluble contaminants, such as the triazines (see also Table II.9), show little
difference between sediment and water concentrations. Experimental evidence,
also, shows that they do not bio-accumulate to the same extent as the persistent
organo-chlorine compounds. Compounds such as the triazines are best analyzed on
water samples taken shortly after application, and near to the point of the compound's introduction.

III.1.4   Determining material transport from studies of bottom sediments

Although the forms of bottom sediment distributions, their composition, and
their physical characteristics, may all be used as indicators of the general
transport of sediments within aquatic systems, this information is usually considered to be qualitative and unsuitable as a basis for quantitative estimates.

Similarly, because the hydraulic conditions which influence the movement of
bed and suspended materials are different, there is no direct association
between the characteristics of suspended particulates and the immediately underlying bed materials. This lack of association is most pronounced in rivers and
the nearshore zones of lakes where hydraulic processes, affecting the sorting of
particulates, are most active; mid-lake conditions, on the other hand, show much
greater similarity between bed and suspended sediments.

In many lakes and river systems, local (or regional) sources and supplies of
sediments have recognizable differences which can be identified in terms of

68

mineralogical, geochemical, and particle-size characteristics. In some situations different deposits of bottom sediments can be distinguished not only by their location but by clear differences in their composition, which reflect derivation from different sources; such deposits are said to be of different provenance.

As an example of natural provenance the sediment contributions from different watersheds may be found to be highly distinct, where different heavy mineral suites are directly related to the different geology and bedrock types in the watersheds (see II.4.3). Similarly, there may be distinct clay mineral assemblages, or the sediments may be characterized by the presence of specific trace elements. If such differences in provenance are apparent, the distribution of the mineral assemblages or the distribution of specific chemical elements may clearly indicate dispersal and transport within the aqueous system.

In many lakes and rivers the sorting of sediments in the nearshore zone is not a smooth and continuous process; rather, it is a hydraulic process the intensity and location of which may fluctuate greatly depending upon variations in current and wave conditions, flow, and sediment supply. Under natural conditions the distributions of clay and silt-size particles are often found to be masked by the fluctuating additions of fine sand and silt (of different chemical and mineral composition). These additions of coarser material effectively dilute the concentration of some trace elements associated with the finer particle sizes, particularly where these occur at micro-concentrations. Samples taken from bottom sediments, which have been affected by this form of natural dilution, may not show the proper distributions of trace element concentrations which are associated with the fine particulates. Hence, it is necessary to apply a form of correction to reduce the significance of masking caused by the diluting effect. Thomas (1972), devised a normalizing technique which, in various forms, is also known as a Quartz Correction Factor (QCF). This has been used with considerable success and it is described in Chapter V.4. Where the quartz composition is not available, an approximation of QCF can be derived using an interpolated empirical relationship between quartz content and mean size. The use of the QCF provides a means of identifying chemical distributions and dispersal patterns which are reasonably unaffected by particle-size interference. QCF is a particularly useful technique for differentiating the transport and dispersal of selected components at river mouths, where sandy silts become admixed with silty clays on the bed of the nearshore zone (in the receiving waters). As described later, in Chapter VI, it is also possible to use percentage composition of select grain size fractions as a means of differentiating separate sedimentological regimes, such as those which reflect deep water transport and dispersal in distal locations. A description of the sediments in the Pallanza Basin (Lake Maggiore) clearly demonstrates how different grain size fractions can be used to distinguish between fine grained materials of similar appearance.

Although studies of bottom sediment type and textural sorting provide only limited information about sediment transport, some inferences can be made on the basis of trends in the distribution of the statistical indices of sorting (such as the standard deviation, and mean sizes, or Skewness/Kurtosis ratio (see Chapter V)); however, in many cases, much supplementary information is required.

Many of the techniques used in determining sediment transport are dependent on the presence of existing tracers, which reflect a lack of homogeneity in the regional sources (different provenance) of the system; or, the introduction of excessive quantities of some material which is a product of man's activities (in a localized part of the drainage basin). In the more heavily developed parts of the world, inputs from man's activities are collectively referred to as 'cultural loadings'. Examples of cultural loading can be seen to take many forms: the (anthropogenic) loading (input) of mercury from a chlor-alkali plant; the loss of lead from a ceramic factory or from an urbanized watershed; the loss of a specific insecticide from an agricultural watershed. In each of these examples the contaminant will 'fingerprint' the finer sediment particles in the form of increased concentrations. These will show up as trends in their concentration gradients in bottom sediments and will usually show a progressive decrease along the main transport routes, followed by the particles as they move downstream and disperse into an open water system.

Indeed, the determination of detailed pathways of sediment dispersal may not be possible in a homogenous sediment without the introduction of artificial tracer materials (e.g., radio-active tracers; antimony, cobalt or tantalum-enriched glass, of specific granular dimensions. See de Groot et al., 1970). These latter techniques are highly specialized and are not discussed further in this Guide.

The determination of sediment transport by the techniques noted above provides a general description of the approaches which can be applied for several different types of survey. Transport studies within an aqueous system should not be attempted without a good appreciation of the physical-sedimentological environment, since this largely controls dispersal, reworking, and deposition of sedimentary materials. The relationships between bed and suspended materials are illustrated in Figure II.3, and will be discussed further.

To obtain quantitative estimates of sediment transport, different techniques are required to measure bed and suspended sediments (see also later sections of this chapter). These measurements are further complicated by the need to use techniques which are individually suited to rivers or lakes, etc.

The transport of bed materials in rivers can be measured by the use of bed load samplers (see III.4.1), whose recoveries can be compared with stage and discharge data to estimate weight or volume of material in transport over selected time intervals. Estimates can be derived, also, from large-scale volumetric changes in the bed form of a channel, measured by means of detailed and precise sounding surveys.

In lakes, especially large lakes, it is very difficult to measure sediment transport. Bed load transport in lakes is usually significant only in the nearshore, where sediment traps and bathymetric changes in bed form can be used to estimate only a portion of sediment transport. More often, quantities are expressed by other forms of measurement such as rates of shore erosion (measured against fixed points), or the difference between inflow and outflow loadings (expressed as concentration x volume of flow). Different rates of sediment accumulation in different parts of a lake basin can be used as an additional quantitative measure.

III.1.5 Determining the source of point and diffuse inputs

The positive identification of a contaminant in a sediment, either accidentally (during a multi-component analysis) or by exploratory testing, leads to the necessity of determining its source. With an understanding of the likely dispersal patterns, defined by studies as discussed earlier, a source can be inferred and sampling of the source area may quickly begin to confirm the origin (be it a river or a direct input to the water-body). Where pre-knowledge is unavailable, a survey program must be designed with a sufficiently close spacing of samples to provide the resolution required for locating the major point input to the water-body. If a river mouth proves to be the source, then a further sampling must be conducted to locate the upstream source. Source determination can only be successfully conducted where point sources (e.g., individual, municipal or industrial discharges) are the principal source of contaminant loading. Where contaminants are derived from diffuse sources, for example the atmospheric loading of lead or PCBs, the distribution of contaminant in lake sediments will display little evidence of 'hot spots', and the concentration gradients will only conform with sediment texture (such as the distribution of the fine clay-size fraction of the recent sediment). If such concentrations are normalized, to compensate for textural variation (QCF, for example), non-specific distributions may be observed. Similar normalization procedures, when applied to sediments contaminated by point sources, show enhancement of the distribution patterns and a clearer indication of source locations and sediment-associated dispersal.

III.1.6 Determination of loading history

The loading history of any parameter may be studied if it is assumed that the parameter is tightly adsorbed by sediment which is, and has been, undergoing undisturbed deposition. In a typical example, a profile is prepared by plotting the concentration of a parameter against depth, from a sediment core taken at a representative location within the water-body. By this means, the concentration gradients may be observed from the sediment surface down to some constant background level, at which point man-made compounds or contaminants approach zero or minimal levels of concentration. Laboratory analysts should extract and analyze the sub-samples from a core, from bottom to top; if the sequence is reversed (from top to bottom), some sub-sample contamination may occur in the lower samples which, for example, represent a time period before man-made compounds such as DDT and PCBs were used.

A careful examination of core concentration profiles can be used to show changes, which may be construed to result from an increased anthropogenic use of some compounds, an example of which has been recently described by Imboden et al. (1980), or, in some instances, decreases may be observed which represent declining usage by man.

Care must be used in the interpretation of data since some variations can be related to:

a) dissolution, upward migration, and precipitation toward the surface of the sediment. This is almost always the case for manganese, the profile of which may be used to assist in the profile interpretation of many trace elements;

b) textural (particle-size) variations in the core;

c) inconsistent dilutions caused by variations in major components, e.g., $CaCO_3$ or SiO_2. For example, forest clearing and development of intensive agriculture will increase run-off and soil erosion, which in turn results in increased sedimentation. Assuming, in this case, that primary production in a lake remains roughly constant, then an apparent decline in the concentration of sedimented organic material will be observed. In fact, organic loading remains constant, but increased sedimentation results in an effective dilution. Conversely, changes in agricultural practice which result from increased irrigation, may greatly alter the watershed hydrology and cause a decline of sediment production. Under these conditions, sedimentation rates in the lake will decrease and, with decreasing dilution by inorganic particles, an apparent increase in the concentration of some other parameters may be observed. Such increases in concentration do not indicate increased loading. It is necessary, therefore, to have some standard against which changes may be defined as apparent or real.

Although the QCF technique provides some compensation for textural variations, it does not provide the type of standard referred to above. However, an approach known as the Sediment Enrichment Factor (SEF), which uses Al as an internal standard, was devised by Kemp et al. (1976) and has been widely applied to many core samples from the North American Great Lakes and elsewhere (see V.4). Under special circumstances, where Al might prove to be an inappropriate standard, it may be possible to substitute other major elements to achieve similar results.

The concentration profiles of both major and trace elements, in many cases, deviate somewhat from their anticipated trends. In such cases it is often useful to compare the aberrant profiles with those of such elements as sulphur, manganese, and zinc, as a means of differentiating the effects of loading variations and post depositional migration within the sediment (under the influence of pore water migration or changing Eh and/or pH conditions in the sediments, as a result of continuing burial and microbial degradation).

In addition, the effects of surface sediment mixing should not be overlooked. This may be due to physical or biological (bioturbation) causes, both of which will tend to produce a relatively constant concentration in the upper few centimeters (in extreme cases this may be as much as 10 cm, as in the western basin of Lake Erie, Kemp et al. (1976)). Over the longer term, such surface mixing does not mask the data but, rather, it smooths the trend of the concentration profiles such as is accomplished statistically by the use of the "moving average" (which smooths highly variable data to delineate trends).

The historical sequence of loadings for many parameters can be defined with a high degree of accuracy when rates of sedimentation can be measured (see Chapter VI). Where sedimentation rates cannot be determined, trends in time can only be inferred, and any estimate of total loading (derived from other forms of information) will be, at best, only approximate.

If sufficient data is available to provide an estimate of sedimentation rates in a complete river or lake system, then the total loadings of sediment and associated components can be calculated as part of a mass balance for the system.

III.1.7 Sediment and geochemical mass balance

The intensity and variety of sampling involved in determining sediment mass balance, and the mass balance of a variety of both natural and anthropogenic sediment-related parameters, requires the use of equipment and resources which are generally beyond a small laboratory. Mass balance studies are difficult in small lake systems (<10 km^2) and extemely difficult, if not impossible, in large lakes. The sampling must include bottom sediment accumulation, river inputs, atmospheric loading, shoreline erosion, and output from the lake to the outlet river; sampling must be representative of both bed and suspended materials. Ideally, sediment loads should be separated into (i) sands, and (ii) silts and clays, since these two groups respond differently in terms of their behaviour during transport and sedimentation.

Sands are usually confined to the littoral and nearshore zone where they are mostly transported as bed load. Under the influence of strong wind-wave action, however, sands may be transported in temporary suspension, particularly in the beach zone.

Because of their smaller particle-size, silts and clays remain in suspension longer than sands, and move a greater distance out into a lake basin where they can be dispersed by the water movements of large-scale circulation. Under some conditions these fine particles may be subject to the effects of seasonal entrained flow (Sly, 1979) and will be transported considerable distances without significant dispersion. Fine sediment accumulation is largely controlled by the large-scale circulation of a water-body, in which both the shape and bottom slope of the basin indirectly influence sediment accumulation (Håkanson, 1981).

Sediment transport and accumulation in rivers is more complex and very much depends upon the flow velocity and channel form. Under high flow and turbulent conditions even coarse sands may be held in suspension for considerable distances; but under normal or low flow conditions the suspended load is composed mostly of fine silt and clay particles. Sediment deposits in rivers are rarely permanent and most are remobilised at least once a year, in response to seasonal rainfall conditions. Accurate mass balance studies in large rivers (as in lakes) are extremely difficult, if not impossible, to accomplish.

Figure III.1 describes the typical components of a mass balance study, and shows their relationships in schematic form.

III.2 Role of Sediment Sampling Programs in Relation to Environmental Assessment

Up to this point, specific objectives for the conduct of sediment studies have been described. However, they have not been considered as a routine component of a water quality assessment program; though such a connotation, with respect to objective, is inferred in many cases. Some reiteration is necessary, therefore, to define the role of sediment quality assessment in the context of a water quality program and as it pertains to the concepts of baseline studies, monitoring, surveillance, and source tracing. Cross-referencing of objectives under these categories is given in Table I.1.

III.2.1 Baseline surveys

Baseline surveys include any studies designed to measure and describe sediment quality at a fixed point in time, against which future surveys may be compared; most baseline surveys sample the bed material rather than suspended material. They embrace some or all of the objectives outlined in III.1.1 to III.1.7. Baseline surveys must be considered at two levels, namely (a) level 1, single system (lake or river), and (b) level 2, regional (composite).

    a) Level 1, single system – This is a moderate to intensive survey of a single lake or river channel, based on an adequate sampling of all sediment types on the river or lake bed surface; it is designed to produce a comprehensive understanding of the sediment quality and of the sedimentary systems of an individual water-body.

    b) Level 2, regional – This type of survey is designed to evaluate sediment quality in a number of water-bodies, which may include both lake and rivers within a specific region. This type of baseline survey is intended to identify the presence or absence of specific compounds or to quantify levels of specified elements. To be effective, it is essential that similar sediment is sampled in each of the water-bodies and that the sediment sampled is always from an area of active accumulation of fine-grained silty clay or clays. In such regional comparative studies it is sometimes possible to enhance the data by using a system of normalization, either by ratio or by analysis of a specific grain-size fraction.

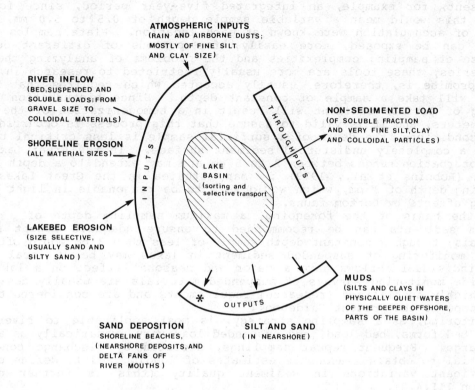

ATMOSPHERIC INPUTS
(RAIN AND AIRBORNE DUSTS;
MOSTLY OF FINE SILT
AND CLAY SIZE)

RIVER INFLOW
(BED, SUSPENDED AND
SOLUBLE LOADS; FROM
GRAVEL SIZE TO
COLLOIDAL MATERIALS)

SHORELINE EROSION
(ALL MATERIAL SIZES)

I N P U T S

LAKEBED EROSION
(SIZE SELECTIVE,
USUALLY SAND AND
SILTY SAND)

LAKE
BASIN
(sorting and
selective transport)

T H R O U G H P U T S

NON-SEDIMENTED LOAD
(OF SOLUBLE FRACTION
AND VERY FINE SILT, CLAY
AND COLLOIDAL PARTICLES)

MUDS
(SILTS AND CLAYS IN
PHYSICALLY QUIET WATERS
OF THE DEEPER OFFSHORE,
PARTS OF THE BASIN)

*   OUTPUTS

SAND DEPOSITION
SHORELINE BEACHES,
(NEARSHORE DEPOSITS, AND
DELTA FANS OFF
RIVER MOUTHS)

SILT AND SAND
(IN NEARSHORE)

*OUTPUTS INCLUDE CHEMICAL PRECIPITATES AND COATINGS

FIGURE III.1   Components of sediment mass balance
(*Outputs include chemical precipitates
and coatings).

III.2.2   Monitoring surveys and frequency of sampling

Monitoring implies a regular or periodic re-sampling by means of a baseline type survey, of either level 1 or level 2, usually to determine changes relating to man's activities, wihch may or may not have been predicted.

In lakes, it is unusual to monitor bottom sediments on a frequent basis since anthropogenic changes may be interpreted from historical sediment core sequences. Additionally, the repeat sampling of bottom sediments must take into account the rates of sediment accumulation which are necessary to enable changes to be observed. Basins in cool temperate climates are often characterized by accumulation rates of 0.1 to 0.2 mm y^{-1} or less, whereas small basins in warm temperate climates may have much greater rates of accumulation. Thus, if the survey samples are taken from the top 2 cm of sediment, and the rate of accumulation is 2 mm y^{-1} (this is a rapid rate of accumulation), the re-sample period should be between five and ten years. Assuming that there is no disturbance of the sediment surface by either physical or biological processes (which is unlikely),

-　Year 1　-　sample is taken from 0 to 2 cm sediment depth;
-　Year 5　-　sample is taken from 1 to 3 cm sediment depth, and
includes 50% new material;

- Year 10 - sample is taken from 2 to 4 cm sediment depth, and is composed of entirely new material.

Because of the considerable differences in rates of sediment accumulation, both within and between lakes (e.g., ranging between 0.1 and 50.0 mm y^{-1} in the North American Great Lakes), a typical sample taken by a grab sampler is a homogenate representing many years of accumulation. In this regard it is obviously impracticable to take a bottom sample of specific thickness at each location to represent, for example, an integrated five-year period, since for the Great Lakes this would mean a variable sample depth of 0.5 to 5.0 mm, even if the rates of accumulation were known at each location. Plate samples and sediment traps can be exposed, more easily, for periods of different duration but, because of sampling complexities and the problems of analyzing the very small recoveries, these tools are more usually restricted to research investigations. A compromise is, therefore, usually accepted which requires that the investigator will take a sample of constant depth. Since bioturbation and physical mixing of surface sediment will result in a homogenization of the surface few centimeters, and it is valid to assume that this process is occurring under most lake conditions, the depth of a surficial sample is less critical than it would be in a completely undisturbed sediment surface. In the Great Lakes, the zone of bioturbation ranges between 2 to 5 cm and may extend to a depth in excess of 10 cm (Robbins et al., 1979). Many studies in the Great Lakes use a sub-sampling depth of 3 cm, which would seem to be reasonable in light of the known mixing effects by bottom fauna.

On the basis of the foregoing, a maximum sampling depth of 3 cm for lake bottom sediments can be recommended to ensure adequate recent material for analysis; though a constant depth sample of less than 3 cm would often be valid.

The monitoring of suspended sediment in lakes may be of local significance when individual inflows have a major and seasonal effect on a lake. However, lakewide monitoring surveys of suspended materials are usually designed to meet more highly specialized (research) requirements and are considered to lie beyond the scope of the present Guidebook.

Monitoring, as a sampling strategy, is most applicable to river systems in which bed forms, bed load, and suspended load vary dramatically as a function of discharge. Frequent repeat samplings, dictated by discharge conditions, are essential to obtain reasonable estimates of loading and to define statistically significant variations in sediment quality (this is further discussed in Section III.4.2).

III.2.3 Surveillance

Surveillance sampling is similar to monitoring, but it implies repeated sediment sampling and observation to determine whether or not changes are occurring, in specific sediment-associated parameters, as a direct result of management or control strategies. Surveillance requires repetitive and intensive sampling of a specific area to provide data which is statistically capable of establishing the probability of observed changes.

III.3 Techniques of Design for Sampling Surveys in Lakes and Similar Environments (including very wide rivers and estuaries)

The design of a sampling program is always a compromise between having all the samples that are wanted, and having the resources and the right conditions in which to collect them.

In most situations resources are limited and it is necessary to use any opportunity to collect them.

The survey techniques should be adequate to meet the needs of the sampling program; if they are not, and it is not possible to improve them, then the requirements of the sampling program must be made less strict. This is particularly true for the use of survey positioning techniques, which must be able to locate sample stations or line surveys with acceptable accuracies. There are no simple solutions to many of the problems that may be encountered and the success of any sampling venture is highly dependent on the initiative, good will, and common sense of the investigator.

In the following discussion on sampling design, it is assumed that the investigator has access to the river and lake sites and that there is the support of moderate resources.

It must be understood that a single sample is taken to be representative of as large an area as possible of any given water-body. For example, the bottom sediment sampling intensity used by Thomas et al. (1972) for Lake Ontario used 326 samples to describe a lake of approximately 18,000 km^2. In this case a geochemical/sedimentological sample of 25 cm^2 x 3 cm deep was taken to be representative of a lakebed area of 55 km^2. This particular survey was designed at the optimum density for the available ship time and, compared to many ocean surveys, it can be construed as being one of high density.

In contrast, Sly (1975) showed in a statistical study that in large lakes, where water depths are 40 m or greater, sample spacing should be between 300 and 1000 m separation in order for sample analyses to distinguish between certain statistically similar or dissimilar populations. Generally speaking there appeared to be a threshold at about the 1000 m spacing, with sample variance at the 1000 to 3000 m interval (and greater) showing little increase. In water depths of 10 to 20 m, spacing should be at about 100 to 300 m separation. However, in water of less than 10 m depth, spacings should be 30 to 100 m separation to provide statistically valid information over bed forms of complex relief. These depths apply to the Great Lakes and are presumably similar in other large, deep, lakes. Smaller lakes with lower wind energy fields will be less critical at commensurately shallower depths. In shallow Dutch lakes one or two samples per 10 km^2 were usually sufficient.

The intensities of the sampling used by Sly (1975), are obviously far too great for most general surveys where resolutions, at such levels of statistical probability, are not required. However, the work does show that the characteristics of individual samples are unique, relative to location and water depth, and that a sample is entirely representative of its location. Hence, the results of even one sample analysis have an inherent validity; and greater numbers of samples progressively refine the extent of environmental variability within the system. As a rule of thumb, 'ensure that there are at least 10 separate samples from each sediment type, from each region of a lake under investigation'.

In explanation of this statement it should be understood that by 'sediment type' it is implied that the sediment appears, from visual observation, to be dominantly composed of gravel, sand, or mud. Because of the difficulty of visually separating samples of clayey silt from those of silty clay it is suggested that, where possible, the number of mud (undefined mixture of silt and clay) samples should be increased.

By using the term 'each region of a lake', it is implied that sample spacing will change to suit the scale of resolution required. Thus, a detailed study of a small embayment or river mouth may be suitably described by a total of 30 to 40 samples and a similar number of samples may be adequate to describe the general characteristics of an entire sub-basin of a large lake.

While there is nothing 'magic' about the number of samples required, experience shows that at least 10 samples from each sediment type are required to make any sort of useful comparative analysis, and that there is little value in comparing different types of sediment with one another (unless for research purposes).

In the following discussions, sampling strategies for lakes and rivers will be described separately. The emphasis is upon bottom sediment sampling in lakes and suspended sediment sampling in rivers.

III.3.1 Seasonal variations affecting lake sediments

Some detailed studies of seasonal variations in the composition of undisturbed lake sediments have been carried out (Mortimer, 1971; Vanderpost, 1972). These indicate that there can be vertical migration of the zero redox potential interface associated with microbial degradation of organic matter, and that this may have an additional influence on the behaviour of mobile elements (such as Mn, Zn) within the sediment column.

In addition to such changes within the sediment column, there is good evidence that the characteristics of accumulating material may change on a seasonal basis. For example, in temperate latitudes during the spring run-off, there is a predominance of inorganic materials in suspension, but during late summer and early fall, increasing quantities of dead and degraded organic material may reach the sediment interface.

Seasonal changes in water temperature may also influence sedimentation; some carbonate is precipitated from the cold waters of hard-water, temperate lakes during the winter months, but much larger quantities of calcium carbonate may precipitate from warm waters during the summer period associated with increased primary production.

The rates of change described above are relatively slow and, in most of these situations, the changes are unlikely to make a significant difference to the bulk characteristics of the uppermost 2 to 3 cm of material.

Other more important seasonal changes have been noted in some large lakes subject to severe winter storm effects, and in lakes subject to large changes in water level. Studies in Lake Ontario (Canada Centre for Inland Waters, unpublished data) have demonstrated that there can be a significant shift in the sand/mud boundary, and unpublished data from the U.S. Corps of Engineers has identified large changes in the concentration of trace metals at dump sites in Lake Erie, on a seasonal basis. In this latter case it has been suggested that the apparent changes in trace metal concentration may be explained as follows: (i) dilution by less contaminated sediments derived from adjacent river inflows (which are of limited influence); or (ii) by the erosion of the uppermost contaminated layers by fall and winter storms, which then expose the underlying and less contaminated materials. Since, even without repeated dumping, there appears to be an increase in the trace metal concentrations during the following summer period (at the same locations), it may be implied that the muds 'creep' back into the shallower waters under calm conditions and re-contaminate the sites.

On the basis of the above information it would seem that, although low density regional sediment surveys and exploratory surveys will be little influenced by seasonal changes, this may not be true for detailed high density surveys of lake bed sediments, particularly in the nearshore zones.

III.3.2   Choosing densities and locations for general sediment sampling programs

In the following discussions, the recommendations are based upon the authors' experience and should be taken as a guide; each investigator should adapt the recommendations to suit the specific conditions with which he is faced.

In general, the density of sampling should be as great as possible, bearing in mind time requirements, capacity of laboratory services, data storage, and handling and processing capabilities. In these types of sampling, it is essential that sufficient numbers of samples are obtained from each sediment type and from each region of a lake, to undertake a limited statistical analysis of the lake bed sediment data. As previously noted, there should be not less than 10 samples from each sediment type in each region of the lake. Assuming that the samples are evenly spread, the more samples available, the better the statistical validity of final data! However, an increase in the number of samples and associated analyses results in a commensurate increase in costs; an excessively intense sampling density, which marginally improves confidence levels, is unlikely to be cost effective. To ensure a reasonable sampling density for these types of surveys it is necessary to obtain some exploratory information about the types of sediment present, and their probable location and extent. There are two ways of obtaining this information, firstly by running simple acoustic surveys, and secondly by sampling at selected locations. Based on this preliminary information appropriate sampling grids can be designed for the final sampling program.

Acoustic survey techniques are a valuable tool for the survey of bottom sediments. They provide continuity of data between sediment sampling sites, which may characterize both the type of surficial material (sand, gravel, or mud) and the presence of layering below the surface. Although both vertical echo-sounders and sideways looking sonar (side-scan sonar) systems are widely available, the use and interpretation of side-scan sonar data is probably beyond the needs of most of the users of this Guide, and it is not discussed further. Boats not fitted with a navigational echo-sounder may be fitted with a portable sounder, with a transducer temporarily mounted over the side.

The sounder must be of the recording type, with an operating frequency of about 30 to 50 kHz or lower (for a detailed discussion on bottom type discrimination and shallow acoustic penetration by echo-sounding see King (1968) and Thomas et al. (1972)). In explanation, it is sufficient to say that the extent to which an acoustic pulse will penetrate the sediment column is largely a function of water content in the sediment. Since fine unconsolidated sediments contain a higher water content than coarse sediments, penetration is usually most effective in soft silts and clays. Little or no penetration will occur in sands, or highly compacted or indurated material; and interpretation of these materials is based on the intensity of the returning bottom signal and on an examination of the form, relief, and appearance of the bottom traces. Some examples from Lake Ontario are shown in Figure III.2. Operator experience has a lot to do with the ability to make useful interpretations, and care should be taken to sample each of the various types of sediment observed on the sounding records, to obtain confirmation of the interpretations.

The presence of gas (such as methane or hydrogen sulphide) and/or large quantities of organic material (such as peat or wood fibres) in bottom sediments has a marked effect on the ability to achieve sub-surface acoustic penetration (or even surface return) by echo-sounding; and there may be a complete lack of signal return from such bottom types. As a further caution, it should be noted that gas production, related to microbial degradation of organic-rich sediments, tends to increase when the overlying waters are warm. To avoid such problems the use of echo-sounding techniques to achieve sub-bottom penetration and/or surface discrimination, should be undertaken during the cooler months of the year.

As an additional complication, it should be noted that the use of the higher frequency sounders may be particularly influenced by the presence of large quantities of suspended material, or air bubbles in the water column; sounding is also best undertaken under calm water conditions.

With some of the more powerful echo-sounders it is possible to receive more than one return signal, since the acoustic returns may bounce back from the (flat) air/water interface or even from the underside of a boat. Sometimes these multiples may provide a clearer image because there is less saturation of the signal and, in any case, they are easy to distinguish because of the regular spacing between the first return and any subsequent returns.

For preliminary or exploratory surveys, the location of survey lines and the position of sample locations depends very much on the size and shape of the water-body (see Figure III.3). It is normal to run at least one line down the long axis of a lake and to run at least three lines across the lake; the axial line is also known as a tie-line because it provides continuity of data between the other shorter lines, at their points of intersection. The minimum number of samples will depend upon the complexity of bottom sediment distributions.

Representative samples should be taken for visual inspection, and both the type of material and depth of water should be recorded. By using acoustic survey and sediment sample data, the probable extent of sediment distributions can be predicted with reference to a bathymetric chart, since sediment/water depth relationships tend to be fairly consistent (within each lake). This forms the basic information upon which to develop the final pattern of sampling, and to establish both the number and locations of samples to be analyzed.

Under some circumstances it may not be possible to carry out a preliminary (exploratory) survey as required, because of a lack of logistical support. In such cases it may be necessary to use 'vessels of opportunity' (fishing boats, ferries or even customs craft), or to add on to the work of some other investigation. Whenever possible, courses followed by such vessels should at least cover a representative part of the lake even if complete crossings are not possible.

For more complex surveys, there are numerous types of sampling patterns from which to choose, e.g., spot samples, random grids, square grids (including nested and rotated grids), parallel line grids and transverse line grids (with equal or non-equal sampling), and ray grids or concentric arc sampling, each of which offers some particular advantage. Once a pattern has been selected, the sampling program should adhere to the original design as far as possible. However, few grids should be considered as being completely inflexible, and it is up to an investigator to ensure that the information recovered, by means of various survey techniques, is representative of actual conditions in the field. If one type of pattern is going to produce excessively biased information, it should be changed before the field work has advanced too far.

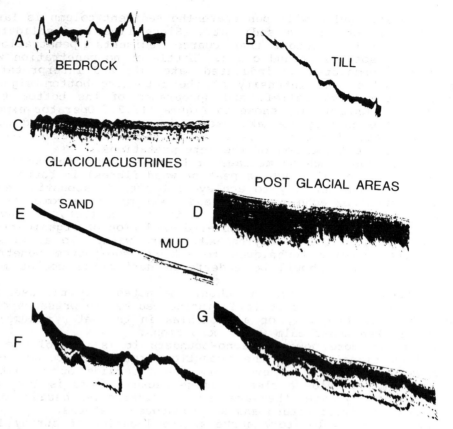

FIGURE III.2 Nonlinear echograms of major Great Lakes sediment types
(after Thomas et al., 1972)

CURVILINEAR ECHOGRAMS OF MAJOR SEDIMENT TYPES
(After Thomas et al., 1972)

A - Bedrock material is characterized by strong acoustic returns and irregular
      relief. Soft, recent mud partly infills surface depressions.
B - Glacial till: this is a hard, overconsolidated clayey material (often
      with coarse gravelly lenses and boulders) which is hard to differentiate
      from bedrock; it usually displays a slightly less irregular surface.
C - Glacio-lacustrine clays: the strong penetration of acoustic signals and
      unique banding in the subsurface layering make these materials easily
      identified.   Individual layers can be traced over wide areas in the
      records, but frequently there is little evidence of such structures in
      sediment cores.
D - Recent muds overlie glacio-lacustrine clays with slight unconformity. The
      changes in acoustic reflectance, and evidence of changes in the subsurface
      layering, allows distinction to be made between these two types of fine-
      grained sediment.
E - Sand and gravelly sand always show a dark and strong acoustic return, with
      no penetration. The surface may be smooth, undulating, ridged, or charac-
      terized by wave forms in shallow water. The change to finer-grained sedi-
      ment in deeper offshore waters is well illustrated by decreasing reflec-
      tance and greater penetration at the lower end of the trace.
F - Complex structures are sometimes evident in the echo trace records; here,
      glacio-lacustrine sediments infill channel-like depressions on the bedrock
      surface.
G - The overstepping relationship, between recent muds and the underlying
      glacio-lacustrine clays, is shown by the internal structures in this echo
      trace.

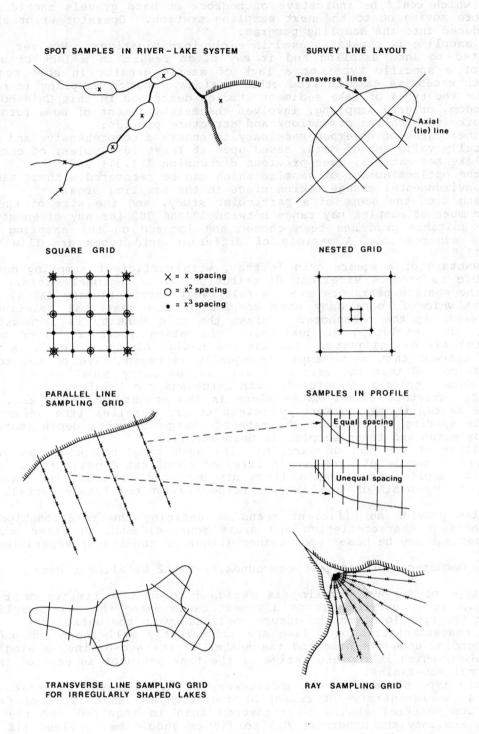

FIGURE III.3 Examples of different types of grid design

Sampling, therefore, should adhere to an accepted plan and, if a sample is not recovered after three attempts with a good sampler (because of a hard bottom), the vessel should not be moved a little to one side until recovery is obtained. The lack of recovery and the presence or absence of rock chips, plants, and pebbles, which could be indicative of bedrock or hard gravels should be recorded, before moving on to the next sampling station. Operator error should not be introduced into the sampling program.

Random sampling is sometimes used in early investigations. However, it is not well suited to lake sampling and it may often result in a lack of sufficient samples of a specific type; or a lack of sample density in some region of a lake, with excessive samples from other regions. Random sampling is not recommended for the types of lake sediment studies described in this Guidebook.

Non-random, or grid sampling, involves the establishment of some form of regular network in which the dimensions and structure provide:

a) the degree of coverage necessary to ensure a comprehensive and statistically valid set of data, based upon at least 10 samples, of each type of lake bed material (see previous discussion III.3); and

b) the optimum number of samples which can be recovered without significant environmental change taking place in the sampling area.

Depending upon the scope of a particular study, and the size of the lake, a typical number of samples may range between 30 and 300 for any given study.

Once a suitable grid has been chosen and located on the sampling plan, it should be adhered to. A variety of different grid types are illustrated in Figure III.3.

The advantage of a square grid is that, with sufficient sampling density, it is possible to produce excellent distributions on a regional basis. However, because the shallow nearshore zone is relatively narrow in many lakes, a bias is introduced which favours many more samples of fine material relative to the coarser sands in the nearshore. Unless the grid density is increased (e.g., squared), the resolution of nearshore information (such as river mouths or embayments) may be inadquate. The use and design of square grids is predicted upon the concept that each sample is equally representative of the total area being sampled and that the values of all samples carry equal weight (statistically). Square grids are useful in both large and small lakes.

Since the greatest change takes place in the onshore-offshore axis, and not along the shore, it may be more efficient to use parallel line grids on which the sample spacing is keyed to the rate of change in water depth (more samples in shallow water and fewer samples in deep water).

A variation of the use of parallel line grid sampling, known as transverse grid sampling, may be of more use in lakes of complicated basin form. In transverse grid sampling, the sample lines are designed to cross the long axis of each arm (or sub-basin of the lake), irrespective of the lake's overall orientation.

Ray grids provide an efficient means of defining the relationships between bottom sediment characteristics and plume sources, such as river mouths; and sample spacings may be based upon either linear or non-linear separations.

III.3.3   Occurrence of specific compounds, level 2 baseline survey

In this type of survey, sampling is designed to meet a limited or restricted objective. It is carried out on a repeat basis using the same sampling techniques at the same locations to ensure consistency in the data.

If the characteristics of a lake are sufficiently well known and understood, then, depending upon its size and the number of its sub-basins, a single sample may be taken, which is representative of the fine sediment in each of the lake's depositional sub-basins.

When this type of sampling is undertaken, it is important to ensure that the sediment is representative of recent accumulation and that it is of fine grain size. More material should be recovered than is required for the specific analyses, and only the uppermost 0.5 to 1.0 cm should be retained (if the sampling equipment is inadequate, as much as 3 cm may have to be retained for analysis, but, as previously stated (III.2.2), more than this is not recommended). Excess material from this sample interval, which is not used for the immediate analyses, can be stored as a reference sample and may be used at a later date to test for previously unrecognized contaminants.

If there are a large number of small lakes, which are being surveyed in a level 2 type program, it is probable that a density of one sample per lake (centrally located) will be sufficient. Where only a few larger lakes are covered by this type of survey, at least five samples should be recovered from each lake (irrespective of a lesser number of major sub-basins). Each lake should be described on the basis of the mean of at least five samples.

This type of sampling may be also referred to as spot sampling, and it can be applied on a site specific basis (such as a river mouth, a point source inflow or contaminant, or a dump site), as well as providing a means of describing a whole basin on the basis of a single sample. Spot samples are used as an indicator of trends; i.e., changes (or no changes) in sediment composition, in relation to set time intervals. For spot samples, it is absolutely essential that temporal variabilities exceed spatial variabilities and, therefore, repeated samples should be carefully relocated at the same location.

III.3.4   Determination of source

If a hazardous compound or element has been identified in a lake survey, then any available information concerning the lake's circulation should be utilized to predict the most probable region of the lake from which the contaminant may be derived. A sample grid should be laid out in this area and sampled for the analysis of the compound. A supplementary analysis of a conservative element should also be made, to serve as an internal standard for the purpose of normalization. It is also important to subject the sample to size fractionation, to ensure that a good intersample comparison by size fraction can be carried out (see previous discussions of SEF and QCF).

In the case where the most likely source appears to be a river (which is frequently the case), the river can be surveyed upstream by means of a transverse sample grid (or by spot samples in a narrow stream). Where more information may be needed to define the zone of transport from the river mouth to the open lake, then an intensive grid may be placed off the river mouth. To reduce the number of samples it is normal to use a ray grid, radiating outwards from the river. Ray grids should be located and designed to include nearshore zones where coastal circulation may interact with the river discharge (see also previous discussion).

III.3.5   History of loading

The history of sediment loading can be determined from an examination of the profiles of textural and elemental concentrations, with depth, through a sediment column. Sampling is carried out by means of a coring device which must be used in an area of a lake which is receiving active accumulation. At least three cores should be recovered in small lakes and at least five in larger lakes or sub-basins. The cores should be spaced equally so as to be representative of the mid-lake sediments, and should be compared with each other before selection of the single core which is to be typical of the lake as a whole. By this means, anomalous cores (due to some local variation in patterns of sediment accumulation or due to poor core sample recovery) are not used to typify a basin.

Sediment has to be carefully extruded from the core tube (see equipment section) and subsampled at specific intervals down the core, often to a depth of 0.5 to 1.0 m. It is normal to subsample at 1 cm intervals for the first 10 cm, and then at 5 or 10 cm intervals down the remainder of the core. Lesser or greater subsample intervals may be used, depending on sedimentation rates; adjustments can be made in additional cores, taken from specific locations, after examination of preliminary analytical data.

Loading studies can be made on cores without the presence of internal features that can be used to date sub-surface materials. In such cases, however, a comparison is made only between the concentrations of specific parameters and their depth below the sediment surface. In more sophisticated studies, it is possible to reduce the effects of variation in texture (normalized particle-size) and to lessen the effects of compaction by compensating for variations in water content. If sediment traps have been used to measure existing sedimentation rates, it is possible to calculate approximate time:depth relationships down a sediment core, assuming constant rates of accumulation.

In most situations, however, cores are preferred in which either the material is suitable for subjecting to various dating techniques (see later discussions) or in which marker horizons (e.g., coarse sediments associated with severe floods or storms, or ash layers associated with forest fires) can act as a common datum plane of regional extent.

III.3.6   Mass balance studies

Both intensive grid (surficial grab) and multiple core samplings are required for mass balance studies in order to establish concentrations and rates of sedimentation. These studies are important but are not recommended for inexperienced staff or laboratories with inadequate technical facilities, because of the care required in core processing and the understanding required for data interpretation.

In particular, they can provide an alternative means of verifying basin-wide loading models which are based on estimates or measurements made in the watershed, but outside the lake itself.

III.3.7   Suspended matter in lakes

The material held in suspension in lake waters is composed of inorganic particles, and both living and dead organic particles, and may be referred to as either total suspended matter or seston. In suspensions, the presence of living matter and degrading organic particles provide complex compositions of variable concentration, which may be quite different from the integrated product of sediment accumulation that is observed on a lake bottom.

This complexity, together with the problem of understanding the relationships between the movements of particulates and mass water circulation, account for many of the reasons why so few studies on the sampling of lake suspended matter have been published. Virtually all published work incorporates the use of sediment traps (Bloesch and Burns, 1980), which have been used to sample materials which are sedimenting through the water column at some specific site and depth within the water-body. Since microbial degradation is proceeding within the traps, and the physics of trap entry are complex, analyses based on such sampling techniques may not be entirely representative of either synoptic conditions or the rates and composition of finally accumulating sediment.

They are, however, a reasonable approximation and represent the most generally available techniques for present application.

For studies which require the analysis of a specific compound it is more useful to recover samples by means of pumping from different depths. This is because, in comparison with sedimentation traps, pumped samples are recovered quickly and because quantities of particulates can be more easily matched to analytical requirements, when suspended load concentrations are measured on site. Pumped samples show greater repeatability than sedimentation traps.

The quantity of suspended solids is best measured by filtration and gravimetric determination of dry weight solids per unit volume. Measurements should be made on large-volume water samples (Van Dorn or similar) and at a number of depths (usually related to stratification of the water column, e.g., surface, mid-epilimnion, top of thermocline, base of thermocline, mid-hypolimnion, and base of hypolimnion (about 1 to 2 m above lake bed)). In lakes where stratification is weak or absent, four or five samples should be equally spaced in the water column, with the lowest 1 to 2 m above the bed.

The location of sites for suspended sediment sampling may be defined on the basis of a coarse square grid or a series of widely spaced parallel or transverse grid sample lines; sampling should be repeated at least four times a year to characterize seasonal variations. A reasonable approximation of the concentrations of suspended matter may be derived from the use of a turbidity meter which can provide continuous readout/depth information and is very much more rapid than the analysis of water samples. Turbidity meters require careful calibration but may be used together with a fluorometer (to approximate chlorophyll content) to provide a crude estimate of the living and non-living components; this information, however, in no way approaches the derivation which is possible from actual water samples.

While the filtration of a 10 l water sample may yield sufficient material to characterize the solids content, it will only provide enough material for a few chemical analyses (however, these may be biologically important as, for example, C, N, P, and Si). Concentrations of suspended solids in most lakes are low, generally less than 1 mg l^{-1} and upon this basis a 10 l sample will give only a 10 mg total sample (at 100 percent recovery). To overcome this problem, water has been pumped from a specific depth and passed directly into a continuous flow centrifuge (such as the Westphalia KDD 605 system discussed later (III.4.2)). Water samples from more than 30 m depth have been successfully obtained but the process is slow. For example, at a lake concentration of 1 mg l^{-1} for seston, a five gram sample requires the processing of 5000 litres; at an optimum centrifuge flow rate of 6 l/min a processing time of 13 hours 53 minutes is required.

Since five grams represents a minimum sample recovery for multipurpose geochemical analyses, the amount of time and effort required is high. This type of sampling should be considered as being of limited application. Centrifuges of the Westphalia type may be used on boats of medium size but should not be subject to violent motion whilst in operation. As an alternative, pumped samples may be held in temporary shipboard tank storage which can be subsequently transferred to land-based units for final concentration. Centrifuge systems should not be used to compute total solids in volumetric samples (see III.4.2).

III.4   River Sampling

At the beginning of the previous section (III.3.1) it was stated that bottom sampling was most usefully applied to lakes, although it was also implied that under the right conditions similar techniques could be used in rivers. In essence, the more a river behaves like a lake, the more useful bottom sampling techniques become. High-flowing rivers, in which bed sediments are at rest for only short periods, can be subject to little more than spot sampling (which is largely limited to natural sediment traps on the inside of channel bends, mid-channel bars, or sheltered areas beyond the influence of the main flow). In rivers where flow conditions are more moderate, comparisons can be made between representative cross channel samples recovered from transverse sample surveys (either equally or non-equally spaced, but the approach must be consistent). Because of rapid local variations in sediment type and the lack of permanent deposition, it is difficult to collect cores which are representative of historical loadings; and studies on historical loadings and mass balance are not well suited to water-bodies whose retention times are measured in hours or days, rather than months or longer.

The design of a program for sampling river sediments is often more complex than that required for the sampling of lake sediments. Lake sediments, after deposition, are generally static; whereas the sediments of rivers are in a perpetual state of flux due to changing conditions in flow and discharge. In sampling, both bottom sediment and suspended solids must be considered but it is not always necessary to sample both at the same location.

III.4.1   Bottom sediment

Sampling for bottom sediment in fluvial systems may be undertaken for two purposes: to quantify the amount of sediment moving in the river, and to recover material for textural and chemical analysis. In rivers, material moves either in suspension, or along the bed as a traction load. It is extremely difficult and complex to measure the quantity in the traction load which, in any case, consists predominantly of coarse sediment particles which are geochemically inert (exceptions to this do occur as, for example, occurrence of wood chips and fibres downstream of a pulp and paper mill). Because of the general lack of importance in terms of its effects on water quality, the sampling and quantification of the traction load is not discussed further; those interested are referred to Guy and Norman (1970), Hubbell (1964), and Inter-agency Committee on Water Resources (1940-1963).

In contrast to sampling the traction load in motion, it is useful to sample the static bed for characterization of the qualitative aspects of the material which is present. The following guidelines can be used in sampling bed material for chemical analyses:
- Sample under low flow conditions when most materials will have settled from suspension.
- Sample near river banks, or behind obstructions which impede flow and create small areas of slack water where sediment accumulation can take place (this technique can be used at river banks during high stage conditions).
- In large rivers, techniques similar to those in lakes are used; samples taken on transverse lines (perpendicular to the flow) should take advantage of channel form and the presence of natural obstructions. Sample lines should be located where the river widens and flow velocities decrease, but not in narrow sections where velocity increases and the channel bed is scoured of all fine material.

- Match the sampling techniques to the site; in large rivers it will be necessary to use vessel support for sediment grabs and corers; whereas, in small streams much of the sampling can be done with rubber boots and a short plastic tube (take consistent recoveries of about 10 to 20 cm in such streams).
- Sample lines should also be placed upstream and downstream of:
  a) the confluence of a major tributary;
  b) towns, industries, and sewage treatment plants;
  c) major changes in land use;
  d) major changes in land form (reflecting changes in surficial material, soils, and bedrock geology).
- Where reaches of a river show little variation in channel form or width, transverse sampling lines may be equally spaced and widely separated.

The type of sampling noted above should provide a clear picture of the effects of land uses within a river basin and of the quality of sediment; it can identify sources of contaminants and it can indicate their dispersion and dilution within the river system. Since the distribution patterns and textural composition of fluvial sediments are subject to large changes under high flow and flood conditions, this type of survey should not be construed as representing a form of baseline; it represents the condition at one point in time only and should be undertaken, as nearly as possible, as a synoptic survey. It can never be duplicated exactly. The data is of particular value as a means of identifying the presence of specific materials and for the identification of sources.

III.4.2   River suspended solids

Some explanation of the relationship between discharge and sediment concentration in rivers is useful for defining the complexities in developing an adequate sampling program. As an example, the relationship of stream flow to sediment concentration, for the River Dart in England, is shown in Figure II.4 (after Walling, 1977). Three high flow events can be seen on the continuous discharge record and these are paralleled, to some extent, by the continuous sediment concentration record. In this case the peaks in sediment concentrations tend to coincide with the peaks in the hydrograph. In many river systems this is not so, and the peak sediment concentration may either precede or lag behind the hydrograph peak. These three situations are defined as advanced, simultaneous, and lagging; sediment concentrations relative to discharge are shown in Figure III.4, from three separate river systems in western Canada (after Tywoniuk and Cashman, 1973). The River Dart (Figure II.4) represents a simultaneous sediment to discharge relationship and it is noticeable, in the three high flow events shown in Figure II.4, that there is a progressive decrease in sediment concentration. This is due to what is known as the exhaustion effect; which means that there is progressively less sediment available for resuspension in the stream system, when high flow events follow closely upon each other. It is obvious from this case that a projected discharge to sediment concentration relationship (rating curve) may not give an accurate estimate of the actual sediment loading. The changing concentration with stream flow during the same period of record is summarized in the inset in Figure II.4. The pattern is complex, though the three events and the exhaustion effect can be clearly seen.

The relationships between sediment concentration and stream flow for the advanced and lagging situations are shown in Figure III.4. It is clear from these examples of events (which could include - heavy rain storms, snow melt, etc.) that intensive sampling of suspended load, relative to the hydrograph, is essential to compute accurate loadings.

Where this is not possible, a rating curve can be developed, based upon the relationship between daily mean discharge and daily mean suspended sediment concentration, as in Figure III.5 (after Walling, 1977). The relationship between concentration (c) and stream flow (Q) is defined by aQ^b, in which (a) is the intercept, and (b) the slope; each stream is, therefore, characterized by a separate rating curve. An approximation of suspended load can thus be devised directly from the measured discharge, or stream flow.

To prepare a rating curve, it is essential to know the discharge, and this is best derived from an automated gauging station. In some cases, these may have been installed already by other programs involved with water quantity, water quality, or flood prediction studies. Generally, however, these are not available and the sediment investigator must try to obtain this information by some other means.

NORTH SASKATCHEWAN
RIVER AT PRINCE ALBERT

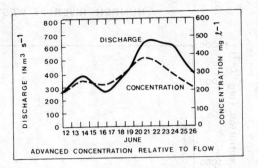

NORTH NASHAAKSIS
STREAM AT ROYAL ROADS.

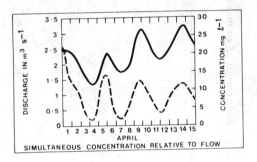

SOUTH SASKATCHEWAN
RIVER AT HIGHWAY 41.

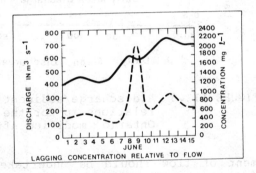

FIGURE III.4 Advanced, simultaneous and lagging concentrations relative
to flow (modified after Tywoniuk and Cashman, 1973)

One of the most simple ways of doing this requires a survey of the river, at a
convenient location, for the preparation of an accurate cross-section of the
river channel, at least to an elevation of the river's surface at maximum flow.
The area of the cross-section should be calculated in m^2, relative to surface
elevations, so that the variable area of the section can be predicted under different flow conditions. A graduated staff, permanently fixed near the river
bank, can be used to gauge the elevation of the water levels (stage height) and
the average flow velocity can be determined by a manually operated flowmeter.
The velocity, in meters/second, should be measured at a series of equally spaced
points and depths across the section line, and averaged. The volume of water
passing through this section, at a particular stage height, can be calculated in
cubic meters/second. With a few measurements, to develop a calibration curve,
the discharge can be read directly from the depth gauge. Close interval (stage)
measurements of discharge should be made during all flow stages of the river
(both rising and falling).

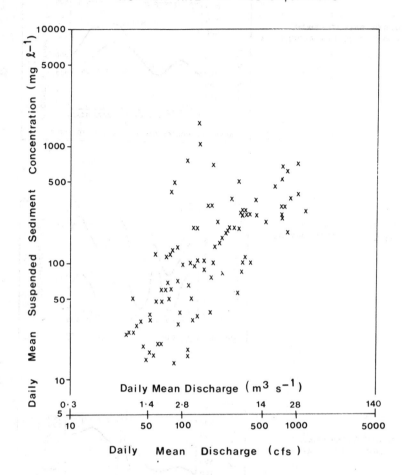

FIGURE III.5   A discharge/sediment concentration rating
relationship for the Humber River at Weston,
Ontario (modified after Walling, 1977)

The measurement of flow should be undertaken with a calibrated (hand-held)
flowmeter. If this is not available then some other technique must be used.
Although almost anything which floats can be used to time the movement of surface water and estimate its velocity, it is desirable to use a vertical float
which rides deep in the water. This is almost unaffected by surface wind stress
and it can integrate motion over as much as the top 1 to 2 m of water (depending
on the length of float, normally a tube or stick which is weighted at one end).
The number of measurements required to calculate average flow is dependent on
stream size. Small streams can be measured at a single location, but large
rivers (under high flow) require a minimum of five cross stream measurements (to
compensate for variability in flow, and bed and bank friction).

The measurement of total suspended solids in rivers, as in lakes, is best
obtained gravimetrically. Ideally, material should be recovered by using one of
the commercially available depth-integrating suspended samplers, but otherwise a
two to ten litre sample (depending on suspended solids concentration) can be
recovered and pressure filtered though a 0.45 μm water quality type filtration
system. From this, the suspended solids concentration may be obtained in units
of mg l^{-1} dry weight of sediment. Using these measured expressions, the amount
of suspended solids passing the sampling site may be estimated as follows:-

Concentration suspended solids (mg l^{-1}) dry weight X discharge (m sec^{-1})/
1000 = weight of suspended solids (g sec^{-1}) at the time of sampling. To obtain
accurate sediment loading values for a river during the first twelve months of

sampling, measurements should be made frequently, i.e., at two to four hour intervals during storm and flood events and at daily intervals for the rest of the year. If this is not possible, adequate loading values may be based on weekly measurements (excluding events) and, after the first year, bi-weekly or monthly measurements may be sufficient to monitor the river (see also V.2.7)

The use of depth-integrating suspended samples, or water bottles, provides very little material for recovery after filtration and, as previously stated (III.3.7), at least five grams of material are required for a comprehensive chemical analysis. The use of centrifuges to process pumped samples provide some solution to this problem and two types of processing systems have been developed:-

1) Laboratory - Large volumes of water are collected in the field (in tanks) and returned to the laboratory for processing in the laboratory-size continuous flow centrifuge. This process is slow because of the low flow rates which are necessary for efficient recovery.

2) Field - Commercial scale centrifuges or separators are used directly in the field, mounted on a suitable vehicle with an auxiliary power supply. Usually a centrifuge is set up at some convenient location, having a permanent power supply, and water samples are returned by a sample collection vehicle. Centrifuges of this type (e.g., Westphalia KDD 605) operate at throughput of six litre/minute and can process samples of many thousands of litres. Normal sample sizes range from 300 to 1800 litres depending on the total solids concentration in the water. With this type of system*, samples are pumped from the river, either to fill a small reservoir (from which the sample is processed) or directly (through a mixing system) into the centrifuge at the required flow rates. An excellent recovery of particles has been demonstrated using both a Westphalia and a Laval system. The two Westphalia centrifuges used by Thomas (CCIW) have measured recoveries of 90 and 95 percent, respectively, in comparison to a standard 0.25 µm filtration. Particles down to 0.01 µm have been observed by electron microscopic examination of the centrifuge-recovered solids.

These systems are expensive and labour intensive in use, but can recover solid samples weighing tens or even hundreds of grams. This makes it possible to undertake even the most complex analyses and to provide sample residues for storage, or repeat or standard analysis. However, it should be noted that the cleanout of the sample from the centrifuge bowls is difficult, and complete recovery is impossible.

Because of the flow conditions at the pump head and the lack of complete solids recovery, these machines should not be used as a means of computing total solids in the volume of water sampled. Filtration and gravimetric analysis of total solids must be used for this determination.

The major advantage of the application of pumped sampling is that it provides recovery of material actually in motion in a stream. These materials are composed of very fine particles which are unlikely to be deposited, even at very low flow, and hence they are rapidly transported to the receiving waters. This is well shown in Figure III.6 (Rainwater and Guy, 1961; and cited in Church and Gilbert, 1975) where the concentration of clay-size particles varies least with discharge.

For the purpose of most quality-related studies on river sediments, it seems unnecessary to use the highly sophisticated techniques of pumped centrifugation. Bottom sediment grab samples and one to ten litre container samples (including integrated-depth suspended water samples) should be able to provide adequate material to characterize gross sediment composition, material mineralogy, and the major geochemistry of the drainage system. Pumped centrifugation is required only where specialized (large volume) analyses are to be undertaken (as, for example, organo-chlorines) and these will need a further back-up by highly sophisticated laboratory analytical services. Centrifugation should not be considered where resources are limited.

---

* Only a few systems are known to be currently operating: at the Canada Centre for Inland Waters (CCIW), in Canada; at Queen's University, in Canada; and the New York State Department of Environmental Conservation, U.S.A.

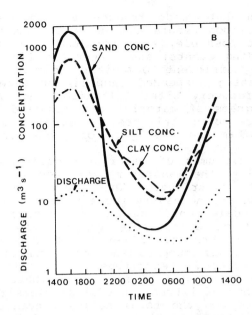

FIGURE III.6   Diurnal pattern of suspended sediment concentration
and stream discharge downstream from Chamberlin
Glacier, Alaska (after Rainwater and Guy, 1961)

III.5   Operation of Equipment and Logistics

The first and probably the most important 'rule' regarding selection of equipment is:

> "Always pick the simplest and most reliable equipment
> that will provide the desired type of sample".

Field work can be expensive and there may be only one opportunity to sample in an area.   Over-complication or over-specialization may result in failure.   The following guidelines are also useful to consider:
- Always carry a spare; samplers are often easily, and surprisingly, lost. Add a safety line!
- Examine all moving parts and attachment points frequently.   Carry spare bolts, pins, shackles, and replace worn parts; watch for corrosion due to electrolysis, caused by proximity of metals having a significantly different potential.
- If a· small sampler is being used by hand and attached by rope, <u>check</u> the knots or splice before every operation.
- Handle equipment gently, even though it may appear robust; damage through rough or careless handling is easily incurred.
- The mechanisms of some samplers may be impaired by silt and sand particles. Always maintain a suitable tool kit to periodically dismantle and clean the sampler; wash or flush with clean water.
- All instruments, which are used to perform some kind of measurement, should be calibrated and tested regularly against some form of known standard (e.g., flowmeters, turbidity meters, D.O. probes, Eh/pH probes, etc.).

Additionally, more specific guidance can be given for the use of grab samplers and coring devices, from which, with experience, improved results will be obtained:
- Understand the triggering mechanisms and the way in which the samplers work.
- Be sure that the boat is stationary and that a sampler is lowered slowly and vertically.   This will ensure that the device does not swing on the line and that it will come to rest properly on the surface of the sediment.
- Recover at a reasonable speed; in many samplers loss of sample may occur with fast and violent recovery.   This is particularly true of coring devices. Smoothness in descent and ascent is important.

- Always check the surface of a sample from grab samplers and the sides of clear plastic tube corers. If there is evidence of disruption, discard and repeat the sample.
- If the sampler has triggered and operated correctly and if there is no recovery of sediment on the first attempt, try at least twice more before abandoning the sample location.
- With spring-loaded samplers, take adequate safety precautions when the instrument is in a cocked position - severe injury can result from accidental triggering at the surface. It is always advisable to wear industrial gloves when handling samplers to prevent minor abrasions and pinching that may easily occur when setting the moving parts of grab samplers.
- Always ensure that staff using the equipment are trained in the use and maintenance of the equipment.
- The composition of sediment samples is just as likely to change in response to oxidation, temperature, microbial activity or de-gassing as with water samples. Sediment samples should be kept in cool dark storage (and not allowed to dry out) in the field before transfer to permanent facilities on shore. If this is not possible, sensitive analyses must be performed in the field before the onset of sediment degradation.

For a description of sampling devices and processing techniques, see Chapters IV and V.

III.6   Positioning

Most river and small lake sampling sites are easily located by reference to either topographical maps or air photos. For data recording purposes, individual locations should be specified by geographical coordinates, either in latitude and longitude or by Universal Transverse Mercator (UTM) coordinates. Where conditions permit, it is perhaps best to locate a small vessel by means of positioning from shore, where it is easiest to plot the results of survey triangulation and, by visual or radio communication between crews, to direct the required navigation.

Larger lakes, wide rivers, and estuaries, however, present more difficult situations. Near shore, a sample location may be positioned from a boat by the use of ranges, which may be formed by the line-up of shoreline features or islands, or by the use of horizontal angle measurements from a sextant to form an intersection. Similarly, a magnetic compass can be used to obtain two or more bearings on shoreline features in order to form an intersection. These bearings must be corrected for magnetic variation and any compass deviation resulting from metal parts in the boat (it is essential to keep well away from the sampler, motor, tools, and cans). In very large lakes, the lack of shoreline resolution presents further difficulties for the positioning of offshore (or mid-lake) samples. In these areas vessels should be equipped with suitable navigation equipment (e.g., Sat. Nav; Loran, Decca, or radar, etc.). Even in most very large lakes, it is quite practical to use a combination of radar and compass heading for the collection of samples from grid locations which cross the lake. Position errors will depend upon the type of equipment used, its calibration, weather conditions, and operator experience, and may well exceed 1:100 (radius of error:length of uncontrolled survey line). In addition, most large survey companies can provide transponder-type radio navigation/positioning systems which provide very high orders of accuracy, with an over water range of as much as 50 to 80 km. These systems are not cost effective for use in low density surveys but may be very worthwhile for high density surveys in small areas of about 200 km^2 or less.

In most lakes and rivers many studies can be completed by using very simple survey techniques and these are usually based on vessel heading and distance travelled. Dead reckoning data, however, requires frequent checks against easily identified shoreline features, by means of bearings taken from the vessel or the shore. Minimum requirements are a small gyro compass (very desirable), a fully compensated and corrected magnetic compass (essential) and either a portable small-boat distance log or an r.p.m. speed rating curve (for boats with inboard motors and equipped with engine revolution counters).

Investigators should familiarize themselves with appropriate survey techniques (and be aware of their limitations) or retain the services of a competent surveyor, before setting up a survey program and before going out into the field (it is easy to become disoriented on a large water-body where familiar landmarks merge into the distance). In most cases, it is less important to be able to locate a sample station precisely over a pre-plotted position than to be sure of the actual location from which the sample was recovered, or over which a survey line has passed. The movement of a vessel along a desired path or track must always take into account drift or leeway induced by winds and currents. Generally, wind effects dominate and these must be compensated for by steering a few degrees off course and into the wind. Vessel drift due to currents, in large lakes, cannot be predicted with certainty. The currents are usually weak but occasionally (near river mouths, or under storm influence) they may cause significant deviation from the desired track. Interpolated correction for sample location is all that can be done under these circumstances.

III.7   Safety Considerations

To many, the description of safety measures that follows may appear to be elementary and obvious. However, many investigators immersed in the complexities of a survey do not give enough attention to the safety which is required for the protection of field parties. In all field endeavours there is some element of risk. Fortunately, major accidents are rare but minor mishaps are common, and probably can never by wholly eliminated. The only way to reduce the likelihood of accidents is to be constantly aware of the need for safety in the field and laboratory, and to anticipate problems before they arise.

Some general guidelines and observations are given as follows:-
- ensure that a boat is adequate for the size of the water-body and climatic conditions;
- never start work in bad weather; be aware of the immediate weather forecast, if such is available;
- learn to recognize weather patterns; in some areas, watch carefully for the development of thunderstorms; trail an electrical ground line if the vessel is fitted with a mast;
- ensure that items in the boat such as the motor and bilge pump are in good working order and carry a set of tools for simple repairs; carry spare fuel;
- ensure that the vessel has adequate safety equiment such as: life jackets for all personnel; flares; fire-extinguisher and an adequate anchor and line, etc. Carry first aid equipment and comply with any regulations that are in effect;
- always advise someone on shore where you will be operating, and your expected place and time of return. Notify them if the place of return is changed; do not work alone;
- on large bodies of water use a chart and aids to navigation. If not available or if on smaller lakes, check with local people on location of natural hazards and use caution. If working in shallow water avoid being stuck in mud, soft sand or quicksand;
- use protective clothing, particularly gloves and footwear. Sampling equipment can cause injuries ranging from abrasions to severe lacerations and/or broken bones;
- ensure that clothing is adequate to meet expected extreme weather conditions appropriate for the site and season;
- take precautions to avoid sunburn and infections (i.e., inoculation for typhus and tetanus or other endemic diseases), protect against parasites (e.g., Bilharzia) and predators, and avoid disturbing large animals;
- carry adequate food supplies, and drinking water.

References

Bloesch, J; Burns, N.M. 1980. A critical review of sedimentation trap technique. Schweiz. z. Hydrol., 42: p. 15-55.

* Canada Department of the Environment. 1973. Fluvial processes and sedimentation. Proc. Hydrol. Symp. Univ. Alberta, Edmonton. Inland Wat. Direct., Ottawa. 759 pp.

* Church, M.: Gilbert, R. 1975. Proglacial fluvial and lacustrine environments. In: Jopling, A.V.; MacDonald, B.C. (eds.). Glaciofluvial and glaciolacustrine sedimentation. Soc. Econom. Palaeon. Mineral, Spec. Publ., 23: p. 22-100.

de Groot, A.J.; Allersma, E.; de Bruin, M.; Houtman, J.P.W. 1970. Cobalt and tantalum tracers measured by activation analysis in sediment transport studies. Proc. Internat. Atom. Energy Symp. Use Isotopes Hydrol., Vienna, March, 1970, p. 885-898.

* Guy, H.P., Norman, V.W. 1970. Field methods for measurement of fluvial sediment. U.S. Geol. Surv., Technique Wat. Resourc. Invest., Book 3, Chapt. 2, p. 598.

Håkanson, L. 1981. On lake bottom dynamics - the energy-topography factor. Can. J. Earth Sci., 18: p. 899-909.

* Håkanson, L. 1981. A manual of lake morphometry. Springer-Verlag, New York, Heidelberg, Berlin, 78 pp.

Hubbell, D.W. 1964. Apparatus and techniques for measuring bed load. U.S. Geol. Surv., Wat. Supply Pap., No. 1748, 74 pp.

Imboden, D.M.; Tschopp, J.: Stumm, W. 1980. Die Rekonstruktion früherer Stoffrachten in einem See mittels Sedimentuntersuchungen. Schweiz. z. Hydrol., 42: p. 1-14.

Inter-agency Committee on Water Resources. 1940-1963. Measurement equipment and analysis of sediment loads in streams. Sub-Comm. on Sedimentation, U.S.A. Reports 1-14.

* Kemp, A.L.W.; Thomas, R.L.; Dell, C.I.; Jaquet, J.M. 1976. Cultural impact on the geochemistry of sediments in Lake Erie. J. Fish. Res. Bd. Can., 33: p. 440-462.

King, L.H. 1967. Use of a conventional echo-sounder and textural analyses in delineating sedimentary facies: Scotian Shelf. Can. J. Earth Sci., 4: p. 691-708.

Mortimer, C.H. 1971. Chemical exchanges between sediments in the Great Lakes - speculations on probable regulatory mechanisms. Limnol. Oceanogr., 16: p. 387-404.

Rainwater, F.H.; Guy, H.P. 1961. Some observations on the hydro-chemistry and sedimentation of the Chamberlin Glacier area, Alaska. U.S. Geol. Surv., Prof. Pap., 414C, 14 pp.

* Sly, P.G. 1979. Sedimentary processes in lakes. In: Lerman, A. (ed.). Lakes; chemistry, geology, physics., p. 65-89. Springer-Verlag, New York, Heidelberg, Berlin.

Thomas, R.L.; Kemp, A.L.W., Lewis, C.F.M. 1972. Distribution, composition and characteristics of the surficial sediments of Lake Ontario. J. Sediment. Petrol., 42: p. 66-84.

Thomas, R.L. 1972. The distribution of mercury in the sediments of Lake Ontario. Can. J. Earth Sci., 9: p. 636-651.

Tywoniuk, N.; Cashman, M.A. 1973. Sediment distribution in river cross-sections. Proc. Hydrol. Symp. Univ. Alberta, Edmonton, p. 73-95. Can. Dept. Environm., Inland Wat. Direct., Ottawa.

Vanderpost, J.A. 1972. Bacterial and physical characteristics of Lake Ontario sediment during several months. Internat. Assoc. Great Lakes Res., Proc. 15th Conf. Great Lakes Res., p. 198-213.

* Walling, D.E. 1977. Natural sheet and channel erosion of unconsolidated resource material. In: Shear, H.; Watson, A.E.P. (eds.). The fluvial transport of sediment-associated nutrients and contaminants, p. 11-33. Internat. Joint Commiss., Great Lakes Reg. Off., Windsor, Ontario.

* Suggested text for further reading.

IV Sampling equipment and analytical methods

Sampling Equipment

IV.1.1   Introduction

In Chapter II the term 'sediments' was used to describe both suspended matter
and deposited matter, and to include all particulate material washed into a lake
or river, or formed in the water. Material is kept in suspension (as suspended
matter) only as long as turbulent motion counteracts sedimentation or sinking.
Therefore, although there is no particular chemical difference between suspended
matter in lakes or rivers, there is some physical difference between the two
systems. In rivers, sedimentation normally takes place only during periods of
low flow, and a major increase of flow may resuspend much of this material. The
coarse sediment fraction is found in suspension only under conditions of very
high flow and, for the most part, sands and gravels are moved downstream as bed
or traction load in which particles are rolled or skip over the bed. Where this
is no longer possible, the sediments may be considered to have entered some form
of dead storage in which they are no longer available to the system. In lakes,
there may be a layer of fluid mud near the bed which has not yet become part of
the solid or compacting lake bed; in such situations the fluid mud should be
considered as remaining in temporary storage. Of course, the boundaries between
bed and suspended load are vague. In rivers, the major transport is horizontal;
in lakes, vertical transport may be as important as, or even more important
than, horizontal transport. Therefore, samplers which are suitable for lakes
may not be suitable for rivers and vice versa.

The boundary which separates particulate and dissolved components is arbitrary. Normally, separation is made using either a 0.45 µm filter or a centrifuge. With either system it is important to check results by repeating the
procedures, and to ensure that filter clogging does not affect results.

Based on this separation, it is convenient to recognize the following components in a water sample: particulate live; particulate dead; mineral; dissolved inorganic (generally ionic); dissolved organic or bound inorganic.
Further, it should be noted that interconversion may occur during sampling or
storage. No single sampling technique is universally applicable!

IV.1.2   Sampling suspended matter

Suspended matter is normally collected with water samplers such as the Van Dorn,
Ruttner, Kemmerer, or Friedinger samplers (Golterman et al., 1978). These have
an open tube of one to three litres capacity with a hinged lid at each end. The
lids may be closed by a messenger. The Ruttner tube is made of Perspex
(~ plexiglass), while the Kemmerer is made of copper. The Friedinger is similar to the Ruttner and Kemmerer types, but its lids are held open at 90°,
parallel to the axis of the sampler, and do not seriously impede water flow.
Metal is not exposed on internal surfaces.

Another method makes use of pump samplers. In these types, a weighted rubber
or plastic tube is lowered to the desired depth and a pump sucks up a continuous

stream of water with which the water sampler is first rinsed and then filled. Both peristaltic and diaphram pumps are suitable, because there is no contact between metal and water. Depending upon the design of the intake head, pumping may cause little disturbance to physical layering (stratification) in the water mass and large volumes can be obtained. Pumps are also suitable for taking a mixed sample from different depths. After recovery, the samples should be transferred to glass or plastic (PVC) bottles in which they can be transported to the laboratory. Normally, glass bottles are used for metal analysis and the organics, while plastic is preferred for nutrients. If insufficient material is collected by these means, a centrifuge may be used. The continuous flow rotors are efficient in collecting even the finest material (Chapter III.4.2).

Suspended matter, sinking or sedimenting in lakes, is usually collected by sediment traps which may be placed directly on the lake bed, or held in suspension within the overlying water column (III.3.7). Many different types of traps have been used successfully, e.g., those by Thomas (1950, 1951, 1955, 1958, and 1963) Kleerekoper (1952), Jarnefelt (1955), Bloesch (1974), and Bloesch and Burns (1980)

The traps should have a flat base and a diameter of between 5 and 20 cm which is considered optimal, and the height should be five times greater than the diameter. The traps can be constructed from PVC or plexiglass material for total organic carbon (TOC) and metal analyses, but should be made of glass or teflon for the analysis of specific organic compounds. No accessories such as lattices, lids, baffles, or collars should be used. Movement of the traps should be avoided and rigid mooring systems should be used (Bloesch and Burns, 1980).

When planning to use sediment traps it is important to recognize that lake morphology and circulation will have an influence on the choice of the apparatus, and that there are many problems related to this technique. Measured sedimentation rates tend to be too high because of trap wall effects. In relatively turbulent waters (shallow lakes, typically 10 m depth or less) the presence of the trap may decrease small eddies, but in deep hypolimnia this effect is not significant. Mineralization (Kleerekoper, 1953) has an influence on the concentration of nitrogen, phosphorus, and organic carbon. At relatively great depths, where biological activity is limited, the effects may be very small and exposure times of less than 14 days may overcome this difficulty. In shallow and highly productive lakes, the technique should not be used at all. Instead, a centrifuge should be used to collect the material from selected depths. Where it is necessary to exclude the presence of resuspended matter derived from the lake bed, traps should be set at least 5 m above the bed. Traps should not be placed too near to areas of major inflow, unless to specifically monitor inflow characteristics.

The use of antibiotics is often recommended if they are able to stop all bacterial activity, and if they do not affect required analyses. $HgCl_2$ crystals may be added for short exposure times. However, it must be realised that the use of toxic agents may kill organisms which otherwise would have remained alive and mobile (and may bias the organic content of the sampler).

In rivers, suspended sediment samples must be representative of the sediment being transported and it is important to note that the distribution of the different grain sizes is not always homogeneous throughout the water flow. The water must enter the sample container at about the same velocity as the stream velocity. The sampler should be kept clear of the stream bed and several samples throughout the whole profile must be taken. The sampler should disturb the water flow as little as possible.

When streams are shallow enough to allow wading, or are accessible from a bridge, a hand sampler can be used; otherwise a cable and reel sampler must be utilized. Automatic pumping is useful, but relatively expensive and, again, the inlet to the pump must be moved through the whole river profile. Samplers can be depth-integrating or time-integrating (see also Chapter III.4). The papers on techniques of water resources investigations of the United States Geological Survey may be used as a reference source (Guy and Norman, 1970; Hubbell, 1964) and publications of the Interagency Committee on Water Resources (1940-1963).

IV.1.3   Corers and dredges

Corers are used to obtain sediment samples in which stratification is preserved, and the sediment water interface is relatively undisturbed. Interface cores may be collected using samplers such as the Jenkin and Kajak devices, and a variety of different types of gravity corers can be used to collect longer sediment cores without preservation of overlying water. Direct sample recovery can be made by using scuba diving and a simple push-tube. The depth of the sediment to be collected will depend on the sedimentation rates; usually a depth of 0.5 to 1 m is sufficient (III.3.5).

Bottom deposits can be also sampled by grab samplers or dredges, such as the Ekman or Petersen dredge (Figure IV.1) which are designed to recover material from the top few centimeters of the lake/river bed. The Ekman sampler is designed to recover soft sediments in the absence of strong currents; the Petersen and Ponar grabs can sample a greater variety of sediment types, and are less affected by current flow.

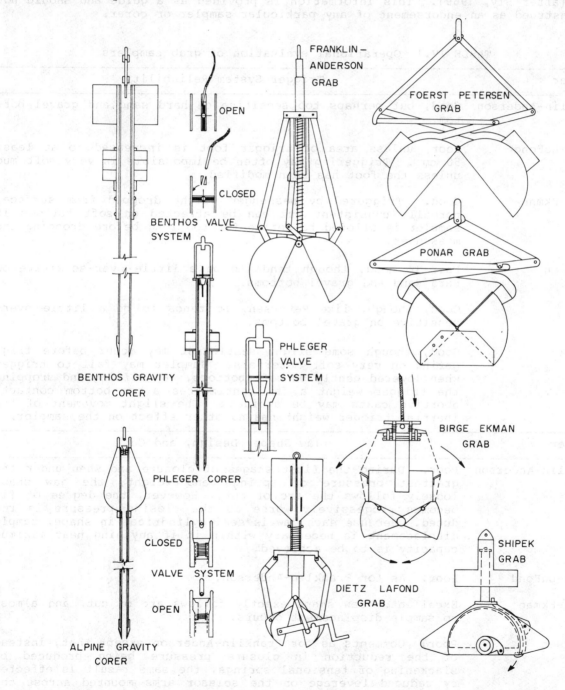

FIGURE IV.1   Corers and bottom samplers tested during equipment trials
(after Sly, 1969)

Under conditions of moderate wave and current motion, none of these samplers recover an undisturbed sample, and they should not be used to study layered structures in the sediments. However, they do provide a rapid means of characterizing the "average" sediment composition over a limited depth range and, indeed, such bulk samples are all that may be required in many cases.

There are several good publications which are available to describe samplers and corers, and a large bibliography is provided in Elliott and Tullett (1978). The variety of types is too great to be fully discussed in this Guidebook; however, Tables IV.1 and IV.2 give an outline of characteristics, methods of operation, and suitabilities of a number of commercially available pieces of equipment (after Sly, 1969). This information is provided as a guide and should not be construed as an endorsement of any particular sampler or corer.

TABLE IV.1 Operational evaluation of grab samplers

Sampler	Trigger System Reliability
Franklin-Anderson	Good, but perhaps too sensitive on hard sand and gravel bottom.
Dietz-LaFond	Poor, unless area of trigger foot is increased to at least 50 cm^2. Triggering may often be impossible in very soft mud unless the foot has been modified.
Birge-Ekman	Good. Triggered by messenger weight dropped from surface, normally consistent but can be affected on soft bottoms if sampler is allowed to settle for too long before dropping the messenger.
Petersen	Fair to good, though tends to be a little over-sensitive on hard sand and gravel bottoms.
Ponar	Good, though, like Petersen, it tends to be a little over-sensitive on gravel bottoms.
Shipek	Good, though some slight settlement may occur before triggering on very soft materials. Sampler may fail to trigger when lowered gently on soft bottoms. By lifting and dropping the trigger weight a few centimetres after bottom contact, abortive casts may be avoided. The slight movement of the inertial trigger weight has no other effect on the sampler.

Sampler	Jaw Shape, Design, and Cut
Franklin-Anderson	Poor. During the first stages of closure and when under the greatest pressure of springs and weight, the jaw shape loosely follows the arc of cut. However, the degree of fit becomes progessively worse as the closing pressure is reduced. Because each jaw is semi-cylindrical in shape, sample displacement is necessary within it if anything near maximum capacity is to be achieved.
Dietz-LaFond	Poor. As for Franklin-Anderson.
Birge-Ekman	Excellent. Jaw shape exactly follows arc of cut, and almost no sample displacement occurs.
Petersen	Poor. Comments as for Franklin-Anderson except that, instead of the reduction in closure pressure being produced by slackening of tensional springs, the same result is effected by reduced leverage on the scissor arms mounted across the hinge line.

Cont'd...../

TABLE IV.1 (Cont'd) Operational evaluation of grab samplers

Ponar	Excellent. Jaw shape exactly follows arc of cut, and almost no sample displacement occurs.
Petite Ponar	As above.
Shipek	Excellent. As for Ponar. In addition, the rotation of the bucket is extremely rapid. In most cases the rotational shear is far greater than the sediment shear strength, thus the cutting action is very clean (producing minimal disturbance), particularly in soft clays, muds, silts, and sands.

Sampler	Preservation and Protection from Washout
Franklin-Anderson	Fair, but the tightness of closure is largely dependent upon the lack of grains trapped between the edges of the jaws. Providing a tight fit between the two jaws is obtained, the sample is well shielded against washout. If the jaws are kept open by material trapped between the jaws, washout can be severe or total.
Dietz-LaFond	Fair. Comments as for Franklin-Anderson.
Birge-Ekman	Good, except when the sampler is used in very coarse or shelly sediment. Under these conditions material may be trapped between the jaws, preventing their closure. In this case, washout may be severe. The jaws are so designed that they slightly overlap one another, thus a slight imperfection of closure can be tolerated.
Petersen	Good. Comments as for Birge-Ekman.
Ponar	Good. Comments as for Birge-Ekman. In addition to the overlap jaws, this sampler has a pair of metal side plates, mounted close to the moving side faces of the jaws. These plates further reduce the possibility of washout.
Petite Ponar	As above.
Shipek	Excellent. The great advantage of Shipek over all of the other samplers described, is that the bucket closes with its separation plane aligned in the horizontal rather than in the vertical. Good samples can be retrieved even when bucket closure is prevented by pebbles or similar material, even 2 to 5 cm across. With the bucket properly rotated, washout is completely avoided.

Sampler	Stability
Franklin-Anderson	Fair. Despite the weight of this grab, it tends to 'stream' at an inclined angle under conditions of rapid ship drift or fast water flow. Providing lowering conditions are calm and stable, the sampler will hold upright during the initial sampling process; if however, the line is allowed to slack, the sampler will fall over.
Dietz-LaFond	Poor. This sampler is very sensitive to 'streaming' and will rarely operate in the vertical position unless used in ideal conditions. Its tendency to maintain an inclined attitude during descent sometimes results in a failure to trigger.

Cont'd...../

TABLE IV.1 (Cont'd) Operational evaluation of grab samplers

Birge-Ekman	Fair. Despite the light weight of this sampler, and its tendency to 'stream', its wide base gives good stability and stance once it has come to rest on the sediment floor. Under poor sampling conditions, however, it becomes impossible to operate because: (a) the sampler, due to its light weight, is continually being lifted and dropped and 'streamed' along the bottom, (b) any slack in the line, particularly near the sampler, is likely to impede the proper function of the trigger's messenger weight. It tends to roll over after triggering on all but soft bottoms.
Peterson	Good. This is a heavy sampler with a wide base line (when the jaws are open). It maintains a near vertical descent under all conditions, but after sampling it tends to fall over (unless on a soft bottom).

Sampler	Stability
Ponar	Very good. Like the Petersen, and because of its weight and wide base line (when jaws are open) this grab has a good vertical descent under most conditions and has a stable stance on the bottom. The presence of the fixed side plates prevents the grab from falling over, after jaw closure, and helps in preserving a near perfect bottom sample.
Petite Ponar	As above.
Shipek	Excellent. Despite the large size of this sampler, its weight ensures a near perfect vertical descent even under conditions of rapid drift or fast water flow. The sampler is also very stable even on bottom slopes 20° or more. This stability ensures the minimum possible disturbance of the sampled material.

The operational suitability of the various corers and grab samplers is summarized in Table IV.2.

TABLE IV.2 Operational suitability of corers and grab samplers

Benthos Gravity Corer	Cores of 3 m or less in soft clays, muds or sandy silts. Particularly suitable for studies of the sediment/water interface, for studies on depositional sediment structures.
Alpine Gravity Corer	Cores of 2 m or less in almost all sediment types. The rugged nature of this corer lends itself to general usage. For studies involving sediment structure or large volumes of material, the corer is unsuitable; for studies of a pilot nature or to prove the suitability of an area for piston coring, this gravity corer is excellent.
Phleger Corer	Cores of 0.5 m or less, in almost all sediment types. Particularly suited to bottom materials containing a high percentage of fibrous organic material. The low cutter angle, the narrow wall thickness and high point loading, and the extremely sharp cutter make it very suitable for sampling shallow lacustrine and estuarine deposits, marsh deposits and thin peat beds.
Multiple Corers	Still under investigation.

Cont'd...../

TABLE IV.2 (Cont'd) Operational suitability of corers and grab samplers

Franklin-Anderson Grab	Suitable for obtaining material for bulk sample analysis. Works best in soft clays, muds, silts and sands. Will occasionally obtain a good gravel sample. Material of no use for structural or other specific analyses.
Dietz-LaFond Grab	Can be used for general sampling but not recommended for any particular use. Of all the samplers tested this pattern proved to be the least suitable.
Birge-Ekman Dredge	Suitable for soft clays, muds, silts and silty sands. This sampler should be used under calm water conditions, typically in small lakes or restricted areas. The lack of sample disturbance, square cross-section, and moderate penetration make this sampler suitable for detailed studies (i.e., biological and geochemical) of the top 2 to 3 cm of bottom sediment. Because of its light weight and easy handling it is well suited to small boat operations.
Petersen Grab	This sampler, like the Franklin-Anderson, is suitable for taking bulk sample material in most types of sediment. It is quite unsuited for studies of detailed and specific sediment properties, though it is perhaps a little more successful in taking gravel samples. Either of these two samplers will do well as a general purpose bulk sampler.
Petite Ponar Grab	As for above, very good for small boat, hand operations.
Shipek Bucket Sampler	An excellent general purpose sampler, though perhaps a little heavy for small boat operation. This sampler is capable of working with almost equal success on all types of bottom material. It provides a sample even less disturbed than the Ponar, making it the most suitable sampler (under test) for detailed geological studies of the sediment surface. The sample volume is significantly less than that of the Ponar, and the quantity of material sampled at maximum cutting depth is also less than the Ponar. These two points may therefore favour the Ponar for certain biological (population) studies. On the other hand, the rapid rotation of the Shipek bucket, as opposed to the much slower closure of the Ponar's jaws, may make it more suitable for sampling sediment containing a significant population of non-sessile forms.

Small hand-held samplers can be effectively used from small boats, canoes, helicopters, and even float planes, and for this a small Ponar, Birge-Ekman or a miniaturized Shipek grab should prove adequate for the recovery of small amounts of material. The Phleger-type corer can be used, also, as a hand-tool but it recovers cores of rather small diameter; a larger core, similar to that recovered by a Benthos gravity corer, is normally preferred. Because of the weight of most gravity corers, and the added weight of core sample, it is advisable to have some form of mechanical winch to aid in their recovery (although two people might be able to handle a Benthos corer, with minimum drop weight in shallow water of about 25 m or less).

Many attempts have been made to overcome the weight problem associated with successful gravity coring, such as the sophisticated wide diameter sphincter corer of Williams and Pashley (1979); however, as yet, there is no single piece of equipment that meets both desired handling characteristics and good core recovery. A recent review of coring techniques and a brief discussion of corer mechanics (Sly, 1981) may assist investigators who must develop their own equipment or who may wish to design equipment to meet local requirements.

The reader should take note of the observations given in Tables IV.1 and IV.2 and make selection on the basis of the specific requirements. More than one type of sampler may be necessary, but care should be taken to ensure that intersample compatibility is maintained by consistent usage of the same sampler for each designated function.

IV.1.4   Processing, further treatment, and storage

If a surface sediment sample has been recovered without disturbance, it may be carefully sub-sampled to retain selected materials of, say, the top 2 to 3 cm of sediment (III.2.2). Usually, however, the total recovery is treated as a bulk sample and the entire sample is mixed thoroughly before taking representative sub-samples for laboratory analysis.

Material can be removed from corers by using a piston to extrude the core; slow extrusion allows thin slices to be taken at selected intervals, from the top of the core. As an alternative, cores may be frozen and cut in a solid state. Although this may be acceptable in some studies, it should be noted that the process of freezing may also destroy internal structures in a core which could be an important aid in subsequent interpretations.

For most analyses (metals, nutrients) the samples are dried at 60° or 105°C, until constant weight is reached, i.e., until the loss of weight is less than one percent of the total loss. Samples containing a large amount of clay may present problems, since they tend to release water over rather prolonged periods. No heating should be applied when sample materials are to be analyzed for volatile organic matter. In some cases, extraction with an organic solvent may be carried out with wet sediment (which has not been previously dried).

In dry sediments, the fractionation of iron, nitrogen, and phosphorus compounds is no longer possible. If this fractionation is required, different extraction steps should be carried out on unfrozen wet sediments.

Freeze-drying provides a relatively quick and simple means of sample preparation for long-term storage. Wet sample materials are placed in special glass containers which are partially emersed in a bath of freezer coolant and quickly cooled to about -40°C. Although the samples can be frozen in dry ice in ordinary vacuum flasks, it is best to use shell freezers in which the special glass containers are rotated as they freeze. This has the effect of coating frozen sediment over most of the inner surface of the glass containers and provides a more easily dried sample. After freezing, the glass containers are connected to a source of high vacuum and the samples are dried as the ice is lost in vapour form under the vacuum. This technique leaves a clean dry powder which is ready to be stored in clean dry vials. Properly sealed vials (to exclude moisture) can be stored for many years without significant degradation of the sample material. The technique is not suitable for the preservation of volatile compounds or gases dissolved in interstitial waters, and analyses must be completed on these components before treatment by freeze-drying. Particle size analyses should also be completed before freeze-drying.

IV.1.5   Interstitial waters

A so-called interstitial water is always present between the particles of bottom sediments, and often it has a much higher concentration of dissolved substances in it than in the water from just above the sediments. If these interstitial waters are to be studied, the samples should not be stored, but processed as soon as possible after collection, preferably within a few hours. Any temperature change should be avoided. Anoxic sediments require to be kept and handled in an anoxic atmosphere, e.g., in a glove box. Any exposure of these samples to oxygen will cause the ferrous-iron to be oxidized rapidly; this will then precipitate, and several other compounds (phosphate, silicate, organic matter) may co-precipitate. Extractions can be made using the following equipment, depending on the quantities required and the compounds to be studied:
1) Centrifuge tubes filled and sealed to exclude air in a temperature-controlled centrifuge. All operations must be carried out under nitrogen atmosphere.
2) Mechanical or pressure-operated squeezers (i.e., Reeburgh, 1967).
3) Direct removal of water by syringe through ports in the wall of the core tube. These ports are closed with a soft seal while coring and needles are later inserted into the core through the seal.
4) In situ extractors or 'sediment peepers' (Hesslein, 1976 and Schindler et al., 1977). In these, a small chamber, filled with distilled water, is covered by a semi-permeable membrane and inserted into the sediment

layer in situ. It is left in place for a sufficient time until pore water and chamber concentrations equilibrate. Only relatively small samples are obtained. This may cause problems if several different elements are to be measured, but concentrations in pore waters, fortunately, tend to be high. Use of sediment peepers in partially consolidated silts and clays is not entirely satisfactory.

Contamination

e presence of heavy metals in sediments is being examined, caution should d with metal samplers, even if they are made from a metal other than that study. Teflon, PVC, or stainless steel samplers are preferable, but if are not available other metal samplers can be used. The samples should be processed rapidly to minimize container effects.

Microbial activity in sediments can lead to rapid changes in composition; this may start when oxygenated sediments become anoxic, resulting in subsequent production of H_2S and/or CH_4. The oxidation state of iron compounds may be changed, also causing release of nutrients. The addition of $HgCl_2$ or formol does not always appear to be successful, due to inactivation (HgS) or adsorption. Temperature changes can also lead to changes in the sample chemical composition.

Caution should be exercised during sampling to avoid contamination from other equipment, oil and grease lubricants, and other surface pollutants on the water.

IV.2   Analytical Methods

IV.2.1   Introduction

The physical structure of sediment provides an important indication of its depositional history and its susceptibility to erosion and remobilization. For instance, water content can be used to indicate its sensitivity to erosion and resuspension or, perhaps, its suitability as substrate for benthic organisms. Also, the diffusion of substances from interstitial waters into the overlying waters is related, to some extent, to sediment porosity and/or compaction.

Parameters which may be used to characterize sediment include:
- Sediment structures (bed form and layering, etc.) and colour. The presence or absence of an oxidized surface layer can have an effect on fluxes across the interface (Mortimer, 1941, 1942, and 1971; for summary, see Golterman, 1975). Additional deeper hard layers, such as iron or manganese oxide layers at greater depth, may also have an inhibitory effect on flux (Sly and Thomas, 1974).
- Density (i.e., dry weight per unit volume) concentration, bulk density, specific density.
- Moisture content per unit volume of sediment.
- Grain size distribution, and its changes with depth of water.

IV.2.2   Preliminary observations and analyses

In the field, sample analyses should begin at the point of recovery; generally, the same types of information should be recorded for both surface grab samples and cores. It is usual to record grab sample and core characteristics on different log-sheets, and Figure IV.2 provides an example of a core log. Record sheets, for grab sample descriptions, can be made up to suit individual requirements; the following outline describes recorded data, common to both types of sample:

Surface condition	- Sample material is undisturbed, partly disturbed or disturbed.
Sub-surface condition	- This usually applies to cores where, although surface materials are apparently undisturbed, materials (of a different composition) may be greatly disturbed lower down the core.
Biota	- Simple description of major types, e.g., pelecypods (clams), gastropods (snails), insect larvae, worms, rooted plants; live or dead material; an indication of abundance (present = very few, common = several, abundant = large numbers).

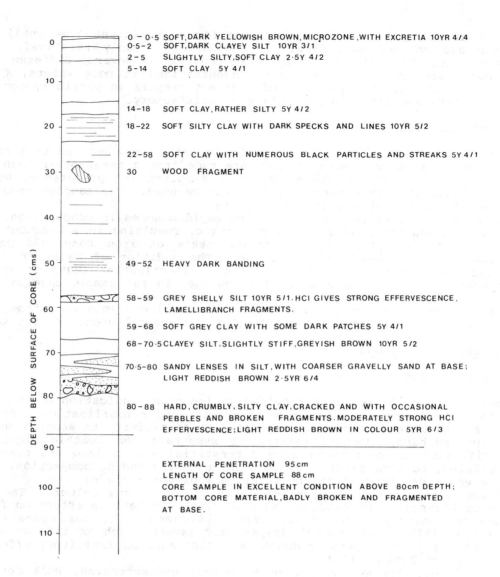

```
0 – 0·5    SOFT, DARK YELLOWISH BROWN, MICROZONE, WITH EXCRETIA 10YR 4/4
0·5–2      SOFT, DARK CLAYEY SILT 10YR 3/1
2–5        SLIGHTLY SILTY, SOFT CLAY 2·5Y 4/2
5–14       SOFT CLAY 5Y 4/1

14–18      SOFT CLAY, RATHER SILTY 5Y 4/2
18–22      SOFT SILTY CLAY WITH DARK SPECKS AND LINES 10YR 5/2

22–58      SOFT CLAY WITH NUMEROUS BLACK PARTICLES AND STREAKS 5Y 4/1
30         WOOD FRAGMENT




49–52      HEAVY DARK BANDING


58–59      GREY SHELLY SILT 10YR 5/1. HCl GIVES STRONG EFFERVESCENCE,
           LAMELLIBRANCH FRAGMENTS.
59–68      SOFT GREY CLAY WITH SOME DARK PATCHES 5Y 4/1
68–70·5    CLAYEY SILT, SLIGHTLY STIFF, GREYISH BROWN 10YR 5/2
70·5–80    SANDY LENSES IN SILT, WITH COARSER GRAVELLY SAND AT BASE;
           LIGHT REDDISH BROWN 2·5YR 6/4
80–88      HARD, CRUMBLY, SILTY CLAY, CRACKED AND WITH OCCASIONAL
           PEBBLES AND BROKEN FRAGMENTS. MODERATELY STRONG HCl
           EFFERVESCENCE; LIGHT REDDISH BROWN IN COLOUR 5YR 6/3


EXTERNAL PENETRATION  95 cm
LENGTH OF CORE SAMPLE  88 cm
CORE SAMPLE IN EXCELLENT CONDITION ABOVE 80 cm DEPTH;
BOTTOM CORE MATERIAL, BADLY BROKEN AND FRAGMENTED
AT BASE.
```

DEPTH BELOW SURFACE OF CORE (cms)

CORE DESCRIPTION LOG
(Colour, consistency, texture, organisms,
HCl effervescence, structure etc.)
CORE TYPE BENTHOS
          GRAVITY
LENGTH OUTSIDE MUD LINE 95 cm

STUDY 42
CORE No 14 WATER DEPTH 42·5 m
DATE 18/05/58 TIME 1015
LOGGED BY J. DOE.

FIGURE VI.2 Core-log example

Quantity recovered	– Sample container is full, 3/4, 1/2, 1/4, trace, or empty. With cores, it is useful to record the external mud line as an indication of penetration depth, and the length of core recovered. These are usually different; the core length being often 10 to 15 percent less, because of the mechanical effects of coring.
Smell	– Most cores and grab samples have an earthy smell, similar to soils. However, certain smells related to various forms of putrefaction are very distinctive; for example, the 'rotten eggs' smell of H_2S is strongly indicative of reducing conditions and the formation of sulphide compounds in sediments.

Layers — The number of layers of different sediment types should be recorded.

For each layer give thickness, visual composition (gravel, sand, mud, etc.), stiffness, and colour.

Stiffness can often provide a guide to water content and age if the sediments have not dried out due to some previous sub-aerial exposure (even temporary exposure such as in reservoirs or rivers); generally, the older they are the stiffer they become, due to compaction and loss of water content. Water loss in clays produces a non-reversible change, whereas temporary water loss in sands will have little effect, unless accompanied by precipitation (e.g., carbonates) which may eventually cause cementation of various layers.

Colour can be measured by comparison with standard soil colour charts (Munsell Soil Colours) and provide a guide to the chemical state of sediments (reddish browns are typical of iron oxides, pale grey colours are typical of somewhat reduced sediments, and black is often associated with sulphide/high organic carbon content). Colours may be indicative, also, of various mineral suites and can be used as a guide to sediment provenance (III.1.4) in some areas.

Other measurements — Apparent redox potential (Eh) and hydrogen ion concentration (pH) profiles can be measured by probes inserted at, for example, 0.5, 1.5, 3.0, and 5.0 cm depths (see also IV.4) to give an indication of chemical states at the surface of the sediment bed (measurements should be made only after readouts have stabilized). The apparent redox potential in a lake as measured with a platinum and reference electrode is different from a thermodynamically well defined redox potential (see Golterman, 1975, p. 156-157). Sediment sample temperature (0.5 to 1.5 cm below surface) gives a reasonable approximation of bottom water temperature, and can be used when recording temperature probes are unavailable. In addition, the use of drops of dilute HCl can given an indication of the amount of carbonate present in the effervescence on the surface of the sample. HCl tests are useful in picking out thin carbonate layers in cores, and areas of carbonate cementation.

IV.2.3   Physical procedures

a) Determination of Dry Weight Per Unit Volume.

The determination of dry weight of suspended matter can be accomplished either by a filtration or by an evaporation method: usually evaporation is used for high concentrations of suspended matter, and filtration is used when concentrations are less than about 100 mg l^{-1}. Above this value the evaporation method must be used.

1) When only small amounts of suspended sediments are present the filtration procedure should be used. Formerly, fritted glass crucibles were often used, but because they tend to clog, they are now usually replaced by glass fibre or membrane filters. For coarse sediments, the crucibles are, nevertheless, still suitable.

The filters, for which several excellent filter holders are commercially available, need little pretreatment. The weight must be noted in advance; and one or two blank filters must be used to check whether they have the same weight after the filtration and drying procedure as before.

Glass fibre filters tend to clog less than membrane filters, but for small amounts of very fine material the membrane filters are more suitable. To ensure consistent results some samples should not be pressure filtered.

The method requires the use of an analytical balance (0.1 mg) having an accuracy of about one percent.

If high concentration samples are to be sub-sampled, they must be vigorously stirred or shaken to prevent settlement of coarse particles before sub-sampling.

Low concentration suspensions will probably require large volume treatment by centrifugation.

2) In the evaporation method, suspended sediments (> 100 mg l^{-1}) are allowed to settle to the bottom of a sample bottle. The supernatant liquid is then decanted and the sediment is washed into an evaporating dish. With suspensions of naturally dispersed clays the method does not work well. If the sediment/dissolved matter ratio is low, a correction must be made for the remaining dissolved solids. Distilled water can be used to prevent the need for this correction during the washing steps, but large quantities of distilled water and long contact times must be avoided in order to prevent solubilization of certain compounds, e.g., $CaCO_3$.

For consolidated sediments, the dry weight can be measured after taking the material from a drying oven; the volume can be calculated from the surface and height of the sample (cores) or by a displacement technique.

b) Determination of Moisture Content.

Standard soil test procedures require that samples of coarse sand should weigh between 250 to 500 g and samples of fine silt or clay about 200 g. It is possible to make non-standard measurements on very much smaller samples but these require a more accurate balance; heating time is largely unaffected. For standard analyses, unprocessed (damp) original material should be sub-sampled and the disaggregated material weighed (wet weight) and placed in a drying oven (105° to 110°C) and reweighed after 16 hours. A drying temperature of 60°C should be used for peats (to inhibit oxidation of organic compounds) and samples rich in hydrous minerals (e.g., gypsum).

Moisture content (M) is expressed as percent of dry soil weight:

$$M = \frac{\text{Sample wet wt.} - \text{Sample dry wt.}}{\text{Sample dry wt.}} \times 100$$

c) Determination of Grain Size Distributions.

Particle grain size can be determined by sedimentation under well-controlled conditions (pipette and accumulation tube methods) and by sieving wet or dry material. The results of wet and dry sieving are generally in closest agreement for coarse materials, but may show marked differences at very fine particle sizes. Sedimentation techniques which measure an equivalent hydraulic diameter (integrating shape, density, and size) may give results which differ substantially from both wet and dry sieving. All grain-size determination methods require some sample pretreatment and sieving requires relatively large quantities of sample material; it is generally unsuitable for small quantities of suspended sediment.

1) Pipette method - The principle of this method is to determine the concentration (dry weight per unit volume) of a laboratory suspension at a predetermined depth, as a function of settling time. Particles having a settling velocity greater than that of the size at which separation is desired will settle below the point of withdrawal, after a certain time lapse. Recommended times and depths are given in Table IV.3 and Figure IV.3 for particle size between 2 and 62 µm. The time and depth are calculated on the basis of Stokes' Law. The table should be read thus: at 20°C, at the withdrawal depth of 15 cm, after 44 seconds, the water

TABLE IV.3 Time of pipette withdrawal for given temperature, depth of withdrawal, and diameter of particles (after Guy, 1973)

(The values in this table are based on particles of assumed spherical shape with an average specific gravity of 2.65, the constant of acceleration due to gravity = 980, and viscosity varying from 0.010087 at 20°C to 0.008004 at 30°C.)

Diameter of particle mm →	0.062	0.062	0.031		0.031		0.016		0.008		0.004		0.002		0.002	
Depth of withdrawal cm →	15	10	15		10		10		10		5		5		3	
Time of withdrawal units →	(sec)	(sec)	(min)	(sec)	(min)	(sec)	(min)	(sec)	(min)	(sec)	(min)	(sec)	(hr)	(min)	(hr)	(min)
Temperature (°C)																
20	44	29	2	52	1	55	7	40	30	40	61	19	4	5	2	27
21	42	28	2	48	1	52	7	29	29	58	59	50	4	0	2	24
22	41	27	2	45	1	50	7	18	29	13	58	22	3	54	2	20
23	40	27	2	41	1	47	7	8	28	34	57	5	3	48	2	17
24	39	26	2	38	1	45	6	58	27	52	55	41	3	43	2	14
25	38	25	2	34	1	42	6	48	27	14	54	25	3	38	2	11
26	37	25	2	30	1	40	6	39	26	38	53	12	3	33	2	8
27	36	24	2	27	1	38	6	31	26	2	52	2	3	28	2	5
28	36	24	2	23	1	35	6	22	25	28	50	52	3	24	2	2
29	35	23	2	19	1	33	6	13	24	53	49	42	3	19	1	59
30	34	23	2	16	1	31	6	6	24	22	48	42	3	15	1	57

collected no longer contains the fraction larger than 0.062 mm (62 µm). It contains particulates of finer size in which the coarser fraction is least represented.

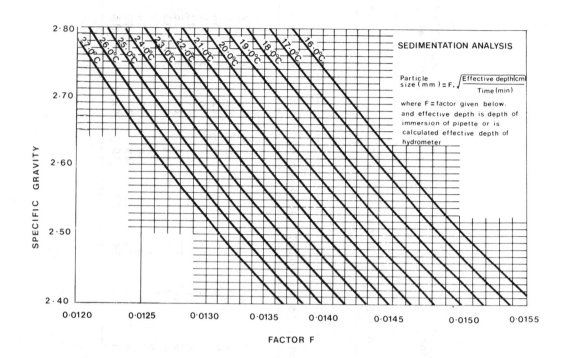

FIGURE IV.3 Nomogram for sedimentation test

Figure IV.4 shows the equipment required (see also Krumbein and Pettijohn, 1938); a manifold operation for multiple samples can be set up following the same principles. Temperature should be held reasonably constant (±2°C) and compensation can be made to accommodate laboratory temperatures outside the range of 18 to 22°C. For samples consisting of suspended matter, sedimentation can be carried out in the native liquid. For consolidated sediments, a few ml of the wet mud may be used, but the dry weight must be known first. Sample splitting may be required as pretreatment when excess (>5 g) silt or clay is present. This can be done in a sample splitter, suitable for splitting wet silt-clay samples, or by other means of representative sub-sampling (such as quartering). For most fine grained sediments it is necessary to use dispersants which greatly reduce the natural tendency of silt and clay size particulates to form aggregates, and settle at an accelerated rate (flocculation). Dispersants cause particulates to settle as discrete grains, thereby allowing a consistent application of Stokes' Law by which particle size is determined from the time a particle takes to fall through a given height of water at constant temperature.

There are many different types of dispersing agents which can be used on fine grained sediments (Akroyd, 1964); however, their effectiveness can be limited by the presence of organics in the sediments, an excessive sensitivity by the sediment to different types of dispersant (which may induce flocculation) or requirements of high alkalinity during dispersion.

As a general rule, it is sufficient to pretreat sediments with H_2O_2 to oxidize organic material, and then to add a small quantity of two percent sodium hexametaphosphate solution. Dilute HCl can

be used to leach the sediment, before the addition of the dispersant, but this is not normally required. Sediment pretreatment
should be kept to a minimum and samples so treated cannot be used
for subsequent chemical analyses. For that, separate sub-samples
must be used.

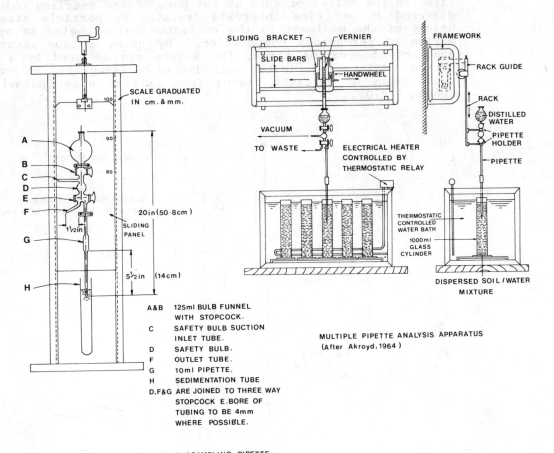

DIAGRAMMATIC ARRANGEMENT OF 10ml SAMPLING PIPETTE
FOR SEDIMENTATION ANALYSIS SINGLE SYSTEM
(After B.S.1377, (1948))

FIGURE IV.4 Apparatus for particle-size analysis by pipette method

It is possible to measure silt and clay size particulates, using
a hydrometer, as an alternative to pipette analysis. In such
tests it is necessary to disperse about 50 g of sediment with
20 ml of two percent sodium hexametaphosphate, in 500 ml of distilled water. After mechanical stirring for not less than
15 minutes, the mixture is poured into a narrow cylinder and made
up to 1000 ml with additional distilled water. The narrow cylinder is brought to constant temperature (in a water bath), at about
25°C.

After end to end shaking for about two minutes (with one hand
over the open end of the cylinder), the test is begun. Hydrometer
readings are made at 0.5, 1, 1.5, 2, 3, 5, 10, 15, and 30 minute
intervals, and at 1, 2, 4, 8, and 24 hours (as with pipette with-
drawals), and conversions made to size/composition using either
tables or nomographs (e.g., Akroyd, 1964). Although the hydrometer analysis is quicker to perform than the pipette analysis,
test results are less reliable (particularly during the early time
intervals); this is because of turbulence in the mixture, float
bobbing, and difficulties in making consistent float level sight-
ings. Pipette analyses are to be preferred.

2) <u>The accumulation tube (Poole, 1957)</u> - In this method, a tube (Figure IV.5 and Table IV.4) is used to determine size distributions, based upon the hydraulic characteristics of the particles; it expresses results in the form of an equivalent hydraulic diameter. In A-Tube determinations the height of sediment accumulated in the collector tube at the base of the settling column, is measured at set time intervals (related to particle size); the height of the sediment in the collector column being an approximation of percentage composition. By using a tape recorder to announce observation times, the A-Tube can be used by a single person. A-Tube and pipette methods can be integrated to provide a rapid means of particle sizing from sand to clay (Rukavina and Duncan, 1970).

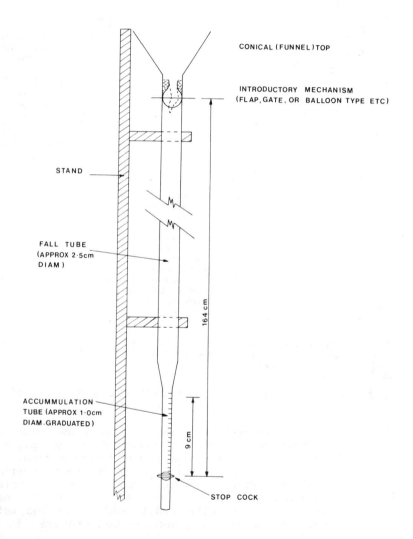

FIGURE IV.5   Schematic diagram of accumulation tube equipment
             for sand-size analysis. Modified after Rukavina
             and Duncan (1970).

    The A-Tube is recommended for rapid determinations of particle size distribution in sand-sized sediments which are typical of stream bed conditions and of the shorelines of lakes. Sample preparation for A-Tube analysis requires that finer material must be removed (e.g., by wet sieving), before a sample is analyzed and that sand particles should be free of attached clay; organic matter should be removed before analysis (by treating 1 g of dry weight in 40 ml H_2O, with 5 ml of six percent H_2O_2 with or without heating). The A-Tube can be used to size particles in the range of about 0.05 to 2 mm. The A-Tube uses a 5 g sediment sample (Rukavina and Duncan, 1970). A-Tube measurements should not be considered as a precise measurement of particle size. Basic equipment consists of:

a) a glass funnel about 25 cm long;
b) a rubber connecting tube with a quick release clamp;
c) glass sedimentation tube with removable collector, giving a fall distance of 164 cm (maximum);
d) a stand;
e) a timer.

TABLE IV.4 Settling tube reading times*

Size		Times, sec					
∅	mm	18°C	20°C	22°C	24°C	26°C	28°C
0.0	1.00	11	10	10	10	10	10
0.5	0.71	15	15	15	14	14	14
1.0	0.50	22	21	21	21	20	20
1.5	0.35	31	31	30	29	29	28
2.0	0.25	48	47	46	45	44	43
2.5	0.18	80	77	74	72	70	68
3.0	0.13	142	137	132	126	121	117
3.5	0.09	261	251	240	232	221	215
4.0	0.06	493	469	448	428	407	392

* Modified from Poole (1957, Table 1) (after Rukavina and Duncan, 1970).

3) Dry sieving (not recommended) - In this method a pre-weighed sample of dry sediment (sand and gravel only) is brushed into a nest of 20 cm diameter 'certified sieves' to obtain separates finer than 4, 2, 1, 0.5, 0.25, 0.125, and 0.062 mm. There is no general optimum sample size but generally speaking a sample of about 50 g will be best for very fine sand, whereas a sample of about 200 g will be required for coarse gravelly sand. Very large samples of several kg are required for analysis of coarse cobble gravels. After shaking for 10 minutes the weight of each fraction is determined. The material which passes through the 0.062 mm sieve may be used in the pipette analysis of fines (subsection 1 above) but this is not recommended. To ensure consistent shaking, a mechanical shaker or electromagnetic vibrator base should be used to shake the nest of sieves.

The dry sieving method gives adequate information about the particle size distribution and an approximate conversion to fall velocity is possible. Dry sieving can be used to size particles in the range of 0.062 to 4 mm, but it is best for the larger particle sizes.

4) Wet sieving - Wet sieving is more suitable than dry sieving for samples containing clay, and both sieves and samples remain wet throughout the analytical process. Subsequently, material retained on each sieve is washed into an evaporating dish, dried, and weighed. The material passing through the 0.062 mm sieve may be retained, and a further separation can be made with either finer sieves or by pipette (subsection 1 above). Wet sieve material can be used for adsorption studies, so long as it has not been dried during a previous stage in storage or sample preparation. Wet sieving may be carried out either in a water bath or by using a gentle water jet that washes the finer particles through the successively smaller sieves.

Normal wet sieving can be used to size particles in the range of 0.04 mm to 4 mm. Special screens are available for sieving at less than 0.04 mm, and dispersing agents (sodium hexametaphosphate + sodium carbonate) may be used if necessary; however, treated samples cannot be used for further chemical analysis.

5) <u>Filtration</u> - When small quantities of a very fine particle size must be studied, filtration and weighing can be undertaken using silver metal (Flotronics) membrane filters (pore size 0.2 to 5 μm) and/or cellulose ester (MF-Millipore) membrane filters (pore size 0.025 to 5 μm). The filters should not be mixed since it has been shown that filtration with two different types of membrane filters under the same conditions and having the same nominal pore size, produces differences in analytical concentrations of iron, aluminium, and silicon, in the respective filtrates (Wagemann and Brunskill, 1974). Care must be taken not to clog filters. The advantage of small quantity filtration is that the material is processed without any chemical changes and can be used again for further studies and chemical analysis, without the introduction of artifacts.

Pretreatment of samples for grain size distribution may be carried out, optionally, by ultrasonic treatment; however, to assure consistency this method should not be mixed with other pretreatment dispersive methods.

6) <u>Presentation of data</u> - Results of size distribution analyses should be combined to provide a complete distribution plot of size/frequency (dry weight) over the full particle size range of each sample (i.e., sieve/A-Tube + Pipette data should be combined, as described by Rukavina and Duncan, 1970, see also Figure IV.6). From the total range of grain sizes occurring in a sediment sample, various statistical parameters may be derived. For most purposes the percentage composition, mean size, and standard deviation are sufficient. Other parameters which can be calculated include:

- Percentage composition, i.e., sand-silt-clay compositions expressed as percent (see also Shephard, 1954).

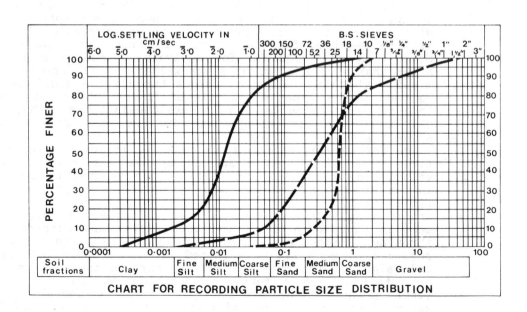

FIGURE IV.6 Chart showing examples of sediment size distribution curves for complete sample analysis (integrating sieve and pipette data) modified after British Standards 1377 (1948).

- Mean grain size, i.e., the arithmetic mean of the grain size distribution.
- Standard deviation, i.e., the spread of the grain size values around the mean.
- Skewness, i.e., the degree of asymmetry from a normal distribution curve.
  Positive skewness signifies the dominance of coarse material and tailing in the finer particle size; negative skewness defines the inverse dominance of fine material.
- Kurtosis, i.e., defines the degree of peakedness of the distribution curve relative to a normal distribution. Positive kurtosis denotes a sharp peaked curve whereas negative kurtosis defines a flattened curve.
- Modes, by size.
  For further details, see Chapter V.

7) Additional characteristics - Surface area - for some fine materials the specific surface area may be used (Oliver, 1973). Further, corrections may be applied to compensate for quartz (Thomas, 1972, after Trostell and Wynne, 1940) and the pelitic fraction (>2 μm).

IV.2.4 Mineralogical analysis

a) Carbonate content - The carbonate content can be determined by gasometric measurement of CO_2 after acidification with HCl. Any gasometric apparatus will be suitable, depending on sensitivity, amount of sediments available, etc.

b) Quartz - Quartz (free silica) can be determined after fusion with potassium pyrosulphate to remove layers of clay (silicates), organic and inorganic carbon, and sulphides, leaving a residue of quartz and feldspars and some resistant heavy minerals. Staining and mineralogical microscope techniques can be used to differentiate between quartz and feldspars.

c) Clay minerals and feldspars - Clay minerals such as kaolinite, montmorillonite, illite, and feldspars can be (semi-quantitatively) determined with X-ray diffraction (XRD). The pretreatment for clay minerals involves air drying, heating to 400°C, and saturation with glycol. The analyses are best undertaken in a laboratory where methods are being applied routinely. Techniques based on differential thermal analysis are not recommended.

d) Extractable material - In several sediments, reproducible amounts of certain substances can be extracted with hot concentrated HCl (90°C) during 20 minutes. The leachate can be analyzed for iron, manganese, lead, copper, zinc, cadmium, beryllium, and vanadium. However, the determination of the total quantities present is often more informative and will be discussed under chemical fractionation (see following).

e) Cation exchange capacity - The determination of cation exchange capacity (C.E.C.) is a cumbersome procedure. The methods are arbitrary and lack precision. C.E.C. is measured by shaking 1 to 5 g of (dry) sediment with 250 ml of a 2 M solution of NH_4^+ or $\frac{1}{2}Ba^{2+}$ (pH = 7), until no change in these concentrations occurs. The amount taken up is measured and expressed as mmol's per 100 g dry material, or as ppm per fraction, e.g., <2 μm, a size which must be specifically determined. For a detailed discussion see Grim (1962), Chapman (1965), and for theoretical aspects Chapter II.6.1.

f) Other methods - Some mineral separations can be made using density fractionation and floatation techniques, in bromoform/methanol mixtures (Milner, 1962); magnetic separations are also possible.

IV.2.5 Chemical fractionation

Chemical fractionation, particularly of man-made organic compounds, may add little useful information for many contaminant studies. However, the information provided by fractionation procedures, applied to metals and nutrient elements, may be extremely valuable for indicating the potential bioavailability of such elements.

No standard methods have yet been established for the fractionation of metals, and many different procedures are presently in use by individual investigators. Recently, Förstner and Wittman (1979) reviewed extraction techniques to determine the forms of metals in sediment materials, and a similar summary of methods is given in Table IV.5. The supposed significance of the metal fractions are described below, using the nomenclature of Tessier et al. (1979).

<u>Easily Exchangeable Fraction</u> - This is generally the result of cation exchange and often metals are defined as loosely sorped to many of the mineral phases, both organic and inorganic, of the sediment. This is believed to be, by far, the most biologically available fraction in normal aerobic environments.

<u>Organic Chelated</u> - This is an extremely important fraction resulting from the formation of organo-metal complexes. Early decomposition processes may result in the release of such metals to the water or, by ingestion, directly to benthic organisms. After deposition and mineralization of the organic matter has been completed, metals associated with this fraction may be considered as non-available.

<u>Adsorption with Hydrated Oxides of Fe and Mn</u> - The co-precipitation of metals with the hydrated oxides of Fe and Mn is well known. Further, these oxides provide sorption sites for metals, some of which may be removed in the easily exchangeable fraction. This fraction may be very significant for many metals and is generally considered non-available under aerobic conditions. Under anaerobic conditions, the resulting reduction of the Fe and Mn oxides may cause solubilization of the associated metals. Under some conditions, however, these can become linked with another fraction of the sediment (e.g., to a sulphide phase).

<u>Carbonate Fraction</u> - Co-precipitation of metals with carbonate is well known and effectively immobilizes the metals with respect to biological availability. However, pH changes in the water may cause dissolution of the carbonate phase and result in metal remobilization.

<u>Resistant Detrital Minerals</u> - A significant proportion of the total sediment-bound metals is often represented by metals incorporated within the lattice of detrital minerals. Concentrations reflect the source materials and may often serve to characterize separate drainage areas. These metals are inert and biologically unavailable.

TABLE IV.5 Summary of metal extractions (Patchineelam and Förstner, 1977)

Chemical Phase	Extraction Methods	Authors
Adsorption and cation exchange	(a) $BaCl_2$ (b) $MgCl_2$ (c) $NH_4 OAc$	Jackson, 1958; Gibbs, 1973
Detrital/authigenic phases	EDTA treatment	Goldberg and Arrhenius, 1958; Gad and Le Riche, 1966
Hydrogenous/lithogenous phases	(a) 0.1 M HCl (b) 0.1 M HNO_3 (c) 0.3 M HCl	Piper, 1971; Jones, 1973; Malo, 1977
Reducible phases	1 M $NH_2 OH \cdot HCl$; 25% v/v acetic acid	Chester and Hughes, 1967
Moderately reducible phases (hydrous Fe-oxides)	Reduction with sodium dithionite complexing with sodium citrate	Aguilera and Jackson, 1953; Holmgren, 1967
Easily reducible phases (Mn-oxide and amorph. Fe-oxides) Carbonates	0.1 M $NH_2 OH \cdot HCl$; 0.01 M nitric acid (a) CO_2 treatment (b) Exchange columns	Chao, 1972 Patchineelam, 1975; Deurer et al., 1978

Cont'd...../

TABLE IV.5   (Cont'd)   Summary of metal extractions (Patchineelam and Förstner, 1977)

Chemical Phase	Extraction Methods	Authors
Organics, sulphides	30% H_2O_2 at 95°C, extract with (a) 1 N NH_4OAc or (b) 0.01 M HNO_3, fat solvents: e.g., chloroform, ether, gasoline, benzene, carbon disulfide	Jackson, 1958; Engler et al., 1974; Gupta and Chen, 1975; Bergmann, 1963; Welte, 1969; Cooper and Harris, 1974
Humic and fulvic acids	0.5 N NaOH; 0.1 N $NaOH/H_2SO_4$	Rashid, 1971; Volkov and Fomina, 1974
Solid organic material	Na hypochlorite, dithionite/citrate	Gibbs, 1973
Detrital silicates	Digestion with $HF/HClO_4$; lithium metaborate (1000°C)	

To improve intercomparisons of data, a report by de Groot et al. (1982) on recent techniques based on laboratory tests was presented at the European Monitoring Group in Lisbon (March, 1981). The extraction procedure is used on the less than 63 μm size fraction only, with the following steps:

1) An extraction with 0.1 M hydroxylamine-HCl for the acid-reducible fraction. This hydroxylamine step includes the extraction of exchangeable cations and of carbonate-bound metals.

2) An extraction with acidified peroxide (30 percent) for the acid-oxydizable fraction. This extraction should be followed by an extraction with ammonium acetate to remove any re-absorbed metal ions.

3) Dissolution of the remaining sample with HF to estimate the metal contents left in the residual fraction (HF may be replaced by aqua regia).

The rather important exchangeable phase (representing very loosely bound trace metals and regulating or reflecting the composition of overlying water) is not included in this scheme. To determine the amount of exchangeable metal ions, an extractant is used which contains cations that are more strongly bound to the exchange positions ($BaCl_2$, $MgCl_2$, and NH_4OAc). Although the ion-exchangeable fraction of trace metals is ill-defined, the use of ammonium acetate seems to offer a suitable compromise.

Many different fractionation schemes for sediment phosphates have been published and one of the earliest of these was Jackson's (1958) work which, unfortunately, gave no relationship to potentially bioavailable phosphate. Better results have been obtained by Golterman (1977), who used extractions with NTA and Ca-NTA solutions (0.01 to 0.1 M; pH 6 to 8), but no standardized procedures have been proposed so far. Williams et al. (1976) developed a modified Jackson procedure which is used to distinguish between apatite and non-apatite phosphate. A useful recent review has been presented by Williams et al. (1980).

In Golterman's (op cit) procedure, the NTA (or EDTA) procedures extract different fractions of the total iron, but these have not yet been chemically defined.

The determination of inorganic $N(NH_3)$, by direct steam distillation of the sediment sample, offers a means of fractionating total N. The fractions may be controlled, however, by the pH during distillation.

The development of the elutriate test (Keely and Engler, 1974; Jones et al., 1978) provides an interesting and relatively simple means of demonstrating the presence of excessive quantities of soluble components that may be of concern as contaminants. Very often these include trace metals and nutrients which may be present in dissolved form in the interstitial water within a sediment sample, and/or in particulate but easily soluble form. The test was originally designed to highlight problems of dredged sediments when recovered from one site and dumped back into a river or lake somewhere else. At the receiving site, soluble contaminants might be released into the natural waters as the sediments fall to the bottom or mixed with it.

For comparative purposes the test can be applied using standard water in a laboratory, rather than a variety of natural water samples.

In the normal elutriate test two litres of wet sediment are mixed with eight litres of unfiltered natural water from the site at which sediment disposal is to take place (or, as stated above, natural waters may be substituted by a local laboratory standard water for comparative tests). The 1:4 volumetric ratio of sediment and water is then shaken continuously for one hour, and allowed to settle for an additional hour. The supernatant is then decanted and filtered four times (3 by glass fibre and 1 by membrane filters).

If the concentration of selected dissolved components is increased by 1.5 times (or more) above that in the original natural water, this is taken to indicate the need for some further examination of the sediment composition as a potential source of contaminants. If the release of soluble components is less than 1.5 times, the sediments are unlikely to be a major source of soluble con- taminants as tested (note there may be other compounds, not included in thi test, which would be released; the test applies only to the compounds tested). Depending upon the characteristics of the local laboratory standard water, the multiplier may be more or less than for the natural water from the receiving site. The use of a laboratory standard, however, provides a means of comparing the general release characteristics of sediments from different locations.

While the test procedure provides a useful guide to the presence of soluble contaminants, it should not be used in an arbitrary way, nor as a rigid stan- dard. The effectiveness of the test is largely influenced by the chemistry of the natural, or local standard, waters (Cheam et al., 1976). In many cases, even though the concentrations of some components may show an increase signifi- cantly greater than 1.5 times, the fact that they nevertheless remain at levels below critical Water Quality Standards (see UNESCO-WHO Report 23, Water Quality Surveys 1.3.2, and Matheson, 1975), means that they should not be a cause for concern.

IV.2.6   Preparations for analysis

Before different chemical elements can be measured in either wet or dry sedi- ments, the sediments must be brought into solution. This solubilization, or digestion, can be accomplished in many different ways. The choice of the method depends very much on which elements or combination of elements are to be measured. The following techniques have found general acceptance:

a) Digestion with H_2SO_4 at 360°C, with or without Cu^{2+} as catalyst; or with dilute H_2SO_4, with or without $K_2S_2O_8$, at moderately elevated temperaures (100° to 150°C). The sample is heated in a normal Kjeldahl flask (with long neck if phosphate is included), on a manifold rack. If much organic material is present, Cu is added as catalyst (colorimetric iron determination is then not possible). The mixture is heated until clear, and then for a further 30 minutes. After dilution the digest can be used for the analysis of P, N, and Fe. SiO_2 forms a white precipitate which can be weighed. Alternatively, the sample may be suspended in 0.15 M H_2SO_4, with or without 1 g $K_2S_2O_8$ (if much organic matter is present). Several Erlenmeyer flasks, covered with normal beakers, can be conveniently placed in a (smaller) laboratory autoclave or pressure cooker. This suspension is heated to between 100 and 160°C depending on the apparatus available. The higher the temperature, the shorter the reaction time. Phosphate can be determined directly in the digest, after correction for the acid (Golterman et al., 1978, Sections 5.6.3 and 5.7.3), and nitrogen can be determined as ammonia after distilla- tion.

It should be noted that, although the H_2SO_4 + $K_2S_2O_8$ mixture does not solubilize all phosphate from clays, it does solubilize most. The method is suitable for most biological materials, and for the analysis of total phosphate, nitrogen, and iron; several trace metals can be determined directly in the digest without concentration (if the sample/ digest volume is not too small).

b) Decomposition with acid mixtures at elevated temperatures under pres- sure. Bomb destruction - Samples, especially if much clay is present, can be digested with hydrofluoric acid at 105° to 150°C in a decomposition vessel, consisting of a stainless steel container fitted with a removable PTFE (Teflon) crucible having a screw cap (e.g., uni-seal decomposition vessel). Hendel (1973) used these vessels for an analysis of glass, digested in an acid solution with HF and H_3BO_3 (extreme caution and protective clothing should be used). Agemian and Chau (1975) used a mixture of nitric acid, perchloric acid, and hydrofluoric acid (3.5 hours at 140°C) to digest many different kinds of sediments including sand and organic silt. In the digest, they were able to measure 20 different elements which included Cd, Cr, Co, Cu, Mg, Pb, Zn, Mo, V, Mn, Fe, Al, Ba, and Ca. Krishnamurti et al. (1976) used a safe HNO_3-H_2O_2 mixture for digestion. A preliminary pre-oxidation of the samples with HNO_3 eliminated the danger of an uncontrollable reaction. In cases of high organic carbon content, pre-ignition of the sample in a furnace at 410°C is essential for colorimetric analysis.

Teflon destruction bombs (without a stainless steel mantle), have recently become commercially available and, although not yet used widely, preliminary experience is most promising. They are very much cheaper than other similar vessels, but can not sustain high internal pressures; they have been used with H_2SO_4/H_2O mixtures up to 150°C. The teflon bombs are most suitable for trace metal analysis and nutrients.

Because $HClO_4$ procedures are extremely dangerous they are not advised for inexperienced analysts; if the analyst insists on using $HClO_4$ it should be mixed with other acids (and ensure that all methods are in order). Fume cupboards must be made especially for all work with $HClO_4$ and they should not be used for anything else.

c) Melting with caustic alkalies - Dry samples can be molten with NaOH in nickel crucibles, or with $KNaCO_3$ in platinum crucibles. The melt and crucible are placed in a beaker with H_2O and, after complete dissolution, the pH is adjusted to between 6 and 9 with HCl. Zirconium crucibles have recently become available and may replace platinum crucibles for most purposes. Nickel crucibles are acceptable for most analyses (not Fe, Ni, Co), but must be of a good quality. Platinum crucibles are extremely expensive and can be damaged when not properly treated. The crucible method is suitable for silicate, (total) phosphate, arsenic, etc. It is normally advantageous to mount a manifold rack, in order to treat some 10 to 12 samples at the same time. Ultraviolet, photo-oxidation methods (Golterman et al., 1978) have been described, and (expensive) commercial apparatus is available. There is some doubt, however, whether this method can be used for samples containing much clay.

Most methods, for which outlines of the principles are given below, are to be found in the I.B.P. Manual No. 8 (Golterman et al., 1978). The I.B.P. numbers given below refer to the method numbers in this manual. (Note: All the classical wet techniques for most total element determinations of sediments, after digestion, are still applicable although time consuming.)

IV.2.7   Methods; major, minor, and trace elements

1) Silicate
   a) Dissolved (I.B.P., 5.8) - Between pH 3 and 4 silicate forms a yellow complex with molybdate ions, which can be reduced to a blue-coloured complex.
   b) Particulate (I.B.P., 5.9) - Particulate silicate is made soluble by fusion with alkali (NaOH, Na_2CO_3, or a mixture of K_2CO_3/Na_2CO_3). Dissolve the melt, neutralize to pH 3 to 4 and proceed as above.
2) Phosphate
   a) Dissolved (I.B.P., 5.6.2) - In strong acid solutions orthophosphate (PO_4-P) will form a yellow complex with molybdate ions, which can be reduced to a blue complex with ascorbic acid. Extraction of the blue complex with an organic solvent increases the sensitivity.
   b) Particulate (I.B.P., 5.9) - Particulate phosphate is solubilized preferably as mentioned under (a), but the melt for silicate can

be used as well. Neutralization is necessary, but if an acid digest is used, the molybdate solution can be made with an adjusted acidity.

3) Nitrogen
   a) Adsorbed NH_3 - Sediments can be submitted to direct steam distillation and ammonia can be measured in the distillate, colorimetrically (I.B.P., 5.1.1, 5.2.4) or titrimetrically (I.B.P., 5.2.2), the pH must be kept at values near 8.
   b) Nitrate - Nitrate can be estimated after reduction to nitrite (I.B.P., 5.3.2), or to ammonia (I.B.P., 5.1.2).
   c) Org-N - Sediments can be digested by a (classical) Kjeldahl digestion and steam distillation, followed by filtration of the NH_3 formed (I.B.P., 5.5). It can also be determined by the COD method (I.B.P., 5.5.4) and I.B.P., 7.3.2).

4) COD
   COD, as a measure of organic carbon, can be estimated after digestion with $K_2Cr_2O_7$ (I.B.P., 7.3.1 or 7.3.2).

5) Ca^{2+} and Mg^{2+} (after digestion of sediment)
   a) Ca^{2+} and Mg^{2+} can be measured, after solubilization (preferably b), by simple colorimetric methods (I.B.P., 4.1.1 and 4.2.1).
   b) Complexometric titrations (I.B.P., 4.3) using indicator or electrode end-point detection.
   c) Flame atomic absorption spectrophotometry (AAS).

6) Fe, Mn, Al
   These metals can be measured in the wet digests (a or b) colorimetrically (I.B.P., 6.4.1, 6.4.2, and 6.5.2), or by AAS.

7) Heavy metals (Hg, Cd, Pb, As, Cr, Cu, Ni, Zn)
   These metals can be measured only by AAS (for Hg, flameless AAS is available).

There are many techniques for determining the concentration of trace elements. The most important ones are colorimetry (often after a concentration step), polarography (classical, cathode ray and anodic stripping voltammetry), and atomic absorption flame spectrophotometry.

The advantage of colorimetric methods is their cheapness and, in some cases, that a distinction between different states (for example ionic or chelated) can be made. If a concentration step is needed, however, this advantage no longer exists. Concentration may be carried out by solvent extraction or by ion-exchange.

Polarographic methods can be sensitive and quick. They are supposed to measure ionic species only, but there is doubt whether this is true (Golterman et al., 1978, p. 122-123). Several chelates can be measured, but colloidal states cannot be so easily measured. The method requires expensive apparatus and skill in the operation.

AAS techniques are among the quickest and most sensitive means of analysis. However, the apparatus is rather expensive and needs proper maintenance, which may be a problem in some locations. The sensitivity is high, especially after an extraction step. No fractionation of species can be made. Some indications of the analytical characteristics of one of the better machines is given in Table IV.6. The ranges of sensitivity vary with different models and equipment manufacturers.

If the concentration of an element is not sufficiently high for a direct aspiration, then a concentration step is needed. Chelation and extraction are the usual techniques. Ammonium pyrrolidine dithiocarbamate (APDC) can be used for Cu, Cd, hexavalent Cr, Fe, Mn, Pb, and Zn, but Cr^{3+} must first be oxidized to the hexavalent form with $KMnO_4$. The Mn complex is not very stable and can cause difficulties if analysis is delayed. The most frequently used solvent for APDC is methyl isobutyl ketone (MIBK). It provides a stable flame in AAS and its physical properties such as viscosity, surface tension, boiling point, and mutual solubility in an aqueous solution, are favourable. It usually gives a low background in the flame. For the procedure see I.B.P., 6.0.3.

In AAS, it is recommended that calibration curves should be prepared and that two points should be measured daily with each series. The usage of IOS*

* Address:- International Organization for Standardization, 1 Rue Varembe, CH-1211, Geneva 20, Switzerland.

standards as reference material is strongly suggested. Precautions to avoid sample and equipment contamination by laboratory dust are essential; dust covers should be used whenever the equipment is not in service.

A few colorimetric methods for Cd, Pb, and Hg have been published, but since interferences occur so often during the concentration steps, these methods are not to be relied upon. The AAS method, with or without solvent extraction for Cd and Pb, is the most acceptable method at present. Mercury should be determined without a flame and good results are obtained for Cd with a graphite furnace. No details are given here, but Table IV.7 may be of use in setting up routine analyses.

TABLE IV.6 Characteristics for several trace elements on a typically good atomic absorption (flame) spectrophotometer

	Sensitivity (Detection Limit)* With or Without Solvent Extraction (mg l^{-1})		Concentration for 1% Absorption (mg l^{-1})	Best Working Range of Concentration (mg l^{-1})
	With Extraction	Without Extraction		
Al	0.05 −1.0	0.1 −1.0	0.4	10 −1000
Cd	0.001 −0.01	0.001−0.01	0.004	0.1− 2
Co	0.001 −0.01	0.01		0.1− 10
Cr	0.0002−0.01	0.01	0.02	1.0− 200
Cu	0.001 −0.01	0.005−0.01	0.04	0.1− 10
Fe	0.001 −0.05	0.004−0.05	0.006	0.1− 20
Pb	0.001 −0.05	0.01 −0.05	0.06	1.0− 10
Mn	0.001 −0.01	0.005−0.01	0.04	0.1− 20
Zn	0.001 −0.01	0.005−0.01	0.02	0.1− 2
Mo	0.0002−0.05	0.05		0.1− 10

* Defined here as twice the fluctuation in background signal (after Golterman et al., 1978).

TABLE IV.7 Characteristics for AAS methods for Cd, Pb, and Hg (after Golterman et al., 1978)

	Cadmium	Lead	Mercury
Detection Limit			
Direct Aspiration	0.01 mg l^{-1}	0.05 mg l^{-1}	0.05 mg l^{-1}
Solvent Extraction	0.001 mg l^{-1}	0.001 mg l^{-1}	
Wavelength	228.8 nm	283.3 nm	253.7 nm
Fuel	Acetylene	Acetylene	special cell
Oxidant	Air	Air	
Type of Flame	Oxidizing	Oxidizing	

IV.2.8 Analysis of organic compounds

The microanalysis of organic compounds in extracts from sediments, water particulates, and benthic flora and fauna, require very sophisticated instruments in order to obtain specific and meaningful results. The extracts consist of multi-component mixtures of organic compounds, with various chemical characteristics in trace amounts. The analysis of natural organic compounds and man-made compounds (so-called pollutants) demands the use of extensive work-up procedures including: extraction, concentration, and separation, before final identification. Gas and liquid chromatography (GC and LC) provide methods which are suitable for the separation of different organic fractions, and which have a degree of resolution; but the handling of extracts during work-up and the ultimate analysis requires well-equipped laboratories and experienced technical personnel for the operation and maintenance of the instruments.

The solvent non-extractable part of the organic matter of samples may be treated in various ways, and practically all lead to degradation and/or polymerization of the biopolymeric residues in the samples. The residues may be investigated using flash pyrolysis in association with mass spectrometers, with or without a separation facility (GC), for the determination of functional groups.

There are no simple ways to determine the composition of the majority of man-made organic micropollutants, and this problem is further enhanced by the very low levels of concentration at which they occur in both sediments and water. Although the overall amount of such substances in an entire drainage basin can be quite large, quantities in individual sediment samples may be very small. To overcome this problem, some estimation of the presence of specific compounds could be made by analysis of other parts of the aquatic ecosystem, such as birds or fish (in which biomagnification may have substantially increased initial concentration, from water and sediment).

In this outline we have attempted to describe useful but simple methods suitable for the gross characterization of organic compounds in sediment and which can be carried out with limited facilities; more advanced techniques are also considered.

    a)   Analyses using simple procedures
- 1) Storage and treatment of sediments - Sediments should be extruded, and stored wet at -10° to -20°C, to minimize bacterial action. When required for analysis, the interstitial water should be separated by centrifuge and the remaining sediment dried at 60°C in vacuum.
- 2) Determine organic C by combustion - Inorganic C must be removed first with dilute HCl. (Since chemical oxygen demand (COD) varies according to the oxidation state of carbon compounds in sediments, it is therefore not an accurate indicator of C content; although it retains its usefulness as a measure of oxidizability.)
- 3) Solvent extractable matter (wax fraction) - In this procedure dry sediment is extracted with chloroform in a Soxhlet apparatus. The extracts are evaporated and the residue is weighed (when analyzing for organo-halogens use hexane for extraction).
- 4) Humic acids - After removal of wax fraction, treat residual sediment with dilute alkali, under N_2 gas, centrifuge the extract and acidify. Collect precipitated humic acids, freeze, then thaw and remove salts. Collect and dry (preferably freeze-drying).
- 5) Hydrolysable amino N - Hydrolyse aliquot of original sediment with 6N HCl at 110°C, in sealed tube. Determine total amino-N in the filtrate, colorimetrically.
- 6) Hydrolysable sugars - Hydrolyse original sediment with 2N H_2SO_4. Analyze filtrate, colorimetrically.

   b)   Analysis using more complex procedures
- 1) Storage and treatment of sediment - Since the previously described method can give artifacts, it is preferable to adopt another method. In this method a mixture of methanol and chloroform is added to wet sediment, to eliminate bacterial action and also to extract the wax fraction. For this, ultrasonic treatment and centrifugation is necessary.
- 2) Organic C - Use a total organic C analyzer in which C is either converted to CO_2 (measured by IR), or CH_4 (measured by flame ionization detector). A CHN analyzer gives all three elements by formation of CO_2, H_2O, N_2 which are then separated on a column (GC).
- 3) Survey of extracts for some classes of organic compounds - One approach involves a separation according to functional groups, using thin-layer chromatography. In this way it is possible to detect various natural compound groups such as hydrocarbons, aromatic hydrocarbons, ketones, fatty acids, fatty alcohols, sterols, triglycerides, various pigments and selected groups of pollutant compounds. Some of the pollutant groups that can be recognized are aliphatic hydrocarbons (derived from fossil fuels), polycyclic aromatic hydrocarbons, and organohalogen compounds (derived from pesticides and herbicides). The detection limit of this method lies generally above the microgram level. LC, GC, and GCMS

techniques are required for the detailed analysis of functional groups.

4) Humic acids - Functional groups analysis possible - COOH, phenolic OH, quinone and ketonic C=O groups, etc.

5) Amino acid N - Use of amino acid analyzer enables the amounts of each amino acid to be determined.

6) Hydrolysable sugars - derivatization with silylating agents will allow for analysis by GLC.

The use of sophisticated techniques to complete separation and identification of organic compounds usually requires complex equipment.

Some of the instrument methods available for the extractable material are:

<u>Separation</u> - gas-liquid chromatography, high pressure liquid chromatography, ion exchange and gel permeation chromatography.

<u>Identification</u> - infrared, ultraviolet and visible spectrophotometers. Mass spectrometry (low and high resolution). Element-specific detectors (N, S, halogens).

<u>Separation and identification</u> - gas chromatography - mass spectrometry, and gas chromatography - infrared spectroscope.

<u>Residual organic matter</u> - can be analyzed by pyrolysis techniques coupled to an instrument for identification.

c) Biocide analysis

In pollution studies, special attention should be given to the so-called biocides (which include pesticides/insecticides, herbicides, and fungicides, etc.). However, for their analysis, it must be realized that great technical skill is required, and it is best to submit samples to a specialist laboratory where these analyses are made regularly. The following gives some ideas about the methods employed at present and the complicated apparatus needed. (Modified after Golterman et al., 1978).)

The most frequent analyses carried out for pesticides in freshwater concern certain fairly persistent organochlorine residues, which can be found almost anywhere if the level of detection is sufficiently reduced. Because of the low concentration of these residues in water and sediments they are detected by gas-liquid chromatography using an electron-capture detector. They include residues of the DDT group, dieldrin and HCH isomers. If the presence of organochlorine residues is suspected in water it may be useful to make preliminary analyses on fish or sediments. For some pesticides, negative results here indicate that the water is free from their contamination.

Other pesticides and herbicides which may be found in water are organophosphorus pesticides. These are mainly non-persistent and are only detectable in the immediate vicinity of a recent discharge. The phenoxy herbicides are also short-lived, with restricted toxicity; their detection requires the preparation of derivatives, if the same GLC technique is used as for the other organochlorines. Carbamates and triazine herbicides are difficult to detect. Because the organochlorine residues are those most frequently examined in water and sediments, some further information is given here on their extraction and analysis.

1) Storage and Treatment of Water Samples - Avoid the use of plastic containers and filter papers. Use all-glass equipment and filter the water, if necessary, through pre-washed glass-wool filters. Add 4 ml of H_2SO_4 (1 + 1) per litre as a preservative. Store the sample in a refrigerator, preferably in the dark. Wash all containers with pure solvent before use.

Large water samples (10 to 20 litres) and relatively large samples of sediments (5 to 50 g dry material) are usually required because of the extremely low concentration of pesticide residues. Rinse the sample containers with a water-miscible solvent such as acetone when the sample has been removed, to ensure that no material remains on the container walls. Combine the rinse with the sample.

2) Principle - The organochlorine residues are extracted either by continuous solvent extraction of the water or sediment, or by passage of the water through absorbent columns of various types of materials (e.g., resins and polyurethane foam). The choice of solvent and material for the column depends on the pesticide being

examined. The residues are removed from the columns by elution with organic solvents.

The eluate or organic extract of water or sediments is then evaporated to a small volume and the concentrate subjected to a cleanup to remove unwanted materials. This cleanup involves either a liquid-liquid partition or passage through a column of adsorbent, such as alumina, silica or florisil. A preliminary separation of residues can be obtained by this chromatographic cleanup. The eluates are then examined by GLC.

Confirmation of the identity of the residue is obtained in part by the relative retention time of the GLC peak, and by the eluate in which it is removed from a chromatographic column. Identification may also be carried out by chemical techniques, or by mass spectrometry.

Thin-layer chromatography has been used for the examination of organochlorine residues but the technique is only useful when several micrograms of material are available.

3) Reagents - High quality reagents must be used throughout. Analytical grade solvents normally require redistillation and adsorbents require pretreatment with solvents before use.

4) Interferences - Blanks should be used to check for possible contamination. An extremely high standard of laboratory cleanliness is essential to avoid contamination from the laboratory itself.

As an example, the following detailed procedure is given for a complete analysis of a sample of Great Lakes sediment for organochlorine insecticides and PCB (Frank et al., 1977):-

'Analysis Procedure

The freeze-dried geochemical sample was prepared by sieving at 20 mesh to remove pebble-size material and ground to pass 100 mesh to obtain complete homogeneity of the sample. Up to 10 grams of sediment was brought to 50 percent field capacity by adding about 2 to 3 ml of water and allowed to stand for 12 hours. A hexane:acetone (1:1 v/v) mixture was used (250 ml) to extract the samples by shaking for two hours on a wrist-action shaker. After filtering the extract, a 100 ml aliquot was mixed with 10 ml saturated NaCl solution and 300 ml water and shaken vigorously for one minute. The hexane phase was passed through a 2 to 3 cm layer of sodium sulfate and evaporated just to dryness with rotary vacuum (Chiba and Morley, 1968).

Twenty-five grams of activated florisil were introduced into a 22 mm i.d. chromatography column. After pre-washing with 50 ml of hexane the sample extract was added to the column. The column was eluted successively at the rate of about 0.5 ml/minute with 200 ml of dichloromethane:hexane (20:80 v/v) and 200 ml of acetonitrile:dichloromethane:hexane (0.35:50:50 v/v). The eluates were evaporated just to dryness with rotary vacuum and the residue was reconstituted in 5 to 10 ml of acetone for the first elution and 5 to 10 ml of hexane for the second elution (Mills et al., 1972).

A 10 mm i.d. chromatography column was prepared containing glass-wool, 1 cm sand and 7.5 cm coconut-charcoal. The column was pre-washed with 1:3, acetone:ether. The first eluate from the cleanup (dichloromethane:hexane (20:80 v/v) fraction) was added and the column eluted first with 180 ml acetone:ether (1:3 v/v) and then with 80 ml benzene to give two fractions. Each fraction was evaporated just to dryness with rotary vacuum and reconstituted for determination (Berg et al., 1972; Holdrinet, 1974).

Micro-Tek Model MT220 and 550 gas chromatographs equipped with NI[63] electron capture detectors were used. These instruments had 1.8 meter U-shaped columns with i.d. of 3.2 mm. Columns were packed with four percent SE-30 and six percent QF-1 on a 80 to 100 mesh Chromosorb W which had been acid washed and treated with dimethylchlorosilicone. Columns were preconditioned for 72 hours at 225°C and 30 ml nitrogen per minute. Operating parameters were:

- Nitrogen carrier gas at 60 ml min^{-1}.
- Injector temperature 200°C.
- Column temperature 180°C.
- Detector temperature 300°C.

Recovery studies were undertaken using natural and spiked samples. The following recovery percentages were obtained: DDE 92.0; TDE 90.5; DDT 90.0; PCB 89.0; and HEOD 87.5. No atrazine was recorded at the levels of detection (10 to 50 µg l^{-1}) and this is not discussed further.'

IV.3 Biological Sampling and Analysis

IV.3.1 Introduction

Aquatic animals are extremely sensitive to pollution. They may be poisoned directly or indirectly either through the food chain or as a result of oxygen depreciation caused by the pollutant. Poisons are absorbed by aquatic animals continuously and few are destroyed metabolically or eliminated; they accumulate within the animal and, if amounts are high enough, may kill it. Suspended solids may destroy the preferred habitat of benthic dwelling animals by settling out and covering a firm substrate with soft sediment. Species depending on the firm substrate will decline or disappear. Where the solids remain in suspension they may inhibit light penetration so that essential food plants (macrophytes or algae) are lost. Organic solids (e.g., fibres or wood chips) may eliminate most macro-invertebrates and fish by utilizing all available oxygen during decomposition processes.

Different species vary enormously in their reaction to different poisons. On the whole, zooplankton are more sensitive than fish. For example, Daphnia magna is more sensitive to many poisons than trout (Ellis, 1937), which is itself a sensitive fish species. Molluscs are killed by levels of copper much lower than those which will kill fish, as is well known in relation to the control against Bilharzia. On the other hand, sandflies, mayflies, and chironomid larvae can be very resistant to lead and zinc poisoning, while oligochaetes, leeches, crustacea, molluscs, and fish (in the same stream) are very susceptible (Jones, 1940). Invertebrates can be used to show the effects of accidental pollution better than fish, which may avoid the pollution and recolonize quickly when the effects have passed. Fish are more difficult to sample than invertebrates so that, for most purposes, invertebrates are a better tool when used as a biological indicator.

IV.3.2 Sampling methods

One of the most simple methods for collecting macrobenthos, in shallow water, is by means of a hand-net. If a standard size net is used in the same manner each time, it gives repeatable results which are well within the range of variation caused by pollution. In both running and standing water, timed collections (e.g., one-half minute) can be taken and, in running water, standard kick samples also give repeatable results (Morgan and Egglishaw, 1965). Three samples should be taken at each site. Where there is a stony bottom, a fixed number of stones should be scrubbed to obtain the epifauna.

For soft sediments, the macrobenthos can be collected by means of a corer. This may be a simple hand-operated tube, in shallow water, or the more sophisticated corer of the Jenkins or Kajak type, for use in deep water. Most animals occur in the top 10 cm of mud but it may be necessary to go as deep as 25 cm; this can only be determined by examination of the samples at the time of collection. Such corers can be used in quantitative studies in which more preliminary work will be required to determine the spatial pattern of sampling and the number of samples per site. Statistical advice should be sought on this (Elliott, 1973).

In large, stony-bottomed rivers, it may be necessary to sample by scuba diving. The methods of separation of animals from the mud, or other material collected with them, depends on the nature of the material. Generally, the samples are worked through a nest of sieves, the lowest having a mesh size of about 0.1 mm for quantitative sampling. Larger mesh sizes may be used for quasi-quantitative methods such as with hand-net sampling, which will vary in size with the study.

After sieving, the animals may be either separated by eye, using head magnifiers, or removed physically. Where the substrate is clean sand, most of the animals may be decanted off by flotation. A concentrated sucrose solution is often successful as a floatation agent, and common salt can be used as well.

Vertical plankton net hauls or plankton traps can be used for zooplankton sampling in lakes. More detailed information on sampling methods can be found in Edmondson and Winberg (1971). For identification of the organisms, both low-power stereo microscopes (mag. X10 to X200) and standard high-power microscopes will be required.

Various general standard works may provide a background reading, e.g., Welch (1958), Ward and Whipple (1966), Macan (1963), and Hynes (1970).

IV.3.3   Macroinvertebrates as indicators of pollution

Many studies have been carried out on the effects of organic discharges, mainly sewage, on macrobenthic fauna. The well known saprobien system of Kolkwitz and Manson (1908), Kolkwitz (1950), and Liebmann (1962), has been used to classify different zones in rivers below organic effluent outfalls, and many modifications have been drawn up. Hynes (1960) has criticized these classifications as being too inflexible and recommends the straightforward comparison of the faunal composition, at a series of stations from above to below the suspected source of pollution. Severe pollution may result in the complete elimination of all macroinvertebrates whereas moderate pollution may result in both a reduction of the number of species and an increase in the population density of a few. Various indices have been proposed which include those based on species composition of the resulting fauna, and those which utilize more complex mathematical indices of diversity (Kaesler et al., 1978). Pollution by sewage in rivers results in a succession of biological conditions downstream, with successive zones of recuperation. The most tolerant species which occur below outfalls are Tubificidae, often with sewage fungus. In slightly better conditions, Chironomus species are dominant. These may be replaced by Asellus aquaticus and then by a clean river fauna. On the other hand, Asellus has not been recorded below sewage outlets in North America. There have been few studies of the effects of pollutants in tropical lakes and rivers, so the characteristic populations developing in these polluted areas have yet to be determined. Sampling sites should be selected carefully, and in rivers they should be comparable between transects (consistently spaced). In flowing water, the transects should run several kilometres from above the source of the pollution to, where possible, an area where the water-body is unaffected. In standing waters, the transects should run from the source of pollution to clean water. The length of transects and number of sampling stations will vary but at least a pair of samples should be taken at each station. The preserved samples should be returned to the laboratory and all animals removed and identified as far as the literature allows. Tables are then drawn up to show the number of each species at each site and placed in order of sites along the transects. Examination of the table will show at which points species disappear or reappear and how their relative density changes between stations (Hynes, 1960). This information will show the regions most affected by the pollution and subsequent sampling can be used to monitor changing conditions. Biological information of this type is particularly valuable in detecting low or moderate levels of pollution. Heavy pollution is usually obvious and often results in complete elimination of the fauna.

Where bottom fauna are being used as a means of monitoring pollution effects, based upon population changes in groups sensitive to pollution or the concentration of contaminants in biological tissues, it may be useful to apply bivariate analysis and display the data on simple control charts (Beak et al., 1959). On these charts the deviations of various group distributions (such as the numbers of oligocheates, snails, bi-valve molluscs and chironomids) can be shown to be statistically significant at some chosen confidence level. This means of display is particularly useful where anomalous changes must be defined against a background of seasonal changes. The technique can be applied to various sampling patterns, and it works well with both Ray sampling and traverse grids. An excellent review of biological impact studies is provided in Ward (1978). The use of biological indicators of river water quality has recently been discussed and reconsidered in a series of papers edited by James and Evison (1979).

IV.3.4   Use of biota in chemical analyses

Aquatic biota are affected by a wide spectrum of pollutants and various faunal components may be used as sensitive indicators of the health of a water-body. A tendency to accumulate certain pollutants, whih may be at a level below the limits of chemical detection in water, makes them very valuable as a sample material. Many pollutants are not discharged continuously, so that the chemical detection of their presence may be difficult without the set-up of an expensive continuous sampling program.

Animals at the top of food chains, such as waterfowl and fish, are good accumulators; but, because of their wide ranging movements and migrations, they may not be useful for the identification of local sources of pollutant.

Filter feeding organisms such as pelecypods (clams), which, in comparison to their size, filter large volumes of water, are also good accumulators. Because they move very little, they are excellent integrators of discontinuous pollutant inputs and they are very useful as an indicator of local sources. Other components of the macrobenthos can be used if pelecypods are not available.

The pollutants can be extracted directly from the animals, using organic solvents; the extracts can be analyzed by the methods previously described. Although the accmulations in the animals may be large, they may not be constant. They can only be used to show the presence of a pollutant. They cannot be used to extrapolate its concentration in the water-body.

IV.4   Oxygen and Gases at the Sediment/Water Interface

As previously noted, oxygen concentrations at the sediment-water interface are important for both chemical processes and the biota. In the following brief outline, consideration is given to both adsorption of oxygen and the release of gas at this interface.

For the in situ measurement of oxygen consumption by the bottom sediments (either in rivers or lakes), measuring bells may be placed over the sediment. Within these bells, a quasi natural flow is generated. The oxygen content of the enclosed water is measured either by slowly pumping the water along an oxygen electrode, or by placing an oxygen electrode in the bell. In this case, an electrode must be selected which consumes only a small quantity of oxygen itself; note that the oxygen demand in the bell is that of the sediments plus that of the water, which must be measured separately in a dark bottle, and the water volume in the bell must be known. The oxygen consumption is expressed in $gm^{-2} y^{-1}$. The method can be applied only where the sediments are sufficiently fine-grained to allow the bell to be sealed against the free water. Oxygen consumption can also be measured on sediment in the laboratory, but extrapolation to lake bottom is difficult; the depth of the core must be considered, and it is not certain whether oxygen consumption depends on sample depth or not.

Although measurements can be made with very small electrodes inserted through holes in a corer, the disadvantages of the laboratory methods are large: the sediment surface is small, the surface may be disturbed, and the results may be influenced by changes in temperature and pressure.

The measurement of oxygen absorption yields information on the activity of the aerobic micro-organisms of the sediment, and is of importance in the balancing of the oxygen budget (see also IV.2.2).

Gas release is determined in situ with the aid of measuring bells or funnels which are suspended in the water to trap the rising gas bubbles. The incubation period must be sufficiently long to obtain a representative sample, as gas bubbles escape irregularly in time. Extrapolating to total lake surface is extremely difficult. Methane bubbles rising through oxygenated water may be partly oxidized by methane-oxidizing bacteria. Also, the quantity which dissolves in the water during the rising cannot be measured. To keep these errors as small as possible, the traps should be suspended as near as possible to the sediment surface, but not in contact with it.

The quantity of gas produced can be measured volumetrically. Identification of the gases (CH_4, N_2, H_2, and H_2S) can be made by simple gas chromatographic techniques.

Gas release can also be measured in undisturbed sediment cores or in undisturbed grab samples, as described in the procedure for the measurement of oxygen consumption. The disadvantages of these laboratory methods are the same as in the case of oxygen consumption measurements. However, in the case of methane production, the influence of temperature changes is even greater; production should be measured at lake bottom temperature.

123

References

Agemian, H.; Chau, A.S.Y. 1975. An atomic absorption method for the determination of 20 elements in lake sediments and some natural waters. Environm. Lett., 9: p. 59-73.

Aguilera, N.H.; Jackson, M.L. 1953. Iron oxide removal from soils and clays. Proc. Amer. Soc. Soil Sci., 17: p. 359-364.

* Akroyd, T.N.W. 1964. Laboratory testing in soil engineering. Soil Mechanics Ltd., Monograph No. 1. London. 233 pp.

Beak, T.W.; de Courval, C.; Cooke, N.E. 1959. Pollution monitoring and prevention by use of bivariate control charts. Sewage Industr. Wastes, 31: p. 1383-1394.

Berg, O.W.; Diosady, P.L.; Rees, G.A.C. 1972. Column chromatographic separation of PCB's from chlorinated hydrocarbon pesticides and their subsequent gas chromatograph quantitation in terms of derivatives. Bull. Environm. Contam. Toxicol., 7: p. 338-347.

Bergmann, W. 1963. Geochemistry of lipids. In: Breger, I.A. (ed.), Organic geochemistry: p. 503-542. Pergamon Press, New York. 658 pp.

Bloesch, J. 1974. Sedimentation und Phosphorhaushalt im Vierwaldstättersee (Horwer Bucht) und im Rotsee. Schweiz. z. Hydrol., 36: p. 71-186.

Bloesch, J.; Burns, N.M. 1980. A critical review of sedimentation trap technique. Schweiz. z. Hydrol., 42: p. 15-55.

British Standards Institution. 1948. Methods of test for soil classification and compaction. British Standard 1377. London. 88 pp. (and more recent editions).

Chao, L.L. 1972. Selective dissolution of manganese oxides from soils and sediments with acidified hydroxylamine hydrochloride. Proc. Amer. Soc. Soil Sci., 36: p. 764-768.

Chapman, H.D. 1965. Cation-exchange capacity. In: Black, C.A. (ed.-in-chief), Methods of soil analysis, p. 891-900. Amer. Soc. Agronomy, Wisconsin.

Cheam, V.; Mudroch, A.; Sly, P.G.; Lum-Shue-Chan, K. 1976. Examination of the elutriate test, a screening procedure for dredging regulatory criteria. J. Great Lakes Res., 2: p. 272-282.

Chester, R.; Hughes, M.J. 1967. "A chemical technique for the separation of ferro-manganese minerals, carbonate minerals and adsorbed trace elements from pelagic sediments." Chem. Geol., 2: p. 249-262.

Chiba, M.; Morley, H.V. 1968. Factors influencing extraction of Aldrin and Dieldrin residues from different soil types. J. Agric. Food Chem., 16: p. 916-922.

Cooper, B.S.; Harris, R.C. 1974. Heavy metals in organic phases of river and estuarine sediment. Mar. Pollut. Bull., 5: p. 24-26.

Deurer, R.; Förstner, U. Schmoll, G. 1978. Selective chemical extraction of carbonate-associated trace metals in recent lacustrine sediments. Geochem. Cosmochim, Acta, 42: p. 425-427.

Edmondson, W.T.; Winberg, G.G. 1971. A manual on methods for the assessment of secondary productivity in freshwaters. I.B.P. Handbook No. 17. Blackwell Sci. Publ., Oxford. 358 pp.

* Elliott, J.M. 1973. <u>Some methods for the statistical analysis of samples of benthic invertebrates</u>. Freshw. Biol. Assoc., Sci. Publ. No. 25. Ambleside, U.K. 156 pp.

Elliott, J.M.; Tullett, P.A. 1978. <u>A bibliography of samplers for benthic invertebrates</u>. Freshw. Biol. Assoc., Occas. Publ. No. 4. Ambleside, U.K. 61 pp.

Ellis, M.M. 1937. Detection and measurement of stream pollution in trout. <u>Bull. Bureau Fish.</u>, 48: p. 367-437.

Engler, R.M., Brannon, J.M.; Rose, J. 1974. A practical selective extraction procedure for sediment characterization. <u>Proc. 168th Meet. Amer. Chem. Soc.</u>, Atlantic City, N.J. 17 pp.

Förstner, U.; Wittman, G.T.W. 1979. <u>Metal pollution in the environment</u>. Springer-Verlag, Berlin, Heidelberg, New York. 486 pp.

Frank, R.; Thomas, R.L. Holdrinet, J.; Kemp, A.L.W.; Braun, H.E.; Jaquet, J.-M. 1977. Organochlorine insecticides and PCB's in sediments of Lake St. Clair (1970 and 1974) and Lake Erie (1971). <u>Sci. Total Environm.</u>, 8: p. 205-227.

Gad, M.A.; Le Riche, H.H. 1966. A method for separating the detrital and non-detrital fractions of trace elements in reduced sediments. <u>Geochim. Cosmochim. Acta</u>, 30: p. 841-846.

Gibbs, R. 1973. Mechanisms of trace metal transport in rivers. <u>Science</u>, 180: p. 71-73.

Goldberg, E.D.; Arrhenius, G.O. 1958. Chemistry of Pacific pelagic sediments. <u>Geochim. Cosmochim. Acta</u>, 13: p. 153-212.

* Golterman, H.L. 1975. <u>Physiological limnology; an approach to the physiology of lake ecosystems</u>. Elsevier Sci. Publ., Amsterdam, Oxford, New York. 489 pp.

* Golterman, H.L. 1977. Sediments as a source of phosphate for algal growth. In: Golterman, H.L. (ed.), <u>Interactions between sediments and freshwaters</u>, p. 286-293. Junk/Pudoc, The Hague.

Golterman, H.L. 1980. Phosphate models, a gap to bridge. <u>Hydrobiologia</u>, 72: p. 61-71.

* Golterman, H.L.; Clymo, R.S.; Ohnstad, M.A.M. 1978. <u>Methods for physical and chemical analysis of fresh waters</u>. I.B.P. Manual No. 8. Blackwell Sci. Publ., Oxford. 213 pp.

Grim, R.E. 1962. <u>Clay mineralogy</u>. McGraw-Hill Publ., New York. 596 pp.

de Groot, A.J.; de Goeij, J.J.M.; Zegers, C. 1971. Contents and behaviour of mercury as compared with other heavy metals in sediments from the River Rhine and Ems. <u>Geol. Mijnb.</u>, 50: p. 393-398.

de Groot, A.J.; Salomons, W.; Zschuppe, K.H. 1982. Standardization of methods of analysis for heavy metals in sediments. In: Sly, P.G. (ed.), <u>Proc. 2nd Symp. Sediment/Freshwater Interaction</u>, Queen's Univ., Kingston, Ontario, June 15-18. (In press.) Junk/Pudoc, The Hague.

Gupta, S.K.; Chen, K.Y. 1975. Partitioning of trace metals in selective chemical fractions on nearshore sediments. <u>Environm. Lett.</u>, 10, 129-158.

Guy, H.P. 1973. <u>Laboratory theory and methods for sediment analysis</u>. U.S. Geol. Surv. Techniques, Wat. Resourc. Invest., Book 5, Chapter 1. 58 pp.

Guy, H.P.; Norman, V.W. 1970. Field methods for measurement of fluvial sediment. U.S. Geol. Surv. Techniques, Wat. Resourc. Invest., Book 3, Chapter 2. 59 pp.

* Håkanson, L. 1981. A manual of lake morphometry. Springer-Verlag, New York, Heidelberg, Berlin. 78 pp.

Hendel, Y. 1973. Replacement of platinum vessels with a pressure device for acid dissolution in the rapid analysis of glass by atomic-absorption spectroscopy. Analyst (London), 88: p. 450-451.

Hesslein, R.H. 1976. An in situ sampler for close interval pore water studies. Limnol. Oceanogr., 21: p. 912-914.

Holdrinet, M. 1974. Determination and confirmation of hexachlorobenzene in fatty samples in the presence of other residual halogenated hydrocarbon pesticides and PCB's. J. Assoc. Offic. Anal. Chem., 57: p. 580-584.

Holmgren, G.S. 1967. A rapid citrate-dithionite extractable iron procedure. Proc. Amer. Soc. Soil Sci., 31: p. 210-211.

Hubbell, D.W. 1964. Apparatus and techniques for measuring bed load. U.S. Geol. Surv., Water-Supply Pap., No. 1748. 74 pp.

Hynes, H.B.N. 1960. The biology of polluted waters. Liverpool Univ. Press, U.K. 202 pp.

* Hynes, H.B.N. 1970. The ecology of running water. Univ. Toronto Press, Toronto, 555 pp.

Inter-Agency Committee on Water Resources. 1940-1963. Measurement equipment and analysis of sediment loads in streams. Subcomm. Sediment. U.S.A., Reports Nos. 1 to 14.

Jackson, M.L. 1958. Soil chemical analysis. Prentice Hall, Englewood Cliffs, New York. 498 pp.

James, A.; Evison, L. 1979. Biological indicators of water quality. J. Wiley and Sons, New York. 597 pp.

Jarnefelt, H. 1955. Über die Sedimentation des Sestons. Verh. Internat. Verein. Limnol., 12: p. 144-158.

Jones, A.S.G. 1973. The concentration of copper, lead, zinc, and cadmium in shallow marine sediments, Cardigan Bay, Wales. Mar. Geol., 14: p. M1-M9.

Jones, J.R.E. 1940. A study of the zinc polluted river Ystwyth, North Cardiganshire, Wales. Ann. Appl. Biol., 27: p. 367-378.

Jones, R.A.; Lee, G.F.; Salek, F.Y.; Mariani, G.M.; Homer, D.H.; Butler, J.S.; Bandyopadhyay, B. 1978. Evaluation of the elutriate test, as a method of predicting contaminant release during open water disposal of dredged sediment and environmental impact of open water dredged material disposal. Vol. 1. Discussion. Vol. 2. Data report. U.S. Army, Corps Engin., Waterways Exper. Stat., Vicksburg, Mississippi, Rept., D-78-45. 217 pp. (Vol. 1) and 611 pp. (Vol. 2).

Kaesler, R.L.; Herricks, E.E.; Crossman, J.S. 1978. Use of indices of diversity and hierarchial diversity in stream surveys. In: Dickson, K.L.; Cairns, J.; Livingston, R.J. (eds.), Biological data in water pollution assessment: quantitative and statistical analyses. ASTM Spec. Publ., No. 652: p. 92-112.

Keely, J.E.; Engler, R.M. 1974. Dredged material research program. U.S. Army, Corps Engin., Waterways Exper. Stat., Vicksburg, Mississippi, Rept., D-74-14.

Kleerekoper, H. 1952. A new apparatus for the study of sedimentation in lakes. Can. J. Zool., 30: p. 185-190.

Kleerkoper, H. 1953. The mineralization of plankton. J. Fish. Res. Bd. Can., 10: p. 283-291.

Kolkwitz, R. 1950. Ökologie der Saprobien. Schriftenr. Ver. Wasser-, Boden-, Lufthyg., Vol. 4. Berlin-Dahlem, Piscator Verlag.

Kolkwitz, R.; Marsson, M. 1908. Ökologie der Pflanzlichen Saprobien. Ber. bot. Ges., 26a: p. 505-519.

Krishnamurti, K.V.; Shpirt, E.; Reddy, M.M. 1976. Trace metal extraction of solids and sediments by nitric acid - hydrogen peroxide. Atomic Absorpt. Newslett., 15: p. 68-70.

Krumbein, W.C.; Pettijohn, F.J. 1938. Manual of sedimentary petrography. Appleton - Century - Crofts, New York. 549 pp.

Liebmann, H. 1962. Handbuch der Frischwasser- und Abwasserbiologie. I. München, Verlag R. Oldenbourg. 588 pp.

Macan, T.T. 1963. Freshwater ecology. J. Wiley and Sons Inc., New York, 347 pp.

Malo, B.A. 1977. Partial extraction of metals from aquatic sediments. Environm. Sci. Technol., 11: p. 277-282.

Matheson, D.H. 1975. Water quality criteria for Great Lakes waters to be used as municipal and industrial water supplies. Inland Wat. Direct., Burlington, Ontario, Sci. Ser., No. 43. 43 pp.

Mills, A.; Bong, A.; Kamps, R.; Burke, A. 1972. Elution solvent system for florisil column clean-up in organochlorine pesticide residue analyses. J. Assoc. Offic. Anal. Chem., 55: p. 39-43.

Milner, H.B. 1962. Sedimentary petrography. George Allen and Unwin Publ., London. 1358 pp.

Morgan, N.C.; Egglishaw, H.J. 1965. A survey of the bottom fauna of streams in the Scottish Highlands. Part I. Composition of the fauna. Hydrobiologia, 25: p. 181-211.

Mortimer, C.H. 1941. The exchange of dissolved substances between mud and water in lakes. J. Ecol., 29: p. 280-329.

Mortimer, C.H. 1942. The exchange of dissolved substances between mud and water in lakes. J. Ecol., 30: p. 147-201.

* Mortimer, C.H. 1971. Chemical exchanges between sediments and water in the Great Lakes - speculations on probable regulatory mechanisms. Limnol. Oceanogr., 16: p. 387-404.

Oliver, B.C. 1973. Heavy metal levels of Ottawa and Rideau River sediments. Environm. Sci. Technol., 7: p. 135-137.

Patchineelam, S.R. 1975. Untersuchungen über die Hauptbindungsarten und die Mobilisierbarkeit von schwermetallen in fluviatilen Sedimenten. Dissert. Univ. Heidelberg, 136 pp.

Piper, D.Z. 1971. The distribution of Co. Cr, Cu, Fe, Mn, Ni, and Zn in Framvaren, a Norwegian anoxic fjord. Geochim. Cosmochim. Acta, 35: p. 531-550.

Poole, D.M. 1957. Size analysis of sand by a sedimentation technique. J. Sediment. Petrol., 27: p. 460-468.

Rashid, M.A. 1971. Role of humic acids of marine origin and their different molecular weight fractions in complexing di- and tri-valent metals. Soil Sci., 111: p. 298-305.

Reeburg, W.S. 1967. An improved interstitial water sampler. Limnol. Oceanogr., 12: p. 163-165.

Rukavina, N.A.; Duncan, G.A. 1970. F.A.S.T. - fast analysis of sediment texture, Internat. Assoc. Great Lakes Res., Proc. 13th Conf. Great Lakes Res., p. 274-282.

Schindler, D.W.; Hesslein, R.; Kipphut, G. 1977. Interactions between sediments and overlying water in an experimentally eutrophied Precambrian Shield lake. In: Golterman, H.L. (ed.), Interactions between sediments and freshwaters, p. 235-243. Junk/Pudoc., The Hague.

* Shephard, F.P. 1954. Nomenclature based on sand-silt-clay ratios. J. Sediment. Petrol., 24: p. 151-158.

Sly, P.G. 1969. Bottom sediment sampling. Internat. Assoc. Great Lakes Res., Proc. 12th Conf. Great Lakes Res., p. 883-898.

Sly, P.G. 1981. Equipment and techniques for offshore survey and site investigations. Can. Geotech. J., 18: p. 230-239.

Sly, P.G.; Thomas, R.L. 1974. Review of geological research as it relates to an understanding of Great Lakes limnology. J. Fish. Res. Bd. Can., 31: p. 795-825.

* Tessier, A.; Campbell, P.G.C.; Bisson, M. 1979. Sequential extraction procedure for the speciation of particulate trace metals. Analyt. Chem., 51: p. 844-851.

Thomas, E.A. 1950. Beitrag zur Methodik der Produktionsforschung in Seen. Schweiz. z. Hydrol., 12: p. 25-37.

Thomas, E.A. 1951. Produktionsforschungen auf Grund der Sedimente im Pfäffikersee und Zürichsee. Verh. Internat. Verein. Limnol., 11: p. 409-421.

Thomas, E.A. 1955. Sedimentation in oligotrophen und eutrophen Seen als Ausdruck der Produktivität. Verh. Internat. Verein. Limnol., 12: p. 383-393.

Thomas, E.A. 1958. Sedimentation und Typeneinteilung des Türlersees. Verh. Internat. Verein. Limnol., 13: p. 191-195.

Thomas, E.A. 1963. Experimentelle Untersuchungen über die Schlammbildung in unberührten und kulturbeeinflussten Seen der Schweiz. Wasser u. Abwasser (1963), p. 1-19.

Thomas, R.L. 1972. The distribution of mercury in the sediments of Lake Ontario. Can. J. Earth Sci., 9: p. 636-651.

Trostell, L.J.; Wynne, D.J. 1940. Determination of quartz (free silica) in refractory clays. J. Amer. Ceram. Soc., 23: p. 18-22.

Volkov, I.I.; Fomina, L.S. 1974. Influence of organic material and processes of sulfide formation on distribution of some trace elements in deep water sediments of Black Sea. Mem. Amer. Assoc. Petrol. Geol., 20: p. 456-476.

Wagemann, R.: Brunskill, G.J. 1974. The effect of filter pore-size on analytical concentrations of some trace elements in filtrates of natural waters. Internat. J. Environm. Analyt. Chem., 4: p. 75-84.

* Ward, D.V. 1978. Biological environmental impact studies; theory and methods. Academic Press Inc., New York, San Francisco and London. 157 pp.

* Ward, H.B.; Whipple, G.C. 1966. <u>Fresh-water biology</u>. (2nd Ed.) J. Wiley and Sons, London and New York. 1268 pp.

Welch, P.S. 1958. <u>Limnology</u>. McGraw-Hill Publ., New York. 538 pp.

Welte, D. 1969. Organic geochemistry of carbon. In: Wedepohl, K.H. (ed.), <u>Handbook of geochemistry</u>. Springer-Verlag, Berlin, Heidelberg, New York. Vol. II-1: p. 6L1-6L30.

* Williams, J.D.H.; Jaquet, J.-M.; Thomas, R.L. 1976. Forms of phosphorus in the surficial sediments of Lake Erie. <u>J. Fish. Res. Bd. Can</u>., 33: p. 413-429.

Williams, J.D.H.; Pashley, A.E. 1979. Lightweight corer designed for sampling very soft sediments. <u>J. Fish. Res. Bd. Can</u>., 36: p. 241-246.

Williams, J.D.H.; Shear, H.; Thomas, R.L. 1980. Availability to <u>Scenedesmus quadricauda</u> of different forms of phosphorus in sedimentary materials from the Great Lakes. <u>Limnol. Oceanogr</u>., 25: p. 1-11.

* Suggest text for further reading.

V Data processing and reliability

V.1   Introduction

The output of a sediment sampling program is in the form of discrete data bits. Since the number of such bits may amount to many thousands (in some exceptional cases it may amount to the hundreds of thousands), handling of results and processing becomes an extremely important component of the program. The system of data storage, handling, and processing of results must be considered during the earliest planning stages since this may well control the amount of data which can be used and the length of time to complete interpretations.

In this Guidebook, we are not concerned with the extremely complex statistical techniques involved in multivariate data analysis nor with the use of massive computer storage and retrieval systems. Rather, we are concerned with the use of simple techniques that are generally available to most investigators. These are suitable for summarizing data, applying confidence limits to interpretations, and for presenting information in most reports and publications.

V.2   Sources of Error

V.2.1   Introduction

The data which are finally used for interpretation in sediment sampling programs, are subject to numerous sources of error which may be summarized (in abbreviated form) in Figure V.1.

There is a potential for errors to become cumulative as illustrated by Figure V.1 and to eliminate this as far as possible, checks should be made at each stage of the sampling-analysis-data-use procedure (referred to, in total, as data collection).

Each data collection program is a compromise between what is actually possible and what is ideal, and it is almost invariably better to collect and process a few samples well than to collect and analyze many samples badly. Because of the ease with which major errors can enter into any part of the data collection program, it is essential to plan ahead and to prepare and test a complete procedure before going ahead with the sampling.

V.2.2   Field sampling

There are three main causes of error in field sampling; taking a sample at the wrong location (which would include, for example, a suspended load sample taken at the wrong depth); keeping a badly taken sample which is NOT REPRESENTATIVE of the lake/river bed or suspended load conditions; and mixing-up the sample numbers. To ensure that errors from these sources are minimal, all position fixes, sampling times and dates, and other general observations must be recorded to allow subsequent scrutiny. If the identity of any sample in any batch of samples cannot be determined from its label, such a sample should be rejected and (if possible) retaken. The greatest source or error, however, is usually the quality of the recovered sample, in terms of how well it represents the environment. Each sample should be carefully checked to ensure that it is satisfactory before moving to the next sample location; if there is any doubt, further samples should be taken and anomalous materials discarded.

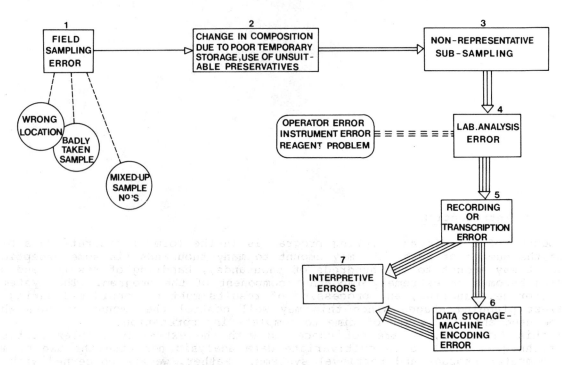

FIGURE V.1 Summary of sources of error

V.2.3 Compositional changes

Because of a variety of complex biological and chemical interactions, changes may take place in sediment samples at any time between sample recovery and laboratory analysis. It is therefore essential to minimize any such changes by the use of preservatives. In particular, it is important to keep samples cool (at about 4°C), to keep them in the dark, and to maintain (as nearly as possible) unaltered levels of O_2. Cool temperatures retard microbial activity and generally reduce the rate of biochemical reactions; but below 4°C water volume expands and, if frozen, textural properties and grain structures may be destroyed. Oxic samples should not be allowed to become anoxic (often as a result of biological degradation), and anoxic samples must be denied exposure to O_2. For studies designed to identify the speciation of certain elements (such as iron and phosphorus), the delay between sampling and analysis should be an absolute minimum (even an hour or so can be detrimental). Careful attention should be given to the choice and use of preservatives since they should not interfere with the chemical determinations to be carried out later. For example, if $HgCl_2$ is added to one set of samples (to inhibit biological activity), it is highly unlikely that a subsequent mercury content determination of the other sets would remain unaffected. In such cases, therefore, it is necessary to split the original sample, in the field, into two or more representative sub-samples and to treat and store these by different means prior to analysis. It is not usually recommended to take multiple samples from the same site because the between-sample variability is often greater than sub-sample variability.

From a practical point of view, it is essential to keep these constraints in mind when planning field operations.

Because of a lack of on-board facilities, samples taken from small boats must be held in temporary storage until they can be delivered to a field laboratory. Since, at most, they should be processed a few hours after sampling, it may be necessary to program 'morning only' sampling so that it is possible to give them laboratory treatment and initial preparation later the same day.

If large lakes or rivers are sampled and it is impossible to return samples to a field laboratory within a few hours, then the sampling vessel must be equipped with suitable laboratory and storage facilities where initial preparation and treatment can be carried out on board (and samples suitably stored for several days or even weeks before delivery to shore facilities).

Test samples should be subjected to analyses, to determine their degradation characteristics under different forms of temporary storage. In addition, a maximum allowable storage period should be determined for both untreated and partly-treated samples. For many parameters it will be inappropriate to carry out analyses on samples whose storage periods exceed the maximum allowable time. A comparison of data, derived from samples which exceed allowable storage by two, four, or more times, followed by extrapolation to zero storage time, is most unreliable.

V.2.4   Sub-sampling

To ensure that sub-samples are representative of the original material, it is essential that the original material is effectively homogenized before sub-sampling. Samples of suspended solids must be well mixed and shaken and they should be sub-sampled by means of a number of small separate draw-offs, which are then recombined into a few sub-samples, each of equal amount. Tests should be run on the sub-sampling technique to demonstrate that sub-samples are properly representative of the original material, and that there is no significant difference between each sub-sample (this applies to the concentration of suspended solids, their particle size distribution, and bulk chemical content).

Bottom sediment samples, also, must be homogenized before sub-sampling. Depending upon the condition of the material (wet or dry), it may be sub-sampled by quartering techniques or by use of sample splitters (in which dry material is poured through a form of box splitter). As with suspended sediment samples, tests must be run to confirm the suitability of sub-sampling techniques.

Sub-samples are generally prepared to allow one or more pre-storage treatments to be made on a single original sample; they will be required where part of each original sample is to be held in long-term storage as a reference; and they may be required where duplicate samples are to be run through laboratory analyses.

V.2.5   Laboratory analyses

Both sedimentological and chemical analyses are subject to operator error, instrument error, and reagent problems. It is wise to select methods having a reasonably high level of accuracy and good precision, rather than to rely upon using an increased number of samples as a means of overcoming the problems of error. Tests in physical analyses (particle size) tend to regard error as total analytical error because operator and instrument errors appear to be of the same order of magnitude. Tests on analytical techniques are usually validated by achieving similar particle size results from two or more separate methods; accuracy may be established by analysis of a standard; and precision may be established by confirming high repeatability of results (when the same sample is subject to repeated analyses).

In chemical analyses, instrument accuracy is determined by the analysis of standards and may be expressed as the difference between absolute and measured value('s) (as individual measurements, standard deviation, or coefficient of variation, etc.). Precision is a measure of repeatability (as defined in the IBP manual, Golterman et al., 1978) and should be derived from the repetition of at least ten tests on the same test material (expressed, commonly, as standard deviation). Sensitivity is a measure of the lowest concentration which can be determined. It can be defined as:

..... 3 × the blank (concentration), as in colorimetric analysis;

..... 3 × the background noise, as in atomic absorption flame spectrophotometry (if noise is high);

..... or 1 percent of full scale deflection (if AAS noise is low).

In chemical analyses, each analytical method for each parameter measured should be subject to a test which will determine the total analytical error. The following list summarizes the more important techniques used for this purpose:

i)   Analysis of standards.
ii) Use of blanks.

iii) Use of duplicate or replicate samples.
iv) Use of spiked samples.
v) Comparative analyses on different equipment.
vi) Interlaboratory comparison (ring testing).

The use of standards (to define accuracy) and blanks (to define sensitivity) has been described previously; similarly, the use of duplicate, or replicate samples, to define precision. In spiked samples, a chemical compound is added to a sample to increase the concentration of a measured element by about 50 percent. Success is determined by the percent recovery of this spike (in excess of the natural concentration).

Unfortunately, a complete spike recovery does not necessarily mean that the analysis is correct. For example, if iodide is present it will be titrated as chloride, while added quantities of chloride will be recovered for 100 percent. This problem will be serious, also, in arsenic, phosphate, and silicate analyses. Furthermore, at low natural concentrations it is possible for interference to occur; under such conditions it can be useful to double the expected quantity of a potentially interfering compound (e.g., add silicate in the phosphate determination, add Ca^{2+} in the SO_4^{2-} determination).

Comparative analyses may be run on different equipment to ensure the most cost-effective and logistically suitable choice of analytical methods, and as a check that equipment is functioning properly.

It must be realized, however, that even with standardized techniques and in-laboratory testing, different laboratories may produce substantially different results (even for the same samples). The use of coded samples, each of which are analyzed blind by a number of participating laboratories (interlaboratory comparison or ring test), provides almost the only way in which laboratory standards can be upheld and validated, particularly at the international level.

Based on such ring tests, important changes may be registered very quickly; typically such changes can be identified with staff changes, changes in methodology, or changes of equipment. It is good practice, in any routine survey or monitoring program, to agree between research/management staff and analytical staff that some samples will be duplicated or spiked, for quality control, and that the results will be discussed jointly.

Ring tests between 'friendly' laboratories are strongly recommended; results of several tests, known to the authors, have been disastrous and in one case the results were so bad that the exercise was stopped (but the overall program did continue).

Several government laboratories may have to use certain legally prescribed procedures; however, all analysts have a duty to ensure that they make a critical examination of their standard methods and manuals before confirming the results of their analytical procedures.

V.2.6 Recording or transcription errors

At no time should results be accepted from any analyses without some form of visual scrutiny to check the likely validity of the results; if data are transcribed it should be subject to an independent check. Look for anomalously high or low values.

V.2.7 Machine storage

At no time should data be fed directly into storage from an automated measuring device without visual checking and inspection by the analyst.

If large amounts of data are coming in from a large survey or monitoring network, computer or punched card data storage may be necessary. Each procedure for data storage or retrieval must be thoroughly checked; if procedures for calculations are used in the computer, a direct inspection of the processed data is necessary via the output of stored data. Data should never be fed into a computer without proper inspection. The programs of programmable calculators should also be checked regularly, e.g., by feeding the machine with a prepared set of data and scrutinizing the output.

Each step in the sampling and processing procedures increases the possibilities of error.

V.2.8   Error in relation to interpretation

In any program of survey, monitor, surveillance, or special process studies, the frequency (temporal) and density (spatial separation) of sediment sampling have a major influence upon the reliability of the data and, therefore, strongly influence potential errors in subsequent interpretations. Because the environmental conditions vary so much between different locations, it is impossible to state repeat intervals or to present a set of exact sample spacings (see previous discussions, Chapter III) which will meet specific experimental requirements. Table V.1, however, provides a guide to what may be considered desirable sampling frequencies for some sediment/water quality sampling studies.

TABLE V.1   Suggested sampling frequencies suitable for some sediment sampling programs

	Frequency Interval	Percentage Acceptable Error in Measurements
Rivers (suspended material)		
Total suspended load (mostly silt and clay)	1 - 2 weeks*	10 - 20
Major elements (Ca,Mg,N,K,Cl, SO₄, HCO₃) in suspended load	2 - 3 months	<5
Minor elements (N,P,Si) in suspended load	1 month or less*	<5
Heavy metals in suspended load	1 month or less*	<10
Pesticides and herbicides	1 month or less*	about 10
Lakes (suspended material)		
Total suspended load (mostly silt and clay)	1 year or less	10 - 20
Major elements	1 year or less	<5
Minor elements	1 year or less	<5
Heavy metals	1 year or less**	<10
Pesticides and herbicides	1 year or less***	about 10
Lakes (bed material)		
Lake bed sediments (textural composition)	5 years****	<5
Major elements	10 years****	<5
Minor elements	5 years****	<5
Heavy metals	5 years****	<10
Pesticides and herbicides	5 years****	about 10

* Or more frequently during flood periods.
** Minimum useful interval about 3 months.
*** Minimum useful interval about 1 year.
**** Or more frequently for special purpose sampling.

It is often necessary to determine if recorded values are significantly different because of natural variation or some other form of total analytical error. To do this it is necessary to show whether the difference between measured values exceeds the likelihood of analytical error (such as previously expressed by the use of the standard deviation or coefficient variation).

Because the objectives of different sediment sampling programs may differ, the forms and amounts of error which are acceptable will differ also. Monitor studies, surveys, and process studies may be designed to demonstrate trends and to quantify the range of values associated with such trends (temporal or spatial). Surveillance programs, on the other hand, are designed to show the presence or absence of some specific compound(s) and to measure their excess in relation to some specific level of concentration (which may be zero, or at some elevated level). In general, the interpretation of trend data tends to be more tolerant of error than surveillance data, in which reference is continually made against some form of standard.

In summary, being assured of the acceptability of cumulative errors up to the point at which data interpretation can begin, it is therefore essential to complete the task of data synthesis with equal care. Because of the complexities of statistical treatments which form a large part of modern data processing techniques, we will present only the most simple and easily understood forms of processing and presentation. The authors would strongly advise the participation of an experienced statistician before proceeding with more advanced techniques, since it is quite possible for improper use of statistics to yield entirely spurious results (and therefore bias or make erroneous interpretations) even though the raw data may have been entirely satisfactory.

It is best to use the simplest statistical techniques which can be matched to the quality of available data, in order to present the most reliable interpretation, as discussed in a subsequent section (V.5).

V.3 Data Handling and Storage

V.3.1 Introduction

The data associated with sediment sampling programs may be available in a number of forms. These are, observations and notes, photographs, maps/charts and diagrams, actual material samples, raw data measurements, and processed data which are in the form of discrete data bits.

Data handling and observational procedures must be designed in advance of sampling, and adhered to and finalized before beginning laboratory analysis.

V.3.2 Archive data

Archive data includes all those forms of recorded information which cannot be held easily on machine data storage, either because of their format or because it may be essential to retain them in original form (such as witnessed documents in support of surveillance work, or regulatory or enforcement activities). Archive data may be in the form of field observations, file notes, sample or other documentary evidence, or as various notations on maps and charts, etc. Good detailed descriptions of what is observed, methods used, and problems faced are essential records to be maintained in a data file. Additionally, photographic records of sampling sites, equipment, and samples recovered, are a useful permanent record, supplementary to the primary data file. Such data should be indexed and, where possible, box-filed. It should be stored for long-term reference under fire-proof and damp-proof conditions, suitable for maintaining such data in good condition for at least several decades (a 50-year period is not unreasonable and allows for selective holding by other agencies at some later date).

V.3.3 Reference samples

Reference samples may be kept to meet any one of three important needs:
   i) to allow substantiation of key data, by providing a source of material for re-analysis (most commonly a requirement of surveillance sampling);

ii) to allow for a subsequent analysis of additional parameters on earlier sample materials, as an expansion of the interpretive phase of data handling and processing; or

iii) as a source of archive material which may be re-examined by new techniques at a much later date, in support of some unspecified future program of sediment analysis (typically of research nature).

There are no set methods which have been established for long-term sediment storage, because of the range of different requirements which may be expected. However, the use of freeze-drying techniques (IV.1.4) seems to provide material which is generally suitable for most needs (after partial loss of more volatile components during the process) and may be recommended as one method of treatment. Typically, samples of 100 to 200 g (dry weight) of material are stored in sealed vials which are kept in a cool, dark, and dry room. Alternatively, samples may be stored after a period of air drying, providing that relative humidity is low; however, this technique is not entirely comparable with freeze-dry processing.

Storage of anoxic materials, living biota, or samples in which certain chemical species are to be retained present special problems. Such materials are rarely held for extended periods of time and require careful pre-storage tests to evaluate the suitability of selected techniques. Because of the specific and somewhat experimental nature of such storage requirements, no further details are provided as guidelines, other than to indicate the need for specialist advice.

V.3.4   Machine processable data

Results are referred to as 'raw data', when in the form of original field measurements or laboratory analyses. Numerical data (and mixed alphabetical and numerical "alpha-numeric" data) may or may not be kept in machine storage, though much of it will be processed or refined by means of calculators or computers. It is referred to as processed data, when the numeric information has been recalculated or otherwise changed as a result of further mathematical manipulation (such as the application of statistics or transposition of measurements).

Irrespective of the exact format, it is essential to maintain a file system so that the data are kept in an organized fashion; a notebook is no longer sufficient when two or more members of the staff are involved in handling the data. A comprehensive data sheet must be developed at the beginning of the program which incorporates field observations, results of analyses, and remarks by the investigator.

Figure V.2 provides an example of the data sheets used in investigations of the sediments of the Great Lakes, and of the survey of suspended solids of rivers tributary to the Great Lakes. These data sheets are not cited for incorporation but merely to serve as a guide.

The data sheets, when completed, must be bound or kept in hard cover; an extra copy should be made, and should be kept in a safe location. The data are absolutely irreplaceable and it is the responsibility of the investigator to ensure its short- and long-term preservation.

We recommend that this type of basic file (described above) should be maintained, even if machine storage and processing is to be used. Machine filing merely requires the information to be coded and transferred to punch cards, either for direct processing from cards or for reading on to disc file or magnetic tape storage systems. Always keep the punched cards on file, either for upgrading or as an additional copy of the data base.

Once the data have been entered for storage in a data filing system, it is sound practice to scan the information by parameter and to check that the data have been correctly entered. To facilitate this, laboratory data should be listed in tabular form against sample number. Mistakes are easily made in transposing from one format to another, so double or triple checking is time well spent. Before commencing any form of data reduction or interpretation, always carefully scan the data sheets by individual parameter; look specifically for samples which show anomalously high or low values, based upon the general levels of concentration observed. If these anomalous values are spurious, then invalid interpretations will result. Always re-analyze for confirmation. If this is not possible, then rejection should be considered unless a plausible or obvious explanation is available. Moderate amounts of numeric and alpha-numeric information (a few thousand data bits will be maximum) can be handled using a calculator and a sheet-type data file. Larger amounts of data will require some form of machine storage, to allow easy recall and selective processing. If machine storage and processing is to be used, it is usual for the agency which provides the computing services to prepare a suitable format for data entry and to specify the storage medium (card, tape, or disc). Investigators should therefore plan ahead to ensure that their own data file systems can be readily transposed into machine storage.

INVESTIGATOR .... STUDY NO. ... __1__ SAMPLE NO. .....

LOCATION .... SAMPLE TYPE ....

POS'N __2__ LATITUDE .... DATE SAMPLED .... TIME ....

      __3__ LONGITUDE .... __4__ WATER DEPTH ....

SEDIMENT TYPE, SHEPHARD (1954) .... MORPHOTYPE ....

ANALYTICAL DATA

__5__ Temp.	__23__ TiO_2	__40__ Cd ....
__6__ Eh	__24__ P_2O_5	__41__ Be ....
__7__ pH	__25__ MnO	__42__ V ....
GRAIN SIZE	__26__ S	__43__ K ....
__8__ % Sand	LECO (%)	__44__ Ca ....
__9__ % Silt	__27__ CO_2	__45__ Mg ....
__10__ % Clay	__28__ Org. C	__46__ Sr ....
__11__ Mean	__29__ $T.Fe_2O_3$	__47__ ....
__12__ Std. Dev.	OTHER (%)	__48__ ....
__13__ Skew.	__30__ Quartz	__49__ ....
__14__ Kurt.	AAS (10^6 or 10^9)	__50__ ....
X.R.F. (%)	__31__ Hg	__51__ ....
__15__ SiO_2	__32__ Pb	__52__ ....
__16__ Al_2O_3	__33__ Fe	__53__ ....
__17__ Fe_2O_3	__34__ Mn	__54__ ....
__18__ FeO	__35__ Cu	__55__ ....
__19__ MgO	__36__ Zn	__56__ ....
__20__ CaO	__37__ Ni	__57__ ....
__21__ Na_2O	__38__ Co	__58__ ....
__22__ K_2O	__39__ Cr	__59__ ....

Page No......

FIGURE V.2 Sample description and observations

138

V.4   Data Units Modification and Normalizing

Just as there is a need for consistency in sediment sampling and laboratory analyses, there is also a need for consistency in the way in which results are presented.

Insofar as it is possible, measurements should conform with the use of the
International System of Units - S.I., which are based on metric units. A few
additional comments, however, may be useful at this point:

1)   Particle size analyses (of both bed and suspended material) may use
the mm or micron (now referred to as micro meter) size scales to
establish various class limits; however, the use of Phi scale defined
as $\phi = -Log_2$ diameter in mm, which presents normally distributed data
in a linear form, may be preferred.

ii)   Geochemical results may be expressed as weight units per weight unit
of dry material (e.g., g kg^{-1}; mg kg^{-1} = ppm) but the use of %, ppm or
ppb expressions should be avoided because of a lack of international
consistency.

iii)   Loading data may be usefully expressed as weight per surface area
unit, such as (m)g m^{-2}; or as annual rates, such as (m)g m^{-2} y^{-1}.

iv)   In studies on river systems it is normal to derive two forms of data,
namely the weight of sediment per unit volume of water and the concentration of specific compounds per unit dry weight of suspended particulate material (besides, of course, concentration of soluble fraction. either as total dissolved solids, specific compounds, or total
bulk element analysis - see recommendations of UNESCO-WHO, Report #23,
Water Quality Surveys, 1978).

v)   In order to calculate the load of suspended material in rivers (often
expressed as kg sec^{-1}) it is necessary to have an accurate measurement
of the river flow (cross-sectional discharge at the sediment sampling
location, or reasonable approximation based on stage-discharge relationships - see Chapter III). Loadings may be expressed as mean
annual load; or for some short period if data are unavailable. A
clear distinction should be made between <u>total annual</u> load and <u>mean
annual</u> load. To calculate such data, it is essential that flood
periods are adequately sampled (see also Chapter III); data interpola-
tion (to fill-in for missing events, or the rise or fall of discharge)
is not recommended since this may substantially bias the calculation
of mean annual discharge.

vi)   Many compounds, considered as potential contaminants, occur in
sediment/water systems as a result of both natural and cultural
causes. When potential contaminants occur naturally (for example the
release of heavy metals as a result of lakeshore, or river bank
erosion) they are usually found at low concentrations which are not
considered significant from the point of view of environmental pollution. Table V.2 (modified after Förstner, 1977) gives some examples of
total metal element background concentrations, based on data collected
in 70 lakes from the least polluted areas of the world.

In Table V.2 many metals are characterized by a relatively small
range of concentrations (e.g., copper, zinc, chromium, nickel, and
lithium); in some cases (Mn) the range is greater because of the
potential effects of diagenetic remobilization (which may be season-
ally effective); the co-precipitation of, for example, $CaCO_3$ and SiO_2
may further influence compositional ranges.

In addition to such effects, it is important to note that source
levels may be naturally high in a few cases; for example, Hg in some
Italian river sediments and in geothermal areas of New Zealand, and Cu
in Uganda.

To enhance interpretations in which concentrations are low or to
ensure size compatibility it is sometimes necessary to express elemental data by selected size-fractions such as concentrations in the
clay-size fraction (less than 2 to 4 µm), or in the combined silt and
clay-size fraction (less than about 60 µm or 0.06 mm). As an example
of this, Vernet et al. (1977) have extracted data for selected elements occurring in the silt and clay-size fraction (less than 0.08 mm)
of unpolluted sediments from a number of Swiss lakes and rivers (see
Table V.3). Despite the fact that the above data cannot be taken as a

representative of world-wide conditions, many elements are reasonably close to Förstner's mean values. The reasons for low values of mercury relative to world-wide values, however, are not immediately clear.

TABLE V.2   Mean metal concentrations (mg kg^{-1}) and major influencing factors in lacustrine sediments; modified after Förstner, 1977

Metal	Metal Contents of Pelitic Sediments		Major Influencing Factors			
	Average Shale	Lacustrine Deposits	Bedrock Lithology		Ca-Mg-Carbonate	
	(Turekian and Wedepohl 1961), (mg kg^{-1})	Median range for 90% of the data, n = 74	Granitoid n = 10	Gabbroid n = 2	Absent n = 50	Present n = 6
Fe	46,700	43,000(12,000-69,000)	49,000	58,000	47,100	16,900
Mn	850	750(100- 1,800)	660	1,100	902	475
Sr	300	142(55- 600)	113	70	118	1,311
Zn	95	110(45- 220)	102	85	124	63
Cr	90	59(25- 180)	42	490	91	42
Ni	68	66(30- 250)	69	1,000	119	46
Li	66	45(15- 200)	40	19	60	81
Cu	45	43(20- 80)	31	44	46	34
Pb	20	28(8- 75)	32	27	29	21
Co	19	15(3- 40)	7	68	19	16
Hg	0.4	0.31(0.15- 1.20)	0.44	0.23	0.41	0.46
Cd	0.3	0.35(0.10- 1.20)	0.49	0.20	0.42	0.39
P			0.07 (0.05 - 0.10)			

TABLE V.3   Natural background values of heavy metals in the less than 80 micron fraction (0.08 mm) of sediments of Swiss rivers and lakes

	mg kg^{-1}		mg kg^{-1}		mg kg^{-1}
Mercury	<0.05*	Chromium	35	Vanadium	50
Cadmium	0.3	Lead	50	Yttrium	25
Copper	25	Tin	5	Cobalt	10
Zinc	75	Nickel	50		

* Corresponds to the original detection limit of the method. More recent investigations indicate values close to 0.02 mg kg^{-1}. (From Vernet et al., 1977.)

   vii) Sediment types and accumulation rates differ widely both within and between rivers and lakes, and low concentrations of selected elements (which are expressed in relation to the unit dry weight of sample) can appear to be anomalously low as a result of various forms of 'dilution'.
   'Dilution' occurs as either textural dilution in which much of the sample is composed of coarse sandy sediment, or as differential dilution in which barren sediments are introduced to the depositional site from another source (often on a seasonal basis, such as the erosion of clay shore bluffs during winter storms). To some extent it is possible to compensate for the effects of 'dilution' and to normalize the values, so that elemental concentrations are related more to the potentially geochemically active (silt and clay materials) components of the sediment sample. Compensation can be made by the use of a correction factor such as the QCF, which is defined as:

$$(QCF) = \frac{E \times 100}{100 - Q}$$

where E = percent element and Q = percent quartz.

Since it is often difficult to precisely define the percent free silica (mineral quartz) in the fine sizes, the correction factor can be used with some transposition of textural (size) data in the silt and clay materials; the net effect is to allow recalculation of the amount of element (E) without the potentially diluting effect of quartz. This technique is of particular value when tracing dispersal patterns of selected elements, where coarse-grained sediments lie between the depositional site and potential sources (e.g., sand deposits lying close to shore and obscuring the sediment originating from small stream inputs, or the presence of complex deltas off major river mouths).

It should be noted, however, that the use of this correction factor may differ from location to location. It is useful, therefore, as an interpretive technique only on a site-specific basis and should not be applied indiscriminately (see also, Chapters III.1.4 and IV.2.5).

Another technique which has been applied to sediment core samples, termed the Sediment Enrichment Factor (SEF), allows discrimination of behavioural trends in different groups of elements. In a study to establish the effects on the geochemistry of sediments by 'cultural impact', Kemp and Thomas (1976) compared compositional data above and below pre-industrial time horizons from Lake Erie cores. By using SEF based upon an Al standard, the authors were able to show compositional groups exhibiting similar behavioral trends. SEF may be derived as follows:

$$SEF = \frac{\dfrac{E_s}{Al_s} - \dfrac{E_a}{Al_a}}{\dfrac{E_a}{Al_a}}$$

where E is the observed elemental concentration and Al is the observed aluminium concentration, subscript 's' is the surface value above the Ambrosia pollen horizon (denoting land clearance and onset of industrial activity in the Lake Erie basin), and subscript 'a' is the value from below the Ambrosia horizon.

In other areas outside the North American Great Lakes, some reference horizon other than Ambrosia may have to be located to provide a suitable datum for pre- and post-industrial change. In other areas, too, the elemental groupings may well differ, depending upon the geochemical characteristics of specific sediment/water systems (see also de Groot et al., 1982).

V.5 Evaluation and Interpretive Techniques

V.5.1 Introduction

The successful evaluation and interpretation of sample data depends largely upon its ability to present information in the form of either distributions, trends, or comparisons, and in the case of comparisons, this may be either on a relative basis or against some form of specific standard.

To achieve these objectives, data may be used in its raw form, or may be modified by the application of some form of adjustment, and much data may be used in a partly synthesized form, after processing by statistical techniques.

Table V.4 summarizes the more frequently used types of data, in relation to forms of presentation. The information given in this table is limited to those forms of output which are most commonly used, and to the most readily available and simple techniques which are required for preparation.

TABLE V.4 Data input (use) in relation to forms of output (presentation)

| | Distributions | Trends | Comparisons | |
			Relative	Specific
RAW DATA	Different sediment types; major, minor elements; heavy metals, specific compounds	(x:y data plots)		
ADJUSTED AND NORMALIZED DATA	Size limited data, "quartz corrected" data, heavy metals and specific compounds	Sediment enrichment factor (SEF) applied to geochemically significant element groupings	RAW AND ADJUSTED DATA CAN BE USED FOR TREND COMPARATIVE ANALYSIS; HOWEVER, IT IS USUALLY PROCESSED FIRST TO SIMPLIFY THE PRESENTATION	
STATISTICALLY PROCESSED DATA	Mean particle size, standard deviation, 3rd and 4th moment measures (rarely); mode (sometimes)	Q-Q plots of selected variables; least squares and regression analysis; trend surface plots of selected variables	Q-Q plots, regressions, comparisons of moment measures, variance, coefficient of variation, student's t test, Chi (χ^2) square test	

V.5.2   Raw data

Raw data in the forms of, for example: composition of sand, silt and clay, elemental concentrations or specific compound concentrations (such as PCB's, DDT, or oils and greases), is largely used for the preparation of spatial distribution maps of surface sediment composition. The same techniques may be applied, also, to the preparation of core profile data which illustrates changes in composition in relation to depth below sediment surface.

Raw data can be used to illustrate the distribution of suspended solids within river cross-sections or in longitudinal sections. Raw data, also, may be used to illustrate the inter-relationships between various measured sediment parameters (such as Hg and organic carbon or clay content) or against some related but independent variable such as water depth (lake) or discharge; in such cases the data can be considered as presenting some form of trend information. Raw data can be used to characterize both trends and comparative evaluations. However, because of the quantities of such information or because of the difficulties in visually comprehending the comparison of numerous sets of distribution data, it is usual to process it first.

V.5.3   Adjusted data

Adjusted data represents only a special case of 'raw data', and the use of selected size fractions has been noted in V.4. When using this technique, however, it is important to note that no single size boundary corresponds with all significant geochemical relationships and that similar relationships are controlled by biochemical reactions and water chemistry, as well as sediment chemistry; these conditions may vary independent of sediment characteristics.

Many important relationships, such as carbonate co-precipitation and heavy metal/org.-C/clay minerals, can be found in broadly similar size fractions but, until their detailed particle-size relationships have been determined, it is best to make comparisons based on textural groupings (i.e., silt or silt and clay fractions) rather than upon some interval within class boundaries (or across class boundaries).

V.5.4   Statistically processed data

Statistics provide a mathematical technique which can be used to simplify (or condense) data and to discriminate (quantitatively) between possible and probable relationships. Generally speaking, if such discrimination is not possible by the use of a simple technique, it will be no more clearly resolved by the use of a more complex technique.

The authors are, therefore, strongly in favour of the use of simple techniques, the use of which can be clearly understood and appreciated. The application of simple statistics greatly assists the investigator by reducing the data to its essential components and characterizing the accuracy and confidence limits of various interpretations. More complex statistical techniques are described in many excellent textbooks (Snedecor, 1956; Davis, 1973; and Sokal and Rohlf, 1973), and if advanced techniques are to be used, it is most sensible to seek the advice and guidance of a competent statistician, to ensure that processing techniques are appropriate for the data and that results are subject to proper interpretation.

Some basic statistical methods which should be used are discussed as follows:

a) Mean ($\bar{x}$)

The mean, which is generally assumed to be the arithmetic mean of a group of numbers, is defined as:

$$\bar{x} = \frac{\Sigma x}{n} \text{ or } \frac{\Sigma f x}{\Sigma f}$$

where f is the frequency of occurrence of x.

It is the first moment measure and the most commonly used statistical fraction. It provides a means by which a large group of numbers can be characterized by a single number. For a data set which corresponds to a statistically normal distribution (see Figure V.3), the mean value and the median value (value at the 50 percent or half-way mark or range of numbers) are coincident. The mean value, for example, can be used to characterize the particle size of a sediment sample, or to characterize the concentration of various elements in a set of samples. Mean values from several samples or groups of samples can be used as the basis of presenting information in the form of distributions, trends, or comparisons.

b) Mode (m_0)

The mode is simply the most commonly occurring value(s), or group(s) of values (as in the case of sediment samples which are analyzed in the form of size-classes), in a set of numbers. The mode is commonly used in comparisons of sediment particle size where contributions from various sources may be characterized by unique size-frequency characteristics (or compositional characteristics) which are reflected by one or more modes in the data set distribution (Figure V.3).

c) Standard Deviation (s)

The standard deviation (or second moment measure) is a measure of spread or dispersion about the mean; it describes how well a set of values are clustered about their mean value. The standard deviation is defined as:

$$s = \sqrt{\frac{\Sigma (x - \bar{x})^2}{n - 1}}$$

Approximately 67 percent of all values will lie within ±1 standard deviation of the mean value; approximately 95 percent of all values will lie within ±2 standard deviations of the mean, and approximately 99 percent of all values will lie within ±3 standard deviations of the mean (see IBP Manual No. 8 pages 5 and 6 for discussion on the difference between population and sample, standard deviation).

In the case of each of the formulations referring to the mean, mode, and standard deviation, their statistical expression is in direct parametric form. Direct comparison between different data sets is possible, therefore, only when the units, used to express the data, are the same.

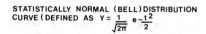

STATISTICALLY NORMAL (BELL) DISTRIBUTION CURVE (DEFINED AS $Y = \frac{1}{\sqrt{2\pi}} e^{-\frac{t^2}{2}}$

WHEN $e = 2.7183$
AND $t^2 = \frac{(X - \bar{X})^2}{s^2}$

NORMAL (S) CUMULATIVE CURVE

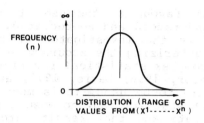

FREQUENCY (n)

DISTRIBUTION (RANGE OF VALUES FROM ($X^1 \cdots X^n$)

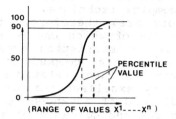

CUMULATIVE FREQUENCY EXPRESSED AS % OF TOTAL n

PERCENTILE VALUE

(RANGE OF VALUES $X^1 \cdots X^n$)

DISTRIBUTION HAS + SKEW TOWARDS SMALL VALUES

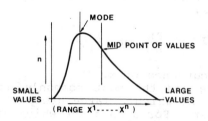

MODE

MID POINT OF VALUES

n

SMALL VALUES

LARGE VALUES

(RANGE $X^1 \cdots X^n$)

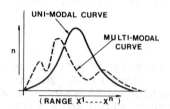

UNI-MODAL CURVE

MULTI-MODAL CURVE

n

(RANGE $X^1 \cdots X^n$)

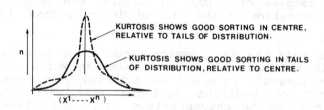

n

KURTOSIS SHOWS GOOD SORTING IN CENTRE, RELATIVE TO TAILS OF DISTRIBUTION.

KURTOSIS SHOWS GOOD SORTING IN TAILS OF DISTRIBUTION, RELATIVE TO CENTRE.

($X^1 \cdots X^n$)

FIGURE V.3 Statistically normal, and other distribution curves

The variance (s^2), which is simply the square of the standard deviation, can be used to describe spread or dispersion about the mean value, but it lacks the advantage of a direct parametric relationship with the original data.

The standard deviation, as a statistical function, is almost as widely used as the mean, and it is applied to almost all forms of data. Typical examples include its use as an indicator of sorting in bottom sediment samples, as an indicator of accuracy in chemical analyses, and as an indicator of consistency of the concentration of particulates in suspended load samples.

d) Skewness (m_3) and Kurtosis (m_4)

Skewness and kurtosis are the 3rd and 4th statistical moment measures, respectively. Skewness is a useful means of qualifying the form of standard deviation and can demonstrate, mathematically, whether or not much of the data is clustered to one side or the other of the mean (Figure V.3). Positive skewness is an expression of bias in the frequency distribution towards smaller values, while negative skewness expresses a bias towards greater values.

Kurtosis is an expression of sorting at the tails of a distribution curve (of some set of numbers), relative to the central part of the curve.

Skewness and kurtosis are sometimes used as a means of characterizing the distribution of river and lake bottom sediments relative to the hydrodynamics of the system, and the following definitions are specifically designed for sediment studies where measurements are based on size-class data (rather than the total count of all the individual particles in a sample):

Measure of skewness (after Coakley and Beal, 1972):

$$M_3 = \frac{X_3}{2(N-2)s^3}$$

Measure of kurtosis:

$$M_4 = \frac{X_4}{(N-4)s^4} - 3$$

where $X_n = \sum_{i=1}^{K} (X_i - \bar{X})^n \cdot \int(X_i)$

where $\int(X_i)$ = frequency of a size class;
X_i = class mid-point;
N = total of frequencies $\sum_{i=1}^{K} \int(X_i)$; and
K = number of class intervals.

As stated by Coakley and Beal (op. cit): 'The above statistics are standardized values and given values of zero for skewness and kurtosis for a perfectly normal and non open-ended distribution. This is not always the case for other moment measure calculations; e.g., the value for kurtosis in a perfectly normal distribution is sometimes given as 3.0 in general statistical formulae (Krumbein and Pettijohn, 1938). In general, the sediment moment measures of skewness and kurtosis can be compared with results from different studies only if care is taken to ensure that the formulae used are rendered compatible.'

As an example of the use of skewness, Thomas et al. (1973) have interpreted skewness in the context of the presence of silt in the (textural) end member size populations of sand and clay. Silt in sand produces a positive skew and silt in clay produces a negative skew. Values approaching zero skewness are characterized by mixed populations (of roughly equal parts).

The results of statistical analyses, using skewness and kurtosis, are presented in non-dimensional form. This can be an advantage where comparisons are required between similar sets of data that differ in unit measurement.

The use of variance or the coefficient of variation (v), defined as:

$$v = \frac{100s}{\bar{x}}$$

provides comparable expressions of spread or dispersion about the mean. When using these techniques on particle size data, it is essential to realize that similar deviation, skewness, and kurtosis values can be produced by the mixing of size populations in the clay and sand series and the sand to cobble series. Therefore, such data should be differentiated. Sly et al. (1982) propose that such statistical interpretations should be separated at the 2.7 ϕ (0.16 mm) mean size boundary, so that statistical trends in high energy sediments (sands and gravels) can be distinguished from similar values in low energy sediments (sandy muds and clays).

The significance of the mean, mode, standard deviation, skewness, kurtosis, and percentile values are summarized in graphic form, in relation to both frequency distribution and cumulative percent distribution, in Figure V.3.

e) Trend Analyses
(Line plots, Q-Q plots, regression, trend surfaces and frequency.)

   i) Line Plots

The simplest means of expressing trend data, which is most often interpreted to mean changes with time, is to plot one or more variable against a common time base. Trends of such data (e.g., concentration of suspended matter, in a series) are then presented in the form of line graphs or histograms. While such presentations are excellent from a qualitative point of view, there is no means of expressing the form of any trend in a quantitative numeration (which will allow a more objective comparison of different sets of trend data). The presentation by line plots may help to select a mathematical formulation for further analyses.

   ii) Q-Q Plots

As a slightly more complex, and partially quantitative technique, the data may be subject to Q-Q plots, in which the percentile value of one set of data is plotted against the same percentile value of its pair. This technique is useful when pairs of data are to be evaluated by trend analysis.

A deviation from a straight line plot indicates that there is a difference between the two sets of data, and a departure of the straight line towards one or other data set is strongly implicit of some change or trend.

The use of bivariate analyses displayed on control charts, as previously described (IV.3.3), provides a useful technique for displaying trend data when this has to be shown in relation to some specified limits.

   iii) Regression and Other Trends

The term trend can be defined, also, as a change which takes place along some sequence of measured data points; with this in mind, the significance of trend analysis to a wide variety of data types can be well appreciated. The most commonly used technique for the quantification and comparison of trend data is by the least-squares method and regression analysis. The simplest relationship between two variables can be expressed by a straight line trend, described by:-

$$y = mx + c$$

where x and y are the measured quantities, m is an expression of slope, and c is the intercept. The best slope and intercept are derived by the use of the procedure of 'least-squares' fit in which the values of m are given by:-

$$m = \Sigma xy - \frac{\dfrac{(\Sigma x)(\Sigma y)}{n}}{\Sigma x^2 - \dfrac{(\Sigma x)^2}{n}}$$

and the values of c are given by:-

$$c = \frac{(\Sigma x)(\Sigma xy) - (\Sigma y)(\Sigma x^2)}{(\Sigma x)^2 - n(\Sigma x^2)}$$

The degree of fit between the data and the theoretical straight line trend is expressed by the correlation coefficient (r), which is defined as:-

$$r = \frac{\frac{1}{n}\Sigma(x - \bar{x})(y - \bar{y})}{s_x \quad s_y}$$

A perfect functional relationship between the observed and theoretical slope occurs when $r = 1$, and complete disassociation when $r = 0$.

More complex relationships, which involve curved trends between two variables, can be expressed by the use of higher degree polynomial and curvilinear regression analysis (see statistical textbooks). Care should be taken in the use and interpretation of log.log plots, since many biological data sets seem to fall on a straight line.

Just as trend analyses may be applied to define linear and non-linear relationships between different pairs of variables, so, too, the spatial distribution data (typical of bottom sediment maps, or suspended concentration distributions) can be investigated by the use of trend surface analysis. This technique is much used in geological studies and serves to differentiate between local and regional effects. The deviation of trend surface and regression analysis frequently becomes complex, involving the use of second degree (quadratic) or third degree (cubic) polynomial expressions and, in keeping with our simple approach to statistics, the reader is referred to appropriate textbooks on this subject for a more detailed explanation.

The application of frequency (harmonic) analysis and power spectrum analysis which express the magnitude of those components of total variance, either at constant time interval or at multiple periodicity, may be considered most useful in the interpretation of flow-related data (such as suspended solids concentration). Those techniques are described in the UNESCO-WHO Report #23 on Water Quality Surveys and will not be repeated here.

iv) Student's t and Chi-square tests

The student's t test is a statistical test which is applied to determine the significance of differnce between paired sets of data. It is defined as:-

$$t = \frac{(\bar{X} - \bar{x}) \sqrt{n - 1}}{s}$$

where $\bar{X} = 0$ for no population discrepancy.

Student's t is one of the most commonly used statistical tests and the significance of relationships between pairs of data is defined by comparing t against the appropriate degrees of freedom $(n-1)$, as shown in Figure V.4 (after Moroney, 1951). A complete example of the application of the student's t test, to paired sets of specific conductance data (Battle River, Saskatchewan), is given in the UNESCO-WHO Report #23 on Water Quality Surveys.

The Chi-square (χ^2) test is used to compare a distribution of actual sample observations against some predetermined or standard distribution. The frequency distribution is compared with some hypothetical form (such as a normal distribution or a log-normal distribution) to see if an assumption of similarity is appropriate. Because of the nature of the test it is possible to replace a hypothetical distribution with another actual distribution (from another set of samples). The test may be used, therefore, to compare sets of data against some hypothetical distribution or against one another (in such cases the sample sets may be composed of a number of different parameters).

The Chi-square value is defined as:-

$$\chi^2 = \Sigma \left(\frac{(f_i - F_i)^2}{F_i} \right)$$

where f_i are the sample counts of individuals and F_i are the corresponding hypothetical (or alternate measured) frequencies.

Figure V.5 shows the significance of Chi-square values in relation to the number of degrees of freedom (after Moroney, 1951).

147

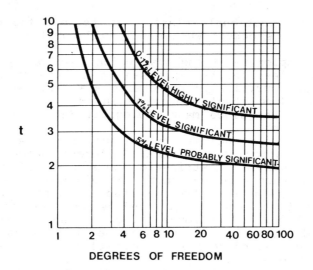

DEGREES OF FREEDOM

FIGURE V.4   Graphs of students' t for 5%, 1%, and 0.1% significance
level. If the calculated value for t is greater than
the value shown for the appropriate number of degrees of
freedom, the indicated level of significance is reached
(after Moroney, 1951)

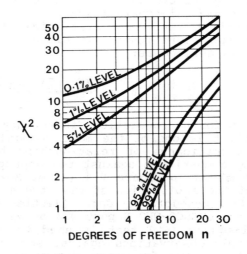

DEGREES OF FREEDOM n

FIGURE V.5   Graphs of χ^2. The 0.1% and 5% levels
indicate suspiciously bad fit. The 95%
and 99% levels are used to indicate suspiciously good fit. For degrees of freedom
greater than 30, $\sqrt{2\chi^2}$ is normally distributed
with unit standard deviation about a mean value of
$\sqrt{2n-1}$ (after Moroney, 1951).

    Statistical techniques offer a wide range of additional and more sophisticated
means of processing data such as multiple regression, multivariate analysis,
cluster analysis and factor analysis. Each of these techniques can provide an
exceedingly powerful means for synthesizing large quantities of data. However,
care must be taken in the preparation of data for such analyses, and it is
essential that the methods and their limitations are clearly understood before
use of such techniques. Th authors therefore recommend that expert advice and
guidance be used before proceeding with such methods of data treatment.

148

Advanced statistical techniques should not be seen as a replacement of the visual scanning and preliminary treatment of data by more simple and less sophisticated techniques.

References

Coakley, J.P.; Beal, G.S. 1972. SEDAN - computer program for sediment particle-size analysis. Can. Dept. Environm., Inland Wat. Br., Rept. Ser., No. 20. 33 pp.

* Davis, J.C. 1973. Statistics and data analysis in geology. John Wiley and Sons, Inc, New York. 550 pp.

Förstner, U. 1977. Metal concentrations in freshwater sediments - natural background and cultural effects. In: Golterman, H.L. (ed.), Interactions between sediments and freshwater, p. 94-103. Junk/Pudoc, The Hague.

Golterman, H.L.; Clymo, R.S.; Ohnstad, M.A.M. 1978. Methods for physical and chemical analysis of fresh waters. I.B.P. Manual, No. 8, Blackwell Sci. Publ., Oxford. 213 pp.

de Groot, A.J.; Salomons, W.; Zuschuppe, K.H. 1982. Standardization of methods of analysis for heavy metals in sediments. In: Sly, P.G. (ed.), Proc. 2nd Symp. Sediment/Freshwater Interaction, Queen's Univ., Kingston, Ontario, June 15-18. (In press.) Junk/Pudoc, The Hague.

Kemp, A.L.W.; Thomas, R.L. 1976. Cultural impact on the geochemistry of the sediments of Lakes Ontario, Erie and Huron. Geoscience Can., 3: p. 191-207.

Krumbein, W.C.; Pettijohn, F.J. 1938. Manual of sedimentary petrography. Appleton - Century - Crofts, New York. 549 pp.

Moroney, M.J. 1951. Facts from figures. Pelican Publ., London. 472 pp.

Shephard, F.P. 1964. Nomenclature based on sand-silt-clay ratios. J. Sediment. Petrol., 24: p.151-158.

Sly, P.G.; Thomas, R.L.; Pelletier, B.R. 1982. Comparison of sediment energy - texture relationships in marine and lacustrine environments. In: Sly, P.G. (ed.), Proc. 2nd Symp. Sediment/Freshwater Interaction, Queen's Univ., Kingston, Ontario, June 15-18. (In press.) Junk/Pudoc, The Hague.

* Snedecor, G.W. 1956. <u>Statistical methods, applied to experiments in agriculture and biology</u>. Iowa State College Press, Ames, Iowa. 534 pp.

* Sokal, R.S.; Rohlf, F.J. 1973. <u>Introduction to biostatistics</u>. W.H. Freeman and Co., San Francisco. 368 pp.

Thomas, R.L.; Kemp, A.L.W.; Lewis, C.F.M. 1973. The surficial sediments of Lake Huron. <u>Can. J. Earth Sci.</u>, 10: p. 226-271.

Turekian, K.K.; Wedepohl, K.H. 1961. Distribution of the elements in some major units of the earth's crust. <u>Bull. Geol. Soc. Amer.</u>, 72: p. 175-192.

Vernet, J.P.; Rapin, F.; Scolari, G. 1977. Heavy metal content of lake and river sediments in Switzerland. In: Golterman, H.L. (ed.), <u>Interactions between sediments and freshwater</u>, p. 390-397. Junk/Pudoc, The Hague.

* Suggested text for further reading.

VI   Sediment dating

VI.1   Methodology

VI.1.1   Introduction

Although it is usually impractical to use measurements of annual sediment accumulation (sediment traps) as a means of extrapolating the age of buried sediments, because of the effects of bioturbation, compaction, and variations in the rates of sedimentation, other techniques are available to give both relative and absolute age. These techniques differ greatly in both certainty and complexity.

There are four main approaches to sediment dating which include a wide range of highly specialized techniques; these include the use of cyclic phenomena, events, identification of specific trends in data sets, and the use of time-dependent dating methods.

VI.1.2   Cyclic phenomena

In this approach, use is made of some sediment characteristic which can be found to repeat itself on a regular basis. This is usually associated with seasonal variations and therefore repeats annually. In moderate to high latitude environments the best known cyclic phenomena is associated with varves. These are composed of fine laminations in which there are alternating bands of different mineralogical and/or particle size composition. In a carbonate-rich lake the summer varves are thicker because of carbonate precipitation in warm water (when solubility of carbonate is reduced). In a textural cycle, summer varves are composed of coarser grains and they are thicker than the corresponding winter varves (when sediment loading is greatly reduced and ice-covered water permits the settlement of fines under quiet water conditions). Under warmer conditions, the development of sulphide bands may reflect the occurrence of anoxia on a periodic basis.

To date varved sediments, it is necessary to count the number of alternating layer sets between the surface and the sample depth, and to express this as years. In long cores, if sections are missing in the sediment column, it may be possible to match similar sequences in different areas and thereby estimate the number of missing layers.

An excellent example of recently varved sediments is cited by Hsü and Kelts (1978) from Lake Zurich where, because of flood control structures on the major inflow, little or no terrigenous material has been carried into the lake since the turn of the century. In Lake Zurich, partial overturn brings cold bicarbonate-rich waters to the surface in the spring. A major diatom bloom occurs in early spring and their tests sink to the bottom to form the base of an annual varve. In response to warm surface temperatures and pH changes, calcite precipitation takes place throughout the summer, forming a distinct lamination. During the later part of the year a thin organic-rich mud accumulates over the calcite (composed of degrading planktonic material, dust particles, and inputs from minor tributaries). The laminated structure of the accumulating varves is preserved in the deepest parts of the lake where bottom water stagnation

inhibits benthic fauna; in these areas, the sediments are not affected by bioturbation.

VI.1.3. Events

Although certain events may re-occur periodically, they are not regular. The
most common internal events in a drainage basin, which are likely to influence
river and lake sedimentation, are associated with major floods, droughts, and
(more rarely) forest fires and landslides. On a larger scale, external events
such as volcanic eruptions and dust storms can introduce exotic materials at
distances thousands of kilometres from their source. Also, magnetic variations
in the earth's field may be preserved as events in the sediment record; they are
discussed later in this section (VI.1.5(b)).

The largest known eruption in recent history was at Mt. Tambora, in Indonesia,
which ejected more than 80 km^3 of material; fine dust from this explosion was
still circulating in the upper atmosphere several years after the event in
1815. Most recently, the 1 km^3 eruption of Mt. St. Helens in the northwestern
United States, carried ash fragments as large as 5 cm in excess of 300 km from
their source and particles of up to 0.5 cm were carried more than 750 km; fine
silt and clay-size materials were carried distances of several thousand kilometres and dust particles (less than 1 µm) were carried substantially further
(Findley, 1981).

By comparison, wind-blown Sahara dust is known to have been transported across
the Atlantic Ocean and has been clearly identified in the Caribbean Islands
(Prospero, 1968).

To make effective use of event data, it is necessary for the date of an event
to be known (from historical record) and that association between the sediment
anomaly and the event is not ambiguous. Although events of internal origin are
well represented in many sediment cores, it is often impossible to use the data
because of confusing ambiguities.

VI.1.4 Identification of specific trends

This is probably the most widely used method of sediment dating but, because it
is often difficult to identify a precise depth within a core at which the value
of some selected parameter departs from background, age determinations resulting
from this technique are not absolute.

Stumm and Baccini (1978) cite a number of examples in which the distribution
of heavy metals in core profiles may be related to cultural impacts caused by
man's increasing industrialization. In Lake Windermere (England), recent concentrations of mercury are about ten times as high as pre-cultural background
levels (Aston et al., 1973) and several step-wise increases can be generally
associated with major changes during the past 1,000 to 1,500 years of human
development.

In Figure VI.1 the interpretation of early changes in mercury concentration is
supported by historic information from additional sources (Aston et al., 1973).

In studies more specifically related to recent changes, Tschopp (1977) has
correlated a five-fold increase in Zn, Pb, Cd, and Cu trace metals in the
Greifensee (Switzerland) with industrialization over the past 50 years
(Figure VI.2). Increases in sediment N, P, and organic-C may also reflect the
greater discharge of domestic wastes, as described by Förstner et al., 1974.

In watersheds where the development of cultural impact occurs in a continuous
and unexceptional manner, it will not be possible to associate elemental concentrations in core profiles with specific dates. Where development has taken
place in an irregular way, or with major expansions and new industries, step-
wise shifts in core profile data may be correlated with precise dates (±2 years
or even better).

In some areas, vegetation changes caused by land clearance may result in a
marked change in pollen types; historic records of land clearance may then provide another and relatively precise form of dating (Pearsell and Pennington,
1947; and Pennington et al., 1972). The use by Kemp et al. (1976) of the 1850
Ambrosia horizon in Lake Erie cores for the development of the SEF technique
(Chapter V.4), provides an important example of this.

The use of multiple dating techniques provides a means of limiting ambiguities
and may make it possible to define a number of separate dates within a sediment
core sequence. This also allows a more precise estimate to be made

where changing rates of sediment accumulation and compaction may influence time interpolations based on core data.

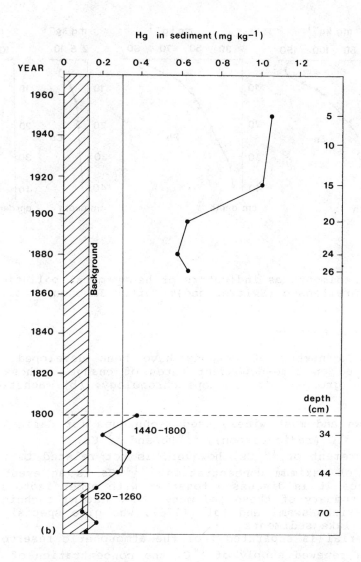

FIGURE VI.1   Sediments as indicators of heavy metal pollution,
mercury in Lake Windermere (England): after Aston
et al., 1973 and cited in Stumm and Baccini (1978)

The preceding examples represent a very limited range of techniques, based on natural and cultural (man-made) events and changes, which are available to assist in sediment dating.   Most of these techniques share similarities in approach; the main differences being in the choice of parameter(s) which are used to establish an association between specific (time-related) events and trends.   There are, in fact, a great variety of natural and man-made materials (including fossil materials, natural minerals/rock fragments, elemental enrichment, and exotic materials) which can be used in these studies on sediment dating.

The choice of method(s) is therefore closely related to local conditions and will be enhanced by familiarity with both the geological setting of an area and the sequence of historical events, which characterize natural conditions and human development.

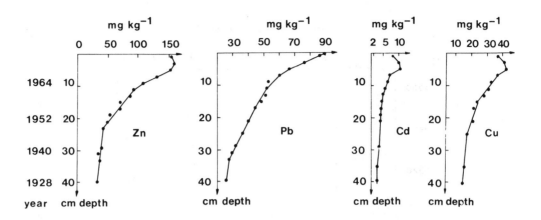

FIGURE VI.2 Sediments as indicators of heavy metal pollution, in Greifensee (Switzerland): after Imboden et al. (1980)

VI.1.5   Time-dependent methods

During recent years, a number of methods have been developed for sediment dating, which are based on time-dependent rates of change. These may be considered in three major groups: (a) isotope chronology, (b) magnetic variation, and (c) other.

a) The best known and most widely used techniques for dating recent sediments include ^{14}C (radio-carbon), ^{210}Pb and ^{137}Cs.

—— The measurement of ^{137}Cs, however, is not related to its decay but to the level of maximum concentration. ^{137}Cs is an event marker, but for convenience it is discussed together with other isotope techniques. An excellent summary of these and many other dating techniques has been prepared by Krishnaswami and Lal (1978), who give special attention to the dating of lake sediments.

—— Once material is separated from the atmospheric reservoir, in which it receives a renewed supply of ^{14}C, the concentration of ^{14}C relative to ^{12}C decreases due to radio-active decay. Although the ^{14}C/^{12}C ratio is not consistent, sensitive instrumentation has allowed the application of this method to sediments of 50,000 years and greater age (^{14}C half life 5,730 years). ^{14}C/^{12}C ratios are influenced by long-term sunspot fluctuations (about nine percent) and show short-term fluctuations of two to three percent at an interval of about 100 years. Radio-carbon dating is most applicable to sediments which are clearly precultural in age (typically measured as several hundreds or thousands of years in age). The ^{14}C/^{12}C ratio has also been affected more recently by the burning of fossil fuels and nuclear weapons testing. ^{14}C is usually measured on organic remains, such as wood fibres (Ralph and Michael, 1974), but it can be measured on carbonate fragments, such as shell materials. Mineral ^{14}C measurements are susceptible to change, as a result of solution replacement by younger carbonates. Dates on organic fragments retained in their place of formation (such as peat layers and tree roots) are usually reliable but dates from fragments of driftwood give only the age of the wood and may not accurately reflect the age of the depositional horizon (for reworked materials this may be a substantial difference).

In contrast to radio-carbon, which is well suited to chronologies of climatic variation, ^{210}Pb provides an excellent means of dating the effects of cultural impact over the past 50 years or so (half life 22.3 years). ^{210}Pb is derived from a number of different sources, in particular the decay of ^{222}Rn escaping from the earth's crust. ^{210}Pb has a short residence time in the atmosphere and most of it enters freshwater systems as a combination of wet precipitation and dry fall. The flux of ^{210}Pb is not constant (being influenced by both natural and man-made causes) and the contribution of ^{210}Pb from ^{226}Ra may be selectively important in some lakes. ^{210}Pb is rapidly removed from waters by particulate scavanging and measurements can be made on sandy silts and fine muds. The contribution of fluvial particulates can be important in the nearshore zone of lakes, whereas the removal of ^{210}Pb from water may be a more important source of this radio-nuclide in mid-lake muds.

^{137}Cs is a radio-nuclide derived as a fallout product from nuclear weapons tests, whose concentration peaked in the years 1959 and 1963. This radio-nuclide is widely distributed globally, and samples may be processed using relatively simple gamma-ray detection equipment and a pulse height analyser (Ritchie and McHenry, 1977).

Figure VI.3 (from Krishnaswami and Lal, 1978) illustrates the intensity of the 1963 fallout peak associated with nuclear testing and its comparable peak in a sediment core profile from Lake Windermere (England), based on data from Pennington et al., 1973. ^{137}Cs is an excellent marker in recent sediments since it is strongly adsorbed on to the fine particulates and shows little evidence of post depositional migration.

The distribution of ^{210}Pb and ^{137}Cs in core profiles is rarely without some form of post depositional change; migration can occur (Lerman and Leitzke, 1975) but more frequently physical resuspension due to storm activity or biological re-mixing modify the original distributions (Robbins et al., 1979). Continuous bioturbation tends to reduce the amplitude of the original anomalies (having an effect similar to the use of a running mean in a mathematical series) and an example of physical re-mixing, by storm effect, is shown in Figure VI.4 (after Krishnaswami and Lal, 1978, and adapted from Robbins and Edgington, 1975, and Robbins et al., 1977).

Although the use of ^{14}C, ^{210}Pb and ^{137}Cs dating techniques are based on well-defined principles, the specialized equipment for these dating techniques are not normally available in routine analytical facilities. Special care is required in the collection and preparation of core materials and the presence of anomalies or ambiguities in data should be checked by using different techniques. For example, Robbins and Edgington (1975) found little satisfactory agreement between Ambrosia pollen dated and ^{210}Pb dated sediments in Lake Michigan. For a number of reasons, the pollen dating appeared to be less reliable; but this is not always the case.

b) Where radio-nuclide dating techniques cannot be used, it may be possible to use other dating methods. Palaeomagnetism, for example, can provide time parallel correlations which may enable some estimation of age based on separate sediment data from more distant sites. High quality oriented cores can be used to study palaeodeclination and inclination which are dependent upon secular variations of the earth's magnetic field with time. A number of distinct variations may be registered in such cores and are most usually correlated with similar cores from elsewhere, age-determined by ^{14}C dating. Palaeomagnetic correlation and ^{14}C dating are complimentary techniques.

c) More recently, hydration rind dating techniques (Friedman and Trembour, 1978) have been applied to age natural glasses (such as obsidian from volcanic eruptions). Although such techniques are of particular application to archaeological studies, the same principles can lend themselves to sediment studies in which the original deposits contained

155

fragments of fresh natural glass. Hydration rates vary, depending upon the chemical composition of the glass and contact moisture, but correlations have been made with several other dating techniques giving a range from a few hundred years to as much as 2×10^5 to 3×10^5 years.

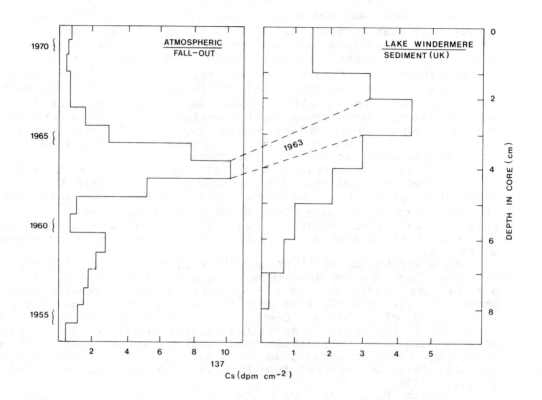

FIGURE VI.3 ^{137}Cs dating in cores, after Krishnaswami and Lal (1978)
^{137}Cs depth profile in sediments of Lake Windermere
and its atmospheric fallout at the same location
(data from Pennington et al., 1973). The peak in the
^{137}Cs concentration between 2 and 3 cm is attributed
to peak in the atmospheric deposition during 1963.

For other methods of determining the age of sediments, the reader is referred to more specialized texts on sediment dating techniques.

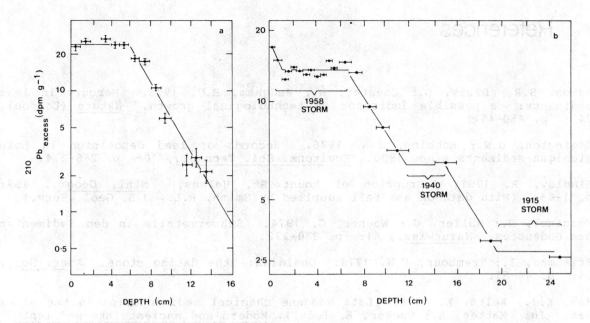

FIGURE VI.4 ^{210}Pb dating in cores, after Krishnaswami and Lal (1978). ^{210}Pb distribution in Huron and Michigan Lake sediments. (a) ^{210}Pb$_{exc}$ distribution of ^{210}Pb$_{exc}$ in the top ~6 cm of the core is due to mixing effects at the sediment-water interface. (b) ^{210}Pb$_{exc}$ distribution in a sediment core from Lake Michigan (adapted from Edgington and Robbins, 1976). The breaks in sedimentation rates caused by storms during various years is clearly discernable in the depth profile of ^{210}Pb.

References

Aston, S.R.; Druty, D.: Chester, R.: Padgham, R.C. 1973. Mercury in lake sediments: a possible indicator of technological growth. Nature (London), 241: p. 450-451.

Edgington, D.N.; Robbins, J.A. 1976. Records of lead deposition in Lake Michigan sediments since 1800. Environm. Sci. Technol., 10: p. 266-274.

Findlay, R. 1981. Eruption of Mount St. Helens. Ntnl. Geogr., 159: p. 1-65. (With data on ash fall supplied by Smith, R.L., U.S. Geol. Surv.)

Förstner, U.; Müller, G.; Wagner, G. 1974. Schwermetalle in den Sedimenten des Bodensees. Naturwiss., 61: p. 270-272.

Friedman, I.; Trembour, F.W. 1978. Obsidian: the dating stone. Amer. Sci., 66: p. 44-51.

* Hsü, K.J.; Kelts, K. 1978. Late Neogene chemical sedimentation in the Black Sea. In: Matter, A.; Tucker, E. (eds.), Modern and ancient lake sediments. Internat. Assoc. Sediment, Spec. Publ. No. 2: p. 129-145. Blackwell Sci. Publ., Oxford.

Imboden, D.M.; Tschopp, J.; Stumm, W. 1980. Die Rekonstruktion früherer Stoffrachten in einem See mittels Sedimentuntersuchungen. Schweiz. z. Hydrol., 42: p. 1-14.

* Kemp, A.L.W.; Thomas, R.L.; Dell, C.I.; Jaquet, J.-M. 1976. Cultural impact on the geochemistry of sediments in Lake Erie. J. Fish. Res. Bd. Can., 33: p. 440-462.

* Krishnaswami, S.; Lal, D. 1978. Radionuclide limnochronology. In: Lerman, A. (ed.), Lakes; chemistry, geology, physics, p. 153-177. Springer-Verlag, New York, Heidelberg and Berlin.

Lerman, A.; Leitzke, T.A. 1975. Uptake and migration of tracers in lake sediments. Limnol. Oceanogr., 20: p. 497-510.

Pearsell, W.H.; Pennington, W. 1947. Ecological history of the English Lake District. J. Ecol., 34: p. 134-148.

Pennington, W.; Cambray, R.S.; Fisher, E.M. 1973. Observations on lake sediments using fall-out ^{137}Cs as a tracer. Nature (London), 242: p. 324-326.

Pennington, W.; Haworth, E.Y.; Bonny, A.P.; Lishman, J.P. 1972. Lake sediments in northern Scotland. Phil. Trans. Roy. Soc. London, Ser. B, 264: p. 191-294.

Prospero, J.M. 1968. Atmospheric dust studies on Barbados. Bull. Amer. Meteorol. Soc., 49: p. 645.

Ralph, E.K.; Michael, H.N. 1974. Twenty-five years of radio-carbon dating. Amer. Sci., 62: p. 553-560.

Ritchie, J.C.; McHenry, J.R. 1977. A rapid method for determining recent deposition rates of freshwater sediments. In: Golterman, H.L. (ed.), Interactions between sediments and freshwater, p. 203-207. Junk/Pudoc, The Hague.

Robbins, J.A., Edgington, D.N. 1975. Determination of recent sedimentation rates in Lake Michigan using ^{210}Pb and ^{137}Cs. Geochim. Cosmochim. Acta, 39: p. 285-304.

Robbins, J.A.; Krezoski, J.R.; Mozley, S.C. 1977. Radio-activity in sediments of Great Lakes: post depositional redistribution by deposit feeding organisms. Earth Planet. Sci. Lett., 36: p. 325-333.

Robbins, J.A.; McCall, P.L.; Fisher, J.B.; Krezoski, J.R. 1979. Effect of deposit feeders on migration of ^{137}Cs in lake sediments. Earth Planet. Sci. Lett., 42: p. 277-287.

* Stumm, W.; Baccini, P. 1978. Man-made chemical perturbation of lakes. In: Lerman, A. (ed.), Lakes: chemistry, geology, physics, p. 91-126. Springer-Verlag, New York, Heidelberg, Berlin.

Tschopp, J. 1977. (Thesis, Swiss Federal Inst. Technol., Zurich).

* Suggested text for further reading.

VII Case histories (1)
Dispersion of contaminants and changes with time

VII.1   Introduction

In this and following chapters, the authors have selected a number of sediment studies which are presented in the form of 'case histories'. Many of the studies were designed as research investigations with the purpose of describing a previously unknown system and, at the same time, providing an explanation of the processes controlling sediment behaviour in it. The interrelationships between environmental chemistry and the physical characteristics of the particulate material are also considered.

Much of the original work goes far beyond the needs of initial investigations related to water quality but, because of this, it provides invaluable background material; the case histories give a feel for the sophistication of sediment-related studies, the complexities of interpretation, and they place less sophisticated studies in perspective. In particular, the work demonstrates a need to appreciate the limitations of this type of data.

The accumulation of sediment in the Borromee Basin of Lake Maggiore (Italy) is used as an example of sediment sorting and selective transport and deposition, and further examples from the North American Great Lakes are used to describe the behaviour of more complex sedimentary environments.

A study of the Bell-Nottaway River system, in northwestern Quebec (Canada), is used to discuss baseline studies and the tracing of point sources by means of particulate materials.

Studies in Lake St. Clair (between Lake Huron and Lake Erie in the North American Great Lakes) are described in order to illustrate the use of sediment monitoring, and to show changes in levels of contaminant concentration with time.

The case histories provide examples of sediment characteristics and the behaviour of particulate material in rivers and lakes. They show how various compounds may be traced and how distinctions can be made between point and diffuse sources. They also provide examples of many of the more important geochemical and biochemical processes by which sediments may become both a source and a sink for contaminants under different environmental conditions.

VII.1.1   Borromee Basin of Lake Maggiore

Whenever a river flows into a lake, the particulate material, carried as suspended load, begins to settle. Sorting occurs during this process so that the larger particles are deposited close to the river mouth and the finer materials are carried further out into the lake, where settlement of silt and clay-size particulates may be influenced by density stratification in the water mass (and the possible effects of chemical precipitation). The distribution of sediments off the mouth of the Toce River, in Lake Maggiore (northern Italy), is used to present an example of selective deposition, and is based on the work of Damiani (1972), translated by J.C. Golterman.

The geological setting of the Toce drainage basin is made complex by the presence of a wide range of metamorphic and intrusive rock types and numerous tectonic structures. Much of the bedrock is composed of mica schists (with garnet, staurolite and tourmaline), and in the south-west of the drainage area granite and gneiss occur. Recent fluvial sediments infill much of the lower part of the river valley.

The river Toce forms a major part (27 percent) of the drainage basin of Lake Maggiore (6599 km^2). It rises in the Monte Rossa massif, on the west side of the lake, and descends over 2200 m, along a distance of only 80 km to the lake. The Toce is a typical mountain stream and at Pallanza, near the mouth of the river, the average annual precipitation is 1.7 m (mostly as rainfall). Peak months are October (0.2 m), November (0.2 m), April (0.18 m), and June (0.2 m); low rainfall occurs in January (0.06 m) and July (0.13 m).

The average annual discharge (1932 to 1963), at a point about 9 km above the mouth of the Toce Rover, was 67.8 m^3 s^{-1} (range 12.9 to 1400 m^3 s^{-1}).

The bathymetry of the Borromee Basin (also referred to as the Pallanza Basin) of Lake Maggiore, and the delta of the inflowing Toce River, are shown in Figures VII.1a and VII.1b.

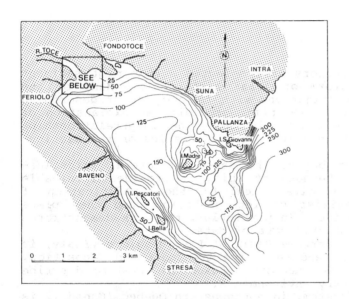

FIGURE VII.1a   Borromee Basin of
                Lake Maggiore, depths (m)
                below lake level (modified
                after Damiani, 1972)

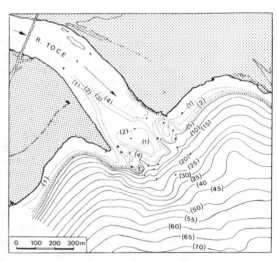

FIGURE VII.1b   Delta of River
                Toce, depths (m)
                below lake level
                (modified after
                Damiani, 1972)

Based on the distribution of bottom sediment types, Damiani was able to distinguish two separate zones of sedimentation in the Borromee Basin. A well-defined area of sands and sandy silts was shown to extend out into the lake, clearly associated with the loss of coarse materials from the entrained flow of the Toce River as it entered the lake (Figure VII.2). Around this area another zone, covered by fine silts and clays, defined sedimentary conditions in which hydrodynamic forces resulted from an interaction of fluvial and lacustrine processes. In this broad zone, both density stratification and large-scale circulation exert a major influence on sedimentation.

On each side of the Toce delta there are areas of fine sediment which noticeably penetrate towards the mouth of the river (Figure VII.3). This distribution is typical of double vortex conditions which may be formed (either side of the river) at the boundary between slow moving lake waters and the relatively high velocity of entrained river inflow. The symmetry of this sediment distribution is strongly indicative that the entrained flow follows the Thalweg (axis) of the Borromee Basin, under high flow conditions.

The lack of very fine sediment along the axis of the Toce inflow within the Borromee Basin, even at depths of as much as 150 m, demonstrates that either

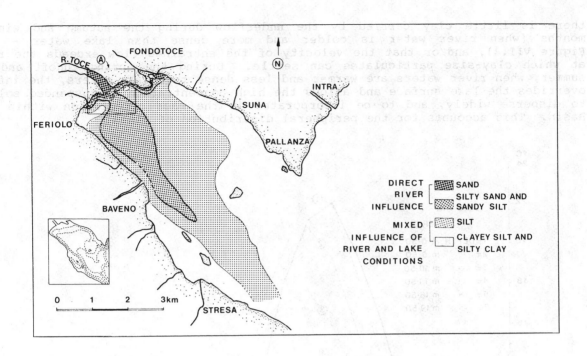

FIGURE VII.2 Distribution of recent sediments, off the mouth of the
Toce River, Borromee Basin of Lake Maggiore (modified after
Damiani, 1972)

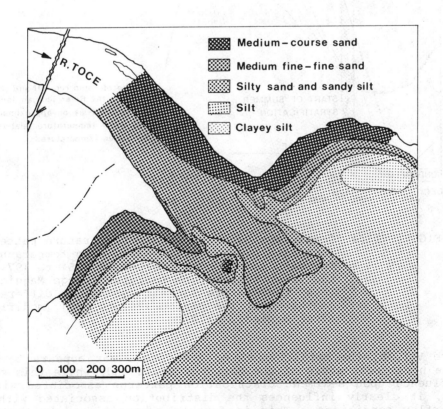

FIGURE VII.3 Distribution of recent sediments on the Toce delta
(modified after Damiani, 1972)

163

there is little clay carried by the underflow during the autumn and winter
months (when river water is colder and more dense than lake water - see
Figure VII.4), and/or that the velocity of the entrained flow exceeds the rate
at which clay-size particulates can settle. During the spring runoff and in
summer, when river waters are warmer and less dense than lake waters, the inflow
overrides the lake surface and allows the high concentration of suspended solids
to disperse widely, and to be incorporated in the mass circulation within the
Basin. This accounts for the peripheral distribution of fines.

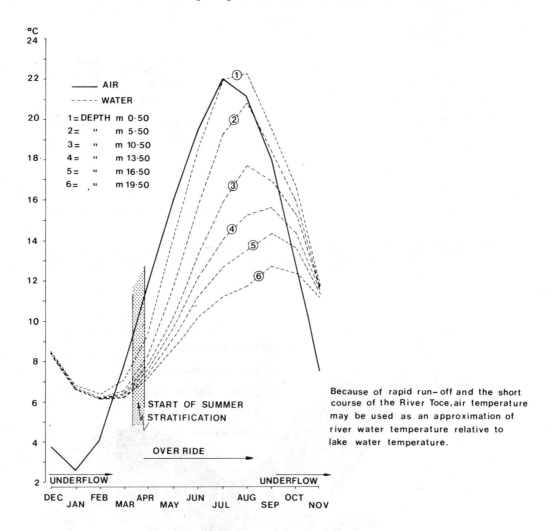

Because of rapid run-off and the short
course of the River Toce, air temperature
may be used as an approximation of
river water temperature relative to
lake water temperature.

FIGURE VII.4   Comparison between the air temperature pattern
                (averaged over several years, mean temperature
                for each month) over the period 1951 to 1971, and
                the water temperature pattern of Lago Maggiore
                (mean temperature for each month) at different
                depths, over the period 1962 to 1971 (modified
                after Damiani, 1972)

    In Figure VII.1b, the main channel of the Toce River appears to be deflected
towards the north-east shore of the Borromee Basin and, while this seems to have
little influence upon sediment distribution patterns associated with underflow
conditions, it clearly influences the distribution associated with spring and
summer overflow conditions. This is further substantiated by the distribution
of mercury in bottom sediments, described by Damiani and Thomas (1974).
    In Figure VII.5a, the highest concentrations of total Hg in the Borromee Basin
lie along the north-east shore and to the north of Stresa, on the south-west

164

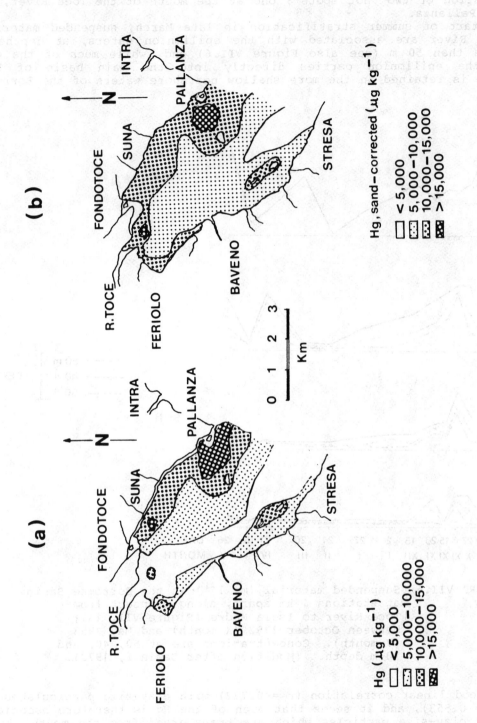

FIGURE VII.5 (a) Distribution of total observed mercury in the surface sediments of the Borromee Basin; (b) Distribution of sand corrected mercury in the sediments of the Borromee Basin (modified after Damiani, 1972)

Hg (µg kg^{-1})

< 5,000
5,000–10,000
10,000–15,000
>15,000

Hg, sand–corrected (µg kg^{-1})

< 5,000
5,000–10,000
10,000–15,000
>15,000

shore. By using a quartz/sand correction factor (Chapter V.4), however, the Hg distribution may be further defined as in Figure VII.5b. In this, the (QCF)Hg shows the location of two 'hot spots'; one at the mouth of the Toce River, and the other off Pallanza.

After the start of summer stratification in late March, suspended materials from the Toce River are associated with the epilimnion waters, at depths of generally less than 50 m (see also Figure VII.6) and, while much of the discharge into the epilimnion carries directly into the main basin of Lake Maggiore, some is retained in the more shallow nearshore waters of the Borromee Basin.

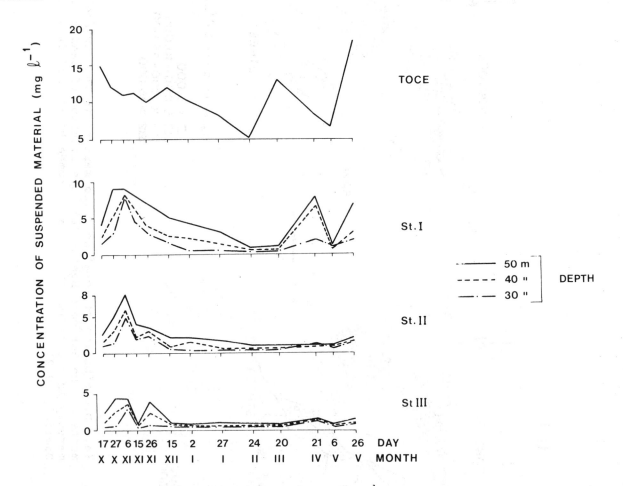

FIGURE VII.6   Suspended material (mg l^{-1}) in the Borromee Basin at stations 1 km apart, along transect from Toce River to Isola Madre (Figure VII, 1a); between October 1952 (X month) and May 1953 (V month). Concentrations are at 50, 40, and 30 m depth. (Modified after Damiani, 1972).

Hg shows a good linear correlation (r = 0.722) with clay-size particulates and with iron (r = 0.553), and it seems that much of the Hg is therefore associated with iron-rich clay-size particles which are transported from the mouth of the River Toce and accumulated in the area between Pallanza and Isola Madre (Figure VII.1a), where rising bathymetry may reduce circulation at depth.

Although no significant correlation between Hg and organic carbon (r = 0.367) was observed, Figure VII.7 demonstrates a significant relationship between Hg and the C/N ratio. Lower C/N ratio values were believed (Damiani, 1974) to be associated with autochthonous (local) organic matter along the shallow north shore of the Basin, and higher C/N ratio values indicated the presence of allochthonous (non-local) organic carbon in the deeper parts of the Basin. The low C/N ratio in the nearshore zone suggests that some of the mercury present in the epilimnion may be taken up by primary producers in shallow water zones (Vollenweider, 1956), and that mercury transfer processes are taking place.

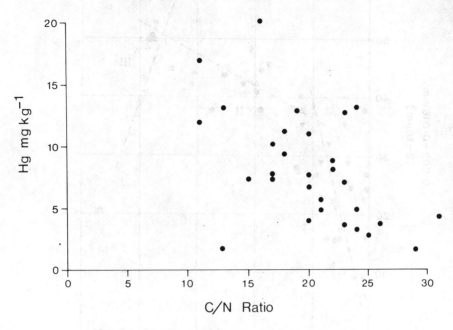

FIGURE VII.7   Relationship of mercury to the C/N ratio
in the sediments of the Pallanza Basin
(after Damiani and Thomas, 1974)

A further substantiation of the differences in sedimentary regime, which influence the settlement of fine sediments within the Borromee Basin, is provided in Figure VII.8. Group I sediments, which form the surface cover of the outward-building Toce delta, are characterized by a low clay content, even though silt increases relative to sand in the deeper waters. These sediments have an almost constant silt/clay ratio of about 4:1 (indicative of a well mixed source). Group II sediments, which occur in the deeper parts of the Basin (and the Feriolo embayment), are characterized by an increased clay content and have a silt/clay ratio of about 6:5. This strongly implies that much of the suspended silt has been deposited on the outer part of the Toce delta and that clay particulates form an increasing percentage of the distal suspended load. Group III sediments have the highest clay content and are characterized by an inverse silt/clay ratio. This strongly suggests that circulation along the north-east shore is rather weak and that only the finest particulate material can be transported within this part of the Basin.

VII.1.2   Niagara River mouth, Lake Ontario

Figures VII.9 to VII.11 are taken from unpublished work on the mouth of the Niagara River, Lake Ontario (Sly). In Figure VII.9, the Niagara River is shown flowing north, from Lake Erie, into Lake Ontario, where it is deflected to the east. The outflow of the river is influenced by a strong eastward moving near-shore sediment transport stream and by an extensive bar (not shown), which has formed on the west and north-west parts of the delta (with material derived both from the discharge of the river and shore erosion). Arrows show the location of major and minor channels, crossing the delta and bar structure.

Most of the sediments forming the upper part of the delta and bar (top set beds) are composed of sands and silty sands having a particle size coarser than 4 φ (63 µm); water depths are usually less than 20 m. Particle size decreases rapidly on the steep outer face of the delta and material having a mean size of 7 φ (8 µm) occurs at depths of 70 to 80 m. Clay-size materials dominate water depths in excess of 100 m.

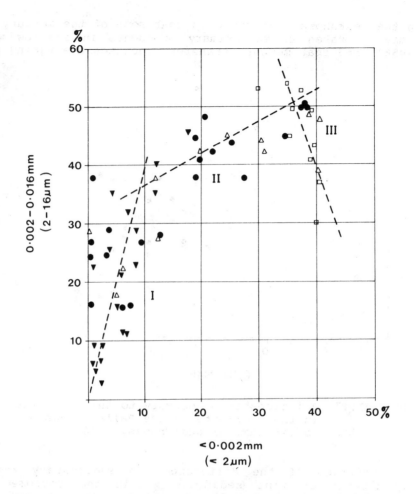

FIGURE VII.8   Sediments of the Borromee Basin showing differentia-
              tion based on percent 2 to 16 μm; percent < 2 μm.
              Group I, Foreset - bottom set of Toce delta; Group
              II, deep central and basin and Feriglo area; Group
              III, north-east shore (modified after Damiani and
              Thomas, 1974)

In Figure VII.9, areas of lag material (defined by skewness/kurtosis sector
relationships; Sly, 1977, and Sly et al., 1982) occur in the channel areas of
the river outflow and on the outer face of the delta, where bottom sediments are
affected by wave action (due to rapid shoaling conditions).   The outflow of
Niagara River water, through the minor channels across the northwestern part of
the bar, also appears to affect the bottom sediments.

   The skewness/kurtosis ratio has been demonstrated as an effective means of
separating sedimentary conditions characteristic of decreasing energy levels
(Thomas et al., 1972 and 1973; Vernet et al., 1972).   The highest energy levels
(sands) are denoted by Sector A, and the lowest energy levels (clays) are
denoted by Sector D.   By making a distinction between samples containing gravel
and those with no gravel, a further separation can be made (Sly, 1977).   The A
to D Sectors then represent a continuous depositional sequence, unaffected by
subsequent erosion.   The E to H Sectors are largely comparable to the A to D
Sectors, but the presence of gravel in these sediments demonstrates a modified
sedimentary regime (usually a lag deposit, although Sectors E to H could contain
ice-drop debris).

   In Figure VII.9, the areas of lag deposits correspond to sediments which lie
within skewness/kurtosis Sectors E to G.   The boundary between Sectors B and C
is also shown in this figure, and shows a close relationship to the 6 to 7 φ
mean size distribution (medium fine silts).

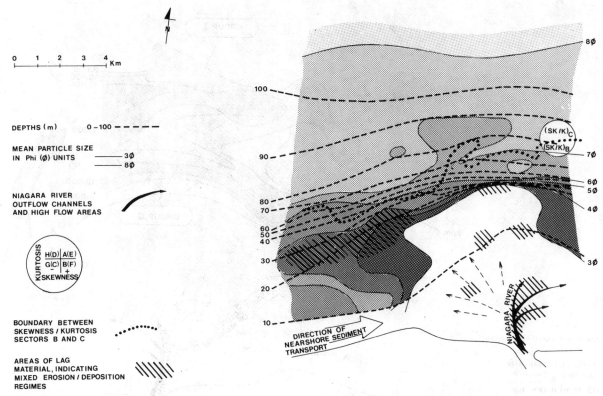

FIGURE VII.9   Plan of the Niagara River mouth showing bathymetry, mean particle
size, and skewness/kurtosis zones B and C.   (Sly, unpublished)

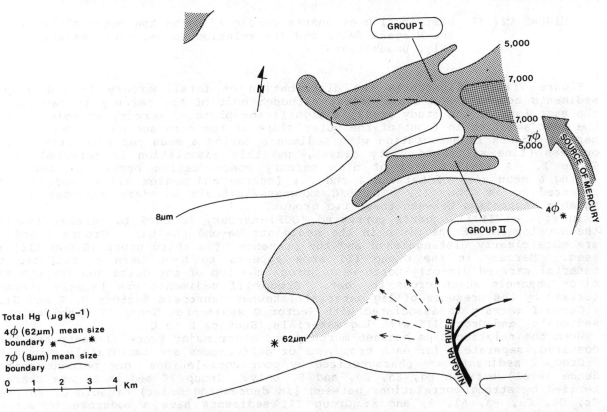

FIGURE VII.10   Distribution of Hg on the outer slope of the Niagara delta
and its relation to sediment texture.   (Sly, unpublished)

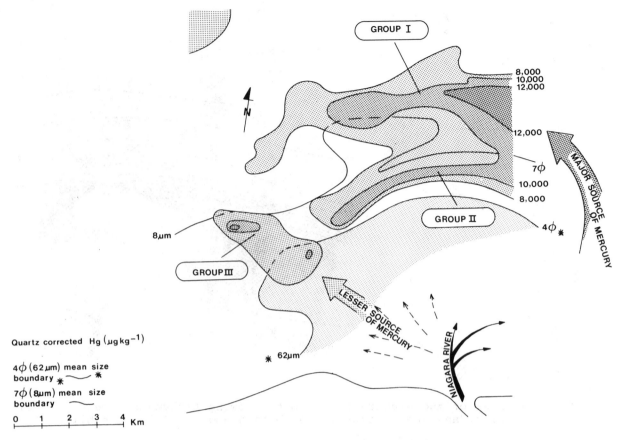

Quartz corrected Hg $(\mu g\,kg^{-1})$

$4\phi\,(62\mu m)$ mean size
boundary

$7\phi\,(8\mu m)$ mean size
boundary

0 1 2 3 4 Km

FIGURE VII.11   Distribution of quartz corrected Hg on the outer slope of
the Niagara delta and its relation to sediment texture.
(Sly, unpublished)

Figure VII.10 illustrates the distribution of total mercury in the deeper
sediments beyond the Niagara delta; although most of the mercury is carried to
the east (out of the study area), a significant plume of mercury extends towards
the west and lies in front of the outer slope of the fore set beds. Most of the
mercury occurs in association with sediments having a mean particle size of $7\,\phi$
or less (fine silts and silty clays), and this association is referred to as
Group I.   A smaller area of high mercury concentration occurs in sediments
having a mean size of between 4 and $7\,\phi$ (coarse and medium silts) and this is
referred to as Group II.   The B/C skewness/kurtosis boundary provides a comparable separation between these two groups.

In Figure VII.11, quartz corrected (QCF) mercury is used to further resolve
the development of the plume in the sediments beyond the bar. Groups I and II
are more clearly distinguished and the presence of a third group (Group III) is
seen.   Mercury in the Group III area appears to have been contributed by
material carried directly north-west across the top of the delta and through the
minor channels which cross the bar.   Group III sediments are largely characterized by the presence of lag material (skewness/kurtosis Sectors E, F and G).

Group I mercury is associated with Sector C sediments; Group II with Sector B
sediments; and Group III with lag materials (Sectors E to G).

When the relationships between mercury and other major trace elements are then
compared, separately for each group, major differences are immediately apparent.

Group I sediments are characterized by poor correlations (one percent confidence level) between Hg, Zn, Cd, and S, only.   Group II sediments are characterized by strong correlations between (in decreasing order) organic C, Zn, Fe,
Cr, Cd, Cu, Pb, Al, S, and K; Group III sediments have a moderate to strong
correlation between S, organic C, Fe, Pb, Cu, Ti, and P.

In Group I sediments, Hg (and Zn and Cd) appears to be weakly associated with
S (probably in the sulphide phase; Thomas, 1972).

170

In Group II, mercury (and other trace metals) has a complex relationship with a number of potential carriers which include organic carbon, iron (as hydroxides and/or sulphides), and clays represented by Al and K (most of the clays in Lake Ontario are illite, Thomas et al., 1972).

In Group III, the association with S, organic C, and Fe, are retained and the presence of phosphorus (probably as iron phosphates) is additional.

In Figure VII.12, the distribution of mercury at Niagara is plotted in relation to water depth. The wide scatter of data points (especially at depths in excess of 70 m) reflects the lack of correlation in Group I sediments. Manganese, interestingly, shows a similar increasing scatter with depth and probably indicates the significance of redox control, associated with bacterial degradation of organics and reduction of iron-sulphur compounds, in deep basin sediments (Sly, 1977, used depth/parameter plots for the comparison of several other elements at this location).

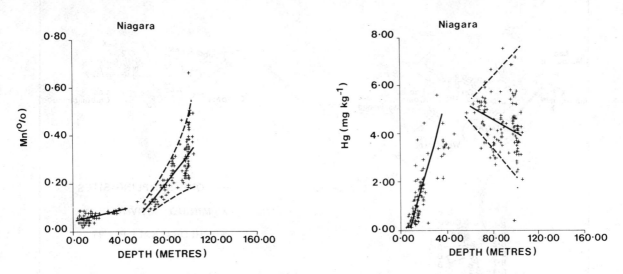

FIGURE VII.12   Scatter diagrams showing the relationship of Mn and Hg to water depth. (Sly, 1977)

By presenting the Niagara data, therefore, further emphasis is given to the normalization of trace element concentrations, as a means of resolving critical distributions. In addition, it has been clearly demonstrated that the behaviour of some contaminants (mercury, for example) may be controlled by quite different geochemical associations which are themselves controlled by separate sedimentological regimes.

VII.1.3   Bell-Nottaway River system, northwestern Quebec

During the early 1970's, mercury contamination was found to be significant in the tissues of many species of fish and birds in northwestern Quebec and, as part of a program to define the possible sources of this contamination, sediment and water samples were recovered from the Bell and Chibougamau Rivers at and above their confluence in Lake Matagami (Figure VII.13). The outflow of Lake Matagami becomes the Nottaway River, which enters into the southern part of James Bay. This study is cited, particularly, as an example of a regional baseline study - level 2 (Winmill, 1972).

Preliminary information indicated that there were a number of mining sites within the drainage basin, a number of small towns with limited sewage treatment facilities, and a chlor-alkali plant on Lake Quevillon.

In 1971, sediment cores (and surface grab samples) were recovered from two to three sites in each lake and from within the rivers, where possible. Their locations are shown in Figure VII.13.

Mercury concentrations in the surface sediments were low, ranging between 0.01 and 0.03 mg kg^{-1} at all sites except Matagami (C-3). Concentration profiles showed little change down any of the cores, except Matagami (C-3). At this core site, surface sediment values of total mercury reached 0.11 mg kg^{-1} and decreased to regional background levels of 0.01 to 0.02 mg kg^{-1} at a depth of greater than 6 cm.

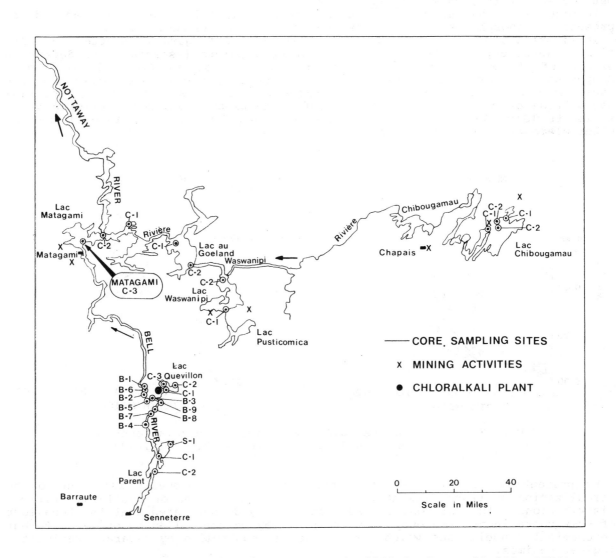

FIGURE VII.13 Nottaway River system (modified after Winmill, 1972)

Mercury concentrations in water in the Chibougamau River system were at detection levels or below, and likewise in the Bell River system, upstream of Lake Quevillon. Mercury in the waters of Lake Quevillon ranged between 0.25 and 0.40 µg kg^{-1}. Mercury in the Bell River water five miles below Quevillon was 0.15 µg kg^{-1}, and at ten miles below Quevillon it was 0.10 µg kg^{-1}.

On the basis of these results, there appeared to be little evidence to support the possibility that much of the mercury was being derived from the leaching or wasting of mine tailings (although some Hg is associated with regional mineralization).

Evidence, however, pointed to an increasing mercury content in the more recent years (upper part) of the Matagami core and to elevated concentrations in the waters of Lake Quevillon (and in the Bell River, below), but still at very low levels (0.4 to 0.1 µg kg^{-1}).

Follow-up studies in the Bell River using pumped suspended sediment sampling, and selected bottom sediment sampling and coring, demonstrated that mercury from urban and mining sources was of limited importance, and that the chlor-alkali plant at Quevillon was a significant source (Thomas et al., 1975a).

Concentrations of mercury in suspended sediments of 180, 220, 175, and 205 µg kg^{-1} were recorded in an upstream direction (from Matagami to the confluence with the Quevillon River), and of 140 µg kg^{-1} above the Quevillon River. Maximum mercury concentrations of 3.8 mg kg^{-1} were found in the surface silts of the Quevillon River, and of 30.0 mg kg^{-1} in silty mud, at a depth of 12 to 14 cm (below layers of high fibre content).

The study showed that most river and lake sediments were devoid of significant concentrations of mercury and that this was largely because of a lack of fine (mud) material on the river bed. The highest concentrations were associated with the suspended load which was probably remobilized from sites of temporary storage within the river, under conditions of increased flow. The highest concentrations in bed materials were in the Quevillon River, just below the plant, and here it was noticeable that the most recent sediments showed a significant decrease relative to the early operations of the plant (marked by the increased fibre content in the river muds).

At the time of the follow-up studies, improved processing techniques had greatly reduced the loss of mercury from the plant and, therefore, downstream mercury levels could be expected to decrease with time, as the temporary storage in the system was depleted.

The levels of mercury contamination in these river systems, caused by the chlor-alkali plant, were significant (Delisle and Demers, 1976), but may not be sufficient to entirely account for the distribution and concentration of mercury observed in the biota. This was likely influenced by additional factors (possible of non-point source origin).

VII.1.4   Lake St. Clair; changes of contaminant levels with time

The occurrence of high levels of mercury in fish from Lake St. Clair was first noted in 1969 (Fimreite et al., 1971). In 1970, a survey was undertaken to describe the distributon and occurrence of sediment-bound mercury (Thomas, 1971) and other contaminants; the results of this survey predicted a significant sediment turnover in the lake and an onward transport of mercury into Lake Erie. A further survey was undertaken in 1974 (Thomas et al., 1975b) to test this hypothesis.

Lake St. Clair is a small body of water between Lake Huron and Lake Erie and having an area of about 1200 km^2, a maximum depth of 6.7 m, and a mean depth of 3.6 m. The most important supply of sediment is derived from Lake Huron and much of the coarser fraction of sand and sandy silt is retained in the delta where the St. Clair river enters from Lake Huron. The remaining finer particulates are carried further out into Lake St. Clair and some portion is taken completely through the lake, and into its outlet to Lake Erie (Figure VII.14).

At the time of the initial studies it was known that mercury was being derived from industrial sources between Lake Huron and Lake St. Clair, and that elevated levels of DDE, TDE, and DDT were entering the system from the Lake Huron area. PCB's from industrial and urban sources were also adding to the contaminant burden from Lake Huron. Also about this time, many of the major sources of contaminant came under regulation and it was therefore anticipated that contaminant concentrations in Lake St. Clair sediments would show a noticeable decline with time.

As a first step, it was essential to demonstrate that the general textural characteristics of Lake St. Clair sediments showed no significant difference between 1970 and 1974.

Surface grab samples were taken by a Shipek grab (IV.1.3), on a 4 km square grid at 55 sample locations. Each sample was then sub-sampled to provide material representative of the top 2 cm of lake bed sediment. Short cores were also taken to establish the thickness of recent sediments (over bedrock and glacial material). Table VII.1 summarizes the textural data and illustrates the lack of significant difference between the sediment types sampled in 1970 and those in 1974.

In Table VII.2, 1970 and 1974 trace metal (excluding mercury) and chloride data are summarized in similar form. The only significant change in this set of data appeared to be cadmium (which is often found together with mercury, as a contaminant), which showed a slight decline. The concentrations of these trace metals appear to be close to the background levels in this area (Thomas et al., 1975b), and show little evidence of contamination.

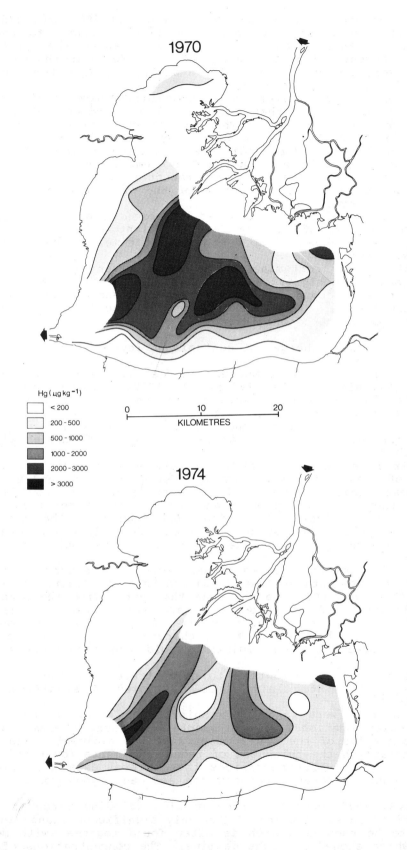

FIGURE VII.14   Distribution of total Hg in the surface sediments of
               Lake St. Clair (modified after Thomas et al., 1975)

TABLE VII.1   Comparative mean values, 1970 and 1974, for sediment texture. After Thomas et al. (1975b)

Year		Sand and Gravel Size Fraction %	Silt Size Fraction %	Clay Size Fraction %	Number of Samples
1970	Mean	53.7	33.0	14.1	50
	Standard Deviation	32.9	24.1	13.0	50
1974	Mean	50.6	35.8	13.6	53
	Standard Deviation	33.1	25.0	10.0	53

On the basis of the textural data, the (conservative) chloride data, and the trace metal data (exclusive of mercury), it was established that the natural sedimentological and geochemical regime in the lake showed no significant change between 1970 and 1974.   The use of a normalizing function was not therefore required.

Mean values for mercury showed a decline between 1974 and 1975.   This trend was confirmed by analyses of the organo-chlorine compounds TDE, DDT, DDE, and PCB, as shown in Table VII.3.   Using the student's t test (0.01 level), changes in the concentrations of mercury and DDT were defined as significant and changes in DDE, TDE, and PCB's were defined as highly significant.   In all cases, the changes resulted in a decrease between 1970 and 1974.

To illustrate the distribution changes, between 1970 and 1974, Figures VII.14, VII.15, and VII.16 map the changing concentrations in the top 2 cm of lake bed sediments.   Despite variations in the geochemical relationships between each of these contaminants and the sediments (ΣDDT is most pronounced), the following differences between 1970 and 1974 distributions can be observed:

  i)   Concentrations in the main sediment plumes, near the source of input (St. Clair delta), have reduced.
  ii)   The size of the areas of most highly contaminated sediments (Hg, <1000 μg kg^{-1}; PCB's, < 20 μg kg^{-1}; Σ DDT, < 8 μg kg^{-1}) have decreased.
  iii)   The areas of low concentration (particularly along the south and east shores of the lake), have increased in size.

These changes are interpreted to mean that (a), contributions from contaminant sources, upstream of Lake St. Clair, have substantially declined (resulting in recent dilution of earlier contaminated sediments) and (b), a combination of resuspension (due to wind/wave action) and flow-through have resulted in removal of some of the previously contaminated lake bed sediment.

Although the changes show an important decrease in contaminant levels, the data, so far presented, give no indication of the quantities of contaminant present nor the magnitude of their decrease.   However, using core data to estimate the thickness of recent sediment, some approximation of the quantities of contaminant can be made.   As an example, Table VII.4 summarizes the calculations used to estimate quantities of mercury.

Based on the concentrations of mercury it is estimated that, in the top 2 cm of Lake St. Clair sediment, there were 6.8 metric tons of mercury present in 1970 and 2.5 metric tons in 1974; a difference of about 4.3 metric tons.

Because Lake St. Clair is extremely shallow, and the average thickness of recent sediment is only about 7 cm, it may be assumed that complete mixing and physical resuspension (by bioturbation, wind/wave action, and ship propulsion in the deeper channels) may affect the entire thickness of recent sediment.   Based on these extrapolations, about 13 metric tons of mercury could have been removed from the lake bed over the four year period; probably, the actual amount lies somewhere between the 4 and 13 metric ton estimates.

Because these calculations refer only to the estimated quantities of mercury present in Lake St. Clair sediments in 1970 and 1974 and include neither estimates of continued (but declining) input, nor a measurement of discharge, they represent only a very crude approximation of a mass balance.

TABLE VII.2 Comparative mean values, 1970 and 1974, for trace metals and chloride (excluding Hg). After Thomas et al. (1975b)

Year	Pb	Cu	Zn	Ni	Co	Cr	Cd	V	Ag	Mo	As	Cl
							in mg kg^{-1}					
1970												
Mean	26.0	16.3	45.2	21.3	10.1	42.1	1.7	49.4	0.7	2.7	2.5	44.6
Standard Deviation	13.8	11.7	25.4	10.4	3.5	45.1	0.5	69.2	0.3	1.2	1.8	9.0
Number of Samples	50	50	50	50	50	50	50	50	49	41	49	49
1974												
Mean	26.7	14.6	46.2	20.8	9.2	58.3	1.4	57.2	0.7	1.8	3.4	45.9
Standard Deviation	13.2	9.7	20.2	9.6	3.3	57.1	0.5	47.1	0.3	0.6	4.5	24.8
Number of Samples	54	54	54	54	54	54	52	54	54	49	54	54
t-value	0.25	0.80	0.22	0.27	1.37	1.61	2.9*	0.66	0.0	-	1.28	-

* Significant at 0.01 level.

TABLE VII.3 Comparative mean values, 1970 and 1974, for Hg, DDE, TDE, DDT, and PCB's. After Thomas et al. (1975b)

Year		Hg	DDE	TDE	DDT	PCB's
				in μg kg^{-1}		
1970	Mean	1549	2.1	3.6	2.0	19.1
	Standard Deviation	2340	1.5	2.2	1.9	8.9
	Number of Samples	50	49	49	23	49
1974	Mean	568	0.7	1.5	0.5	10.0
	Standard Deviation	777	0.6	1.6	0.4	6.3
	Number of Samples	54	53	54	19	54
t-value		2.8*	6.1*	5.5*	3.7*	6.0*

* Significant at 0.01 level.

TABLE VII.4 Data used in computation of mercury tonnages in Lake St. Clair sediments for 1970 and 1974. After Thomas et al. (1975b)

	1970	1974
Lake area, (km^2)	1,190	
Sediment volume (top 2 cm), (cm^3)	2.4 $\times$ 10^{13}	
Water content* (top 2 cm), (% weight)	85	
Dry sediment content, (% weight)	15	
Dry sediment content, (% volume)	7	
Dry sediment density, (g cm^{-3})	2.6	
Hg content dry sediment, (μg g^{-1})	1.549	0.568
Hg content wet sediment, (μg g^{-1})	0.282	0.103
Tonnage (top 2 cm), (metric tons)	6.8	2.5
Difference 1970-1974, (metric tons)	4.3	
Tonnage 7 cm, extrapolated, (metric tons)	22	9
Difference 1970-1974, (metric tons)	13	

* Inferred from Lake Erie data.

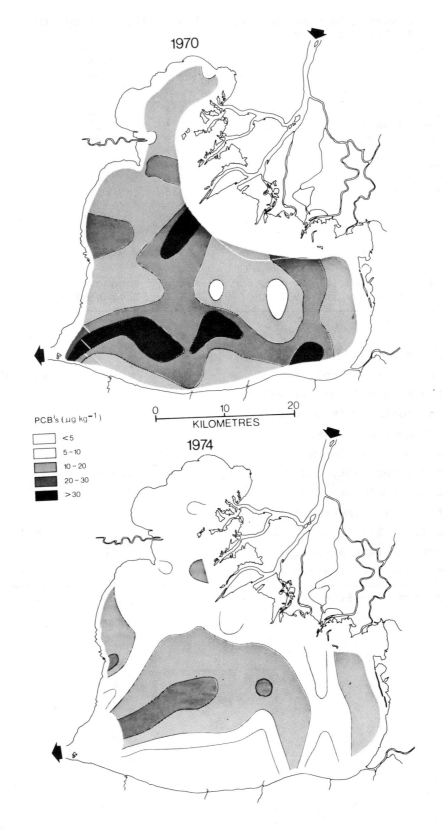

FIGURE VII.15   Distribution of PCB's in freeze-dried sediments from
Lake St. Clair (0 to 2 cm).   (Modified after Frank et al.,
1977.)

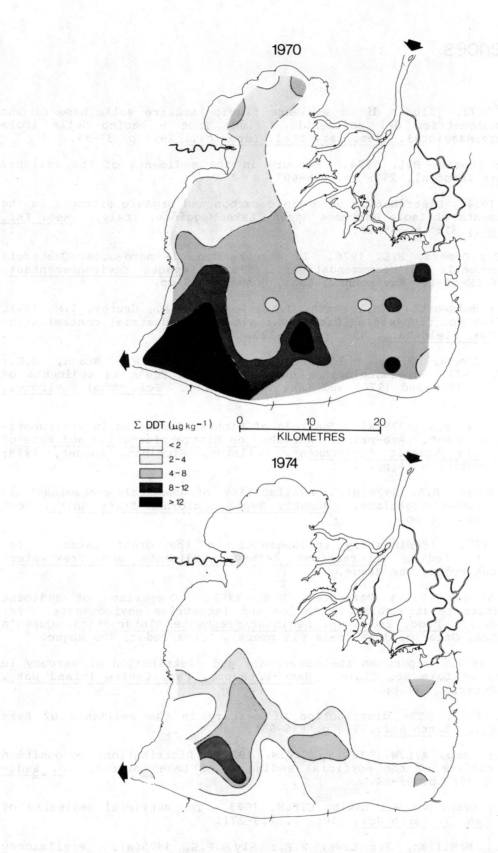

1970

Σ DDT (μg kg⁻¹)

☐	< 2
☐	2 – 4
▨	4 – 8
▦	8 – 12
■	> 12

0   10   20
KILOMETRES

1974

FIGURE VII.16   Distribution of ΣDDT in freeze-dried sediments from
Lake St. Clair (0 to 2 cm). (Modified after Frank
_et al._, 1977)

References

Damiani, V. 1972. Studio di un ambiente fluvio-lacustre sulla base di una analisi granulometrica dei sedimenti: fiume Toce e bacino delle isole Borromee (Lago Maggiore). Mem. Ist. Ital. Idrobiol., 29: p. 37-95.

Damiani, V.; Thomas, R.L. 1974. Mercury in the sediments of the Pallanza basin. Nature (London), 251: p. 696-697.

Damiani, V. 1974. Distribution of organic carbon and organic nitrogen in the surface sediments of Isole Borromee Basin (Lake Maggiore, Italy). Mem. Ist. Ital. Idrobiol., 31: p. 45-60.

Delisle, C.E.; Demers, R.L. 1976. Le mercure dans le nord-ouest Québecois (situation actuelle et recommendations) 1976. Impacts Environnementaux, Rapp. 8-RQ-76-CE-5R-1. Environnem. Can., Québec. 55 pp.

Fimreite, N.; Holsworth, W.N.; Keith, J.A.; Pearce, P.A.; Gruchy, I.M. 1971. Mercury in fish and fish-eating birds near sites of industrial contamination in Canada. Can. Field-Nat., 85: p. 211-220.

Frank, R.; Thomas, R.L.; Holdrinet, J.; Kemp, A.L.W.; Braun, H.E.; Jaquet, J.-M. 1977. Organochlorine insecticides and PCB's in sediments of Lake St. Clair (1970 and 1974) and Lake Erie (1971). Sci. Total Environm., 8: p. 205-227.

Lee, G.F.; Jones, R.A. 1979(a). The role of biotransformation in environmental hazard assessment. Pre-print. Workshop on Biotransformation and Fate of Chemicals in the Aquatic Environment, Pellston, Michigan, August, 1979; Amer. Soc. Microbiol. 24 pp.

Lee, G.F.; Jones, R.A. 1979(b). Availability of chemical contaminant in sediments to higher organisms. Unpubl. Rept., Colorado State Univ., Fort Collins, Colorado. 6 pp.

Sly, P.G. 1977. Sedimentary environments in the Great Lakes. In: Golterman, H.L. (ed.), Interactions between sediments and freshwater: p. 76-82. Junk/Pudoc, The Hague.

Sly, P.G.; Thomas, R.L.; Pelletier, B.R. 1982. Comparison of sediment energy - texture relationships in marine and lacustrine environments. In: Sly, P.G. (ed.). Proc. 2nd Symp. Sediment/Freshwater Interaction, Queen's Univ., Kingston, Ontario, June 15-18 (in press). Junk/Pudoc, The Hague.

Thomas, R.L. 1971. Report on the occurrence and distribution of mercury in the sediments of Lake St. Clair. Unpubl. Rept., Can. Centre Inland Wat., Burlington, Ontario. 11 pp.

Thomas, R.L. 1972. The distribution of mercury in the sediments of Lake Ontario. Can. J. Earth Sci., 9: p. 636-651.

Thomas, R.L.; Kemp, A.L.W.; Lewis, C.F.M. 1972. Distribution, composition and characteristics of the surficial sediments of Lake Ontario. J. Sediment. Petrol., 42: p. 66-84.

Thomas, R.L.; Kemp, A.L.W.; Lewis, C.F.M. 1973. The surficial sediments of Lake Huron. Can. J. Earth Sci., 10: p. 226-271.

Thomas, R.L.; McMillan, J.; Lowe, W.E.; Sly, P.G. 1975(a). Preliminary report on a 1975 survey on the distribution of mercury in the sediments of the Bell-Nottaway River system, N.W. Quebec; between Lake Quevillon and Lake Matagami. Unpubl. Rept., Can. Centre Inland Wat., Burlington, Ontario. 69 pp.

Thomas, R.L.; Jaquet, J.-M; Mudroch, A. 1975(b). Sedimentation processes and associated changes in surface sediment trace metal concentrations in Lake St. Clair, 1970-1974. Proc. Internat. Conf. Heavy Metals in the Environm., Toronto, Ont., October, 1975: p. 691-708.

Vernet, J.P.; Thomas, R.L.; Jaquet, J.-M.; Friedli, R. 1972. Texture of the sediments of the Petit Lac (western Lake Geneva). Eclogae Geol. Helv., 65: p. 591-610.

Vernet, J.P.; Thomas, R.L.; Jaquet, J.-M.; Friedli, R. 1972. Texture of the sediments of the Petit Lac (western Lake Geneva). Eclogae Geol. Helv., 65: p. 591-610.

Vollenweider, R.A. 1956. L'influenza della torbidita provocata dalle acque di piena nel bacino di Pallanze (Lago Maggiore). Mem. Ist. Ital. Idrobiol., 9: p. 85-111.

Winmill, A.E. (ed.). 1972. An investigation into the source and distribution of mercury in the environment in northwestern Quebec. Cooperative investigation by the Government of Canada and the Government of the Province of Quebec. Unpubl. Rept. 42 pp.

VIII Case histories (2) Major and trace elements, and anthropogenic organic compounds

VIII.1 Major Elements

It is generally accepted that increasing concentrations of conservative elements in surface waters result from aging during the hydrological cycle. Major changes can be caused by groundwater inflow, irrigation and evaporation, runoff, and receiving wastewaters; suspended sediments, however, may also act as another source of dissolved constituents.

Few mineral grains, with the possible exception of quartz, are in equilibrium with the surrounding aqueous medium, and the long exposure time (in suspension) and large surface areas of fine silt and clay-size particles (many orders of magnitude greater than their apparent surface based on grain diameter) make the fine particulates most susceptible to dissolution.

In the following quotation, the significance of suspended sediment as a source of major ions, is illustrated by examples based on the Sacramento River and Los Angeles Aqueduct (California) described by Gunnerson and Morris (1963). Although these examples indicate that suspended sediments can be the source of measurable increases in the concentration of dissolved ions, they also show that these changes are not of major concern (as an environmental hazard).

'Streams and Aqueducts

'Studies of the concentrations of various constituents in natural streams often show increases which have not been adequately accounted for. Such increases are usually ascribed to the difficulties of obtaining truly representative samples of the stream and its tributaries. However, sampling or analytical errors should be randomly distributed and, when the data are plotted on a trilinear chart, changes in water character which cannot be accounted for by inflows should also be randomly distributed. A study of the Sacramento River in northern California indicated a persistent trend for such changes (Gunnerson, 1962). Figure VIII.1 shows that the character of Sacramento River water is generally determined by the inflows. However, close examination of the figure shows that throughout most of the river there is an unexplained trend towards increasing proportions of chloride and decreasing sulfate. The significant point here is that evaporation and inflows do not account for the changes.

'Much more data (R.L. Derby, personal communication) are available for the city of Los Angeles' aqueduct which imports water from the Owens Valley in the Sierra Nevada. The aqueduct carries about 13.7 m^3 sec^{-1}. Table VIII.1 lists average annual changes in this water computed from monthly analyses at two points in the system separated by about 290 km (180 miles) and about 7.7 days.

'The absolute increases in concentrations of various ions are small and do not affect the utility of the water supply. However, these increases are, with the single exception of chloride in 1958–1959, typical features. The increases in ionic concentrations cannot be explained by corrosion of the concrete aqueduct. The general reductions in turbidity, however, are consistent with the postulated solution of suspended sediment. Although turbidities are poorly related to sediment concentrations (American Public Health Association, 1960), the data strongly suggest that some of the sediment is going into solution.

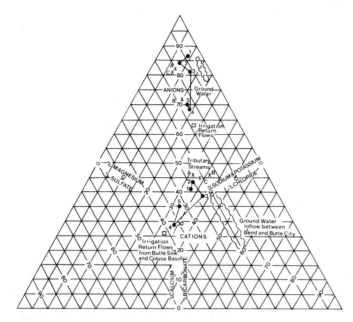

1 – RIVER AT KESWICK, km 485 (mile 300)
2 – RIVER AT BEND, km 412 (mile 256)
3 – RIVER AT BUTTE CITY, km 271 (mile 168)
4 – RIVER AT KNIGHTS LANDING, km 180 (mile 112)
5 – RIVER AT SACRAMENTO, km 102 (mile 63)
A – TRIBUTARIES BETWEEN KESWICK AND BEND
B – TRIBUTARIES BETWEEN BEND AND BUTTE CITY
C – TRIBUTARIES BETWEEN BUTTE CITY AND SACRAMENTO.

FIGURE VIII.1 Changes in character of Sacramento River water, May 1960 (after Gunnerson and Morris (1963))

TABLE VIII.1 Water quality changes in Los Angeles' aqueduct (Haiwee Reservoir to Upper Van Norman Reservoir). After Gunnerson and Morris (1963)

	Average Influent 1958–62 (mg l⁻¹)	Percentage Change During Transit				
		1958–59	1959–60	1960–61	1961–62	Average
Calcium	24.0	+ 4.9	+ 4.5	+ 3.7	+ 1.6	+ 3.9
Magnesium	5.54	+ 6.9	+ 8.7	–	+ 3.8	+ 6.5
Sodium	34.4	+ 5.5	+ 1.4	+ 6.6	+ 1.4	+ 3.7
Potassium	4.22	+ 0.8	+ 1.5	–	+ 2.4	+ 1.6
Total Alkalinity	112.3	+ 2.0	+ 0.5	+ 3.9	+ 1.8	+ 2.0
Sulfate	21.5	+ 18.1	+ 5.5	+ 11.5	+ 2.7	+ 12.6
Chloride	18.0	– 1.7	+ 4.2	+ 3.1	+ 4.0	+ 2.4
Turbidity[1]	4.6	+ 0.3	– 17	– 39	– 16	– 18

[1] Jackson candle turbidity units (American Public Health Assoc., 1960).

'Data for the Delta-Mendota Canal which flows south for 174 km from the Sacramento-San Joaquin Delta in California show more pronounced changes. Water entering the canal during the irrigation season has about 200 mg l⁻¹ dissolved solids and 100 mg l⁻¹ suspended sediment (U.S. Bureau of Reclamation, 1953 et seq., U.S. Geological Survey, 1962). Conductivity data for the period 1953 to 1955, when the most complete records are available, indicate that, during three to five days travel, dissolved solids have increased by some 10 percent. Sediment concentrations at the lower end of the aqueduct have not been adequately measured. Evaporation, dust falls, waste discharges, and corrosion of the concrete lining account for only a portion of the increases. The high concentrations of fine-grained sediment and decreased turbidity, together with the relatively small increases in dissolved solids, again may suggest solution of sediment.'

Similar increases in concentration of dissolved major elements have been described for the River Rhine by Golterman (1982).

VIII.2   Trace Elements in the Aqueous Environment

VIII.2.1 Introduction

Trace elements occur in all lithogenous materials in variable quantities, but generally in amounts measurable in parts per million (μg g^{-1}). Many, like Cu and Zn, are essential micronutrients for living organisms, but which can become toxic, however, when biologically available levels become too high. Wood (1974) provided a classification of elements according to toxicity and availability, and is reproduced in Table VIII.2.

TABLE VIII.2 Classification of elements according to toxicity and availability

Non Critical			Toxic But Very Insoluble or Rare		Very Toxic and Relatively Accessible		
Na	C	F	Ti	Ga	Be	As	Au
K	P	Li	Hf	La	Co	Se	Hg
Mg	Fe	Rb	Zr	Os	Ni	Te	Tl
Ca	S	Sr	W	Rh	Cu	Pd	Pb
H	Cl	Al	Nb	Ir	Zn	Ag	Sb
O	Br	Si	Ta	Ru	Sn	Cd	Bi
N			Re	Ba		Pt	

Environmental concern with trace elements rests, not so much with dietary deficiencies, but rather with an over-supply (caused by human activity), which raises environmental concentrations to levels that produce toxic effects in the aquatic biological system, and ultimately impact on human health. Since trace metals occur naturally, increases in levels due to anthropogenic (man-made) sources should be separately identified.

Sources of man-derived metals are multitudinous and include, for example, atmospheric emissions due to combustion of oil and coal, and direct household disposal of a wide array of metal-containing refuse. However, experience has shown that environmental enrichment of metals occurs, in its most spectacular form, in waters closely associated with major industrial activity. Sources within these industrial areas include direct loss from industrial effluent discharge, overland wash-off during rainstorms, leaching, and inadequate disposal of industrial wastes.

Sediment-bound metals have proved to be a most useful indicator in determining sources and mass balances (see VII.1.3 and VII.1.4), yet the exact role in transfer of metals to the biological component of the aquatic system has not been resolved. Few studies to date have provided clear evidence of the existing relationships between sediment/trace metal concentration and levels in aquatic organisms, or to direct toxicological effects. This statement obviously does not include catastrophic introductions of metals into aquatic systems such as mine waste discharges.

The fact that clear sediment/biota relationships have not been established is of considerable interest and indeed has resulted in a complete failure, to date, in producing sediment bio-assay tests of sufficient simplicity and reliability to be used in routine assessment of sediment metal concentrations for legislative purposes. As an example, the United States Environmental Protection Agency provides a listing of total metal concentrations as a guideline for the aquatic disposal of dredged sediment (cited in Thomas and Mudroch, 1979). These do not take into consideration the forms of the metal or the physical and chemical conditions of the receiving waters, and they tend to be overly conservative. However, they are the only guidelines available to indicate sediment quality standards presently available. This situation may be partly ameliorated by the use of the elutriate test, which has been discussed in Chapter IV.

VIII.2.2 Forms of trace metals, with reference to the Rivers Rhine and Ems

Many detailed studies have been conducted on the sediments of the River Rhine to evaluate the significance of metals in a variable and heavily industrialized river system. The metal load carried by the river is large and was estimated, in 1970, for the following metals, in metric tons y^{-1}: Hg, 100; Cu, 3000; As, 1000; Co, 200; Pb, 1500, and Zn, 9000. Using a simple approach, de Groot et al. (1971) measured the concentrations of several metals in Rhine River sediment which were compared to similar studies in the River Ems. This latter river was considered to be unpolluted and observed metal levels were used as a baseline for comparison with the Rhine. The results are summarized in Table VIII.3.

TABLE VIII.3 Heavy metal content in Rhine and Ems sediments as mg kg^{-1} of the < 16 μm fraction (after de Groot et al., 1971)

	Rhine	Ems		Rhine	Ems
Fe	54000	112	As	310	60
Mn	2600	3300	La	80	80
Zn	3900	700	Co	43	40
Cr	760	180	Hg	18	3
Pb	850	100	Sc	12	12
Cu	470	150	Sm	7	9

From an evaluation of the data cited (Table VIII.3), de Groot et al. (1971) concluded that the higher values for Zn, Cr, Pb, Cu, As, and Hg in the Rhine River sediment should be regarded as indicating pollution and further demonstrated clearly that analysis of filtered water samples by government agencies was producing misleading results. In this study by de Groot et al. (1971) the use of the River Ems sediment in setting baseline levels is interesting and has some validity in highlighting the extent of contamination of Rhine River sediment. However, inspection of the data quoted for the River Ems, particularly for Pb, Cu, As, and Hg, would suggest that this river is far from being non-polluted. Background or natural levels for these elements would be in the order of 30, 40, 3 and 0.1 mg kg^{-1}, respectively (Thomas and Mudroch, 1979). Background levels, however, have to be treated with caution since they are only valid when determined in the same region and from the same sediment type under investigation.

The mineral associations of metals in Rhine River sediments have been examined by Förstner (1977a) and Förstner and Patchineelam (1980), and the results of Förstner (1977a) are summarized in Figure VIII.2. Förstner distinguished two main metal groups: one in which high percentages of Fe, Ni, Co, Cr, and Cu were found in the detrital fraction and the other for Pb, Zn, and Cd, in which bonding occurs predominantly in forms other than in the detrital fraction. This latter grouping includes those metals most related to human or cultural activities. The same pattern was observed by Förstner (1977b) in analyses of deep sediment cores taken from the Rhine, in the Cologne area, in which he compared ancient Rhine sediment to recent deposits. He found, for example, that 98 percent of the Cd in the Lower Rhine particulates could be ascribed to cultural activities.

Further refinements have been made to studies on metal partitioning in sediments from the River Rhine and Lake Constance (Förstner and Patchineelam, 1980). In this latter study, both size and chemical fractionation were used to achieve a greater degree of understanding of metal/sediment bonding. Some of the results of this work are summarized in Figure VIII.3 which shows the concentrations of total zinc and phosphorus, three sedimentary phases, and grain size surface area as a function of particle size, in two samples from the Rhine and Lake Constance. The surface area shows similarity between both samples and increases with decreasing particle size. Both total P and Zn increase with decreasing particle size in like fashion to the Fe, acid reducible fraction. Humic substances increase in the finer sizes but also show increased concentrations in the coarse clay size. Förstner and Patchineelam (1980) did not explain this in terms of physical-chemical processes, but ascribed the relationship to

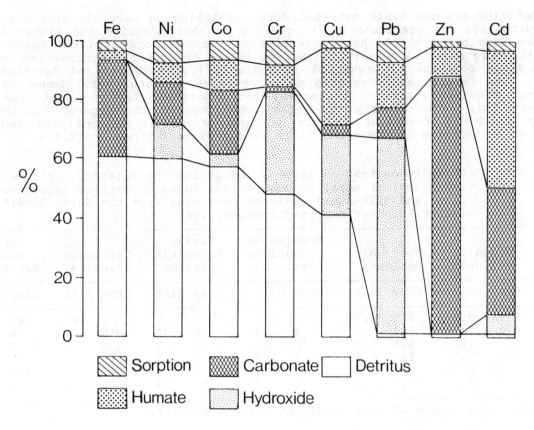

FIGURE VIII.2   Forms of metal bonding in Rhine sediments
(after Förstner, 1977a)

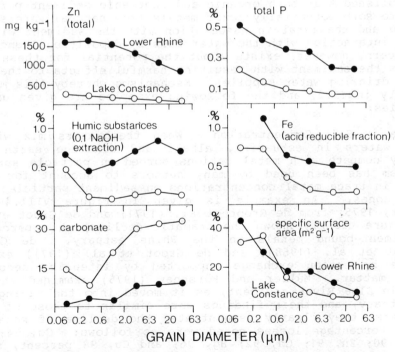

FIGURE VIII.3   Percentages and concentrations of zinc, various sedimentary
phases, and specific surface area in different grain size
intervals of sediments from the Rhine River and Lake Constance
(after Förstner and Patchineelam, 1980)

loss of fine-grained humic material during settling in particle size recovery. The carbonates are particularly interesting in that, despite the higher levels in Lake Constance, the higher concentrations tend to occur in the coarse clay and silt fractions. A summary of the results of the metal fractionation for the Rhine River sediment is presented in Table VIII.4 (Förstner and Patchineelam, 1980). The results are presented as percentages of total metal bound in each chemical fraction (carrier substances) for separated clay and silt-size particles. This table clearly shows the importance of the organic (humic) and easily reducible fractions in the bonding of metals in polluted sediment samples. Phosphorus in the Rhine River is discussed further in IX.1.3.

TABLE VIII.4 Phase concentration factors indicating the relative enrichment (or reduction) of metal concentrations in major carrier substances of clay- and silt-sized sediment particles from the Rhine River* (after Förstner and Patchineelam, 1980)

	Organic Residues		Inorganic Residues		Moderately Reducible Fraction		Easily Reducible Fraction		Carbonate Fraction		Humic Acid Fraction	
	Clay	Silt	Clay	Silt	Clay	Silt	Clay	Silt	Clay	Silt	Clay	Silt
Fe	<0.01	0.01	0.5	0.7	–	–	–	–	2	<1	40	30
Mn	0.2	0.2	0.4	0.5	2	2	30	30	10	4	6	4
Cr	3	1	0.5	0.7	16	22	5	7	0	0	3	3
Cu	0.5	0.3	0.1	0.1	8	10	6	4	15	5	50	35
Pb	0.03	0.05	0.2	0.2	8	15	3	5	<1	<1	100	100
Zn	0.1	0.2	<0.1	<0.1	4	7	55	55	25	8	8	17

* Percent metal phase of total sediment/percent carrier.

VIII.2.3 Examples of mobilization of trace metals from sediments

It is well established that both organic and inorganic sediment particles have a great capacity to sorb potentially toxic metals from natural waters. Binding is generally strong and the metal in association with the sediment will ultimately be removed from interaction with the water mass by depositional and accumulation processes. Concern, however, exists about the potential for these metals to be remobilized from the sediment with resulting harmful effects to the aquatic eco-system and even drinking water supplies. Mechanisms whereby this may occur were discussed briefly in II.2, and the following examples are given using the same process categories:

a) Increase in Salt Concentration – When freshwaters mix with receiving marine waters in estuaries, alkali and alkaline earth cations can actively compete with metal cations sorbed on particle surfaces. This mechanism has been used by many authors to account for the dramatic decline in trace metal concentrations on sediment particles in estuarine mixing zones. An example is given in Figure VIII.4 (Müller and Förstner, 1975) from de Groot et al. (1971) and de Groot et al. (1973). This figure clearly shows the dramatic decline, on a percentage basis, of sediment-bound metals in the Rhine estuary. de Groot (1966), de Groot et al. (1968), and de Groot et al. (1971) explained this decrease by cation exchange supported by intensive decomposition of organic matter. Müller and Förstner (1975) examined the decline of metals in Elbe River sediment, as it moved into the mixing zone of the Elbe estuary, and their findings were similar to those of de Groot and co-workers; they clearly demonstrated the decline of metal concentrations. Percentage losses noted were as follows: Co, 34; Ni, 64; Pb, 76; Cr, 90; Zn, 91; Cd, 92; Hg, 96; and Cu, 98 percent, respectively. However, the interpretation of the available data by Müller and Förstner (1975) strongly suggested that the observed decreases were not due to remobilization of metals from particle surface; rather, they were rela-ted to estuarine mixing of the Elbe sediment with North Sea sediment which contained low metal concentrations. This mechanism is now more generally accepted to account for observed declines of metal concentrations as freshwater sediments enter estuarine environments. It does not discount cation exchange which presumably does occur, but it certainly provides a most satisfactory explanation for the large declines that have been observed in the Rhine, and elsewhere.

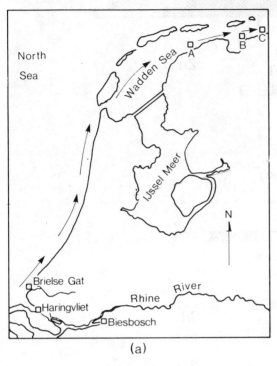
(a)

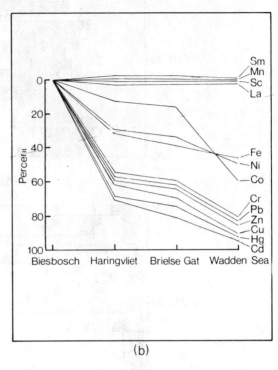
(b)

FIGURE VIII.4   (a)   Direction of movement of sediments in the Rhine estuary, North Sea, and Wadden sea.
              (b)   Mobilization of metals in the Rhine estuary, North Sea, and Wadden Sea, expressed as a percentage of the original contents. (Both parts after Groot et al., 1971, 1973, as used by Müller and Förstner, 1975)

b)   Changes in Redox Conditions - Decreases in redox potential occur due to depletion of oxygen under eutrophic conditions. Under these conditions the hydrated oxides of Fe and Mn are reduced and dissolved, allowing all or some of the sorbed or incorporated metals to be released. This type of re-mobilization has been observed in Lake Erie under anoxic conditions where dramatic increases of iron, manganese, and phosphorus occur in the hypolimnion waters (Burns and Ross, 1972). Further, Chau et al. (1970) described increases in the concentrations of Fe, Mn, and Zn in the bottom waters of Lake Ontario. This finding, together with observed sediment redox potentials in the sediments, was used by Cronan and Thomas (1972) to account for the source of Fe, Mn, and trace metals occurring in ferro-manganese concretions along the north shore of the lake. It would appear that this release mechanism is particularly significant in lakes and is related in large measure to primary production.

c)   Lowering of pH - This results in the dissolution of carbonates and hydroxides as well as increased desorption of metal cations by competition with H^+ ions. This process is currently under intensive investigation in lakes, particularly in Scandinavian and northeastern North America due to the major concern with the acidification of soft-water lakes resulting from acidic precipitation.

Short, dated, sediment cores can be used to provide information on the specific chemical associations of heavy metals, as a means of

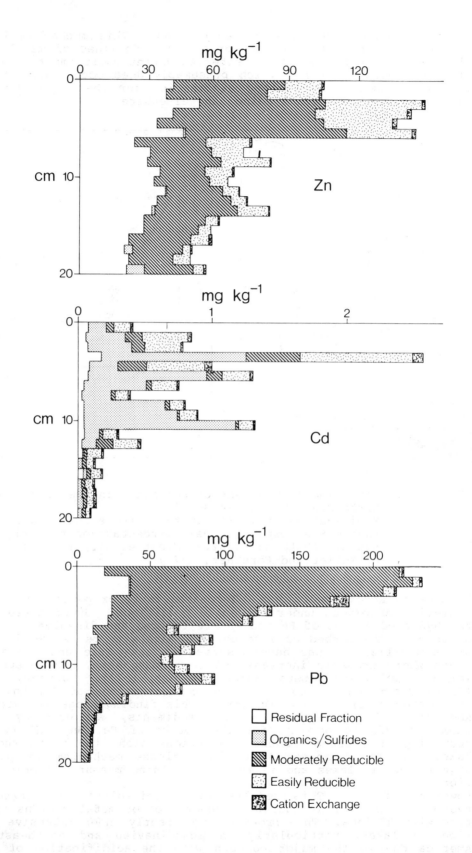

FIGURE VIII.5   Depth profiles of Zn, Cd, and Pb, as well as their chemical forms, in a sediment core from Lake Hovvatn, Norway. (From Reuther et al. (1981) and cited in Förstner (1982).)

deciphering the individual processes. In Figure VIII.5 (adapted from Reuther et al., 1981, quoted in Förstner, 1982) data is presented from Lake Hovvatn in southern Norway, which has been subjected to lime treatment. Before treatment in 1980/81, this lake had a pH of 4.4 and had been barren of fish since the 1940's. The total concentrations of zinc and cadmium increase significantly in the lower part of the sediment record (reflecting approximately 100 years in that lake), but fall drastically in the uppermost layers; whereas lead concentrations increase continuously from the bottom to top of the sediment core profile. In this case, leaching of metals by the acid lake water is apparent only for zinc and cadmium. A comparison of the associations for these and other metals reveals that the decrease of zinc occurs in the easily reducible fraction, whereas the remobilization of cadmium occurs chiefly in the organic fraction. A significant decrease of the reducible fractions is also observed for cobalt and nickel. Lead and copper are affected by these changes only to a small and insignificant degree. The fact that these effects were not discerned in another lake of the same area, which exhibits a water pH of 4.9, indicates that an increase in pH of half a point (0.5) may be enough to limit the mobility of these elements (Reuther et al., 1981).

d) Natural and Synthetic Complexing Agents - Increased use of these agents may result in the formation of stable, soluble metal complexes with metals which might otherwise be adsorbed to sediment particles.

e) Biological Transformations - This process has been well described for mercury, both in the laboratory and in the environment. Similar transformations have also been recognized for Cd, Sn, As, Se, and Pb in laboratory studies but have not been well documented in the environment. This is the subject of much current research.

A recent example of the process of mercury transformation, and the effects upon the aquatic food chain, has been presented by Jackson (1980) from the English-Wabigoon river/lake system in northwestern Ontario, Canada. The river/lake system, from Wabigoon Lake to Ball Lake, is shown diagramatically in Figure VIII.6. A chlor-alkali plant situated on the Wabigoon River at Dryden

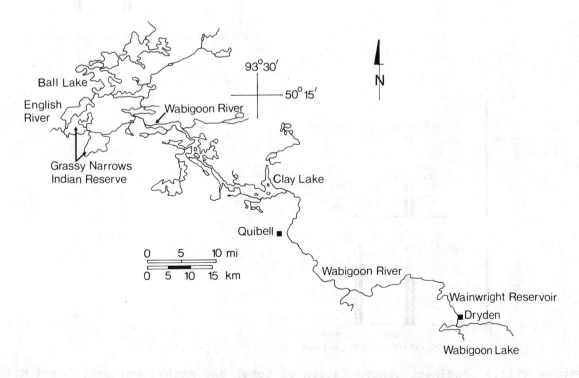

FIGURE VIII.6 The river-lake system, Wabigoon Lake to Ball Lake
(after Jackson, 1980)

has released massive amounts of mercury, most of which has been incorporated into the sediments. Jackson (1980) notes that anomalously high levels of mercury have been found in sediment as far as 240 km downstream of Dryden, and in fish at least 270 km downstream. Total Hg concentrations in the sediment decrease exponentially with distance downstream, and are paralleled by a decline in org C and N, increasing N/org C ratio, and an increase in pH (Figure VIII.7). In contrast, sediment methyl mercury (CH_3Hg^+) showed no significant variation with distance from the mercury source at Dryden. This data is explained by Jackson (1980) as follows: (i) the decline of total mercury reflects a downstream change in sediment type from deposits of decomposing wood fragments near Dryden to clay-silt mud associated with humic matter and Fe–Mn oxides further down the system; i.e., decreasing org C and N and increasing N/org C ratio. Dispersion also results in a decreased concentration downstream;

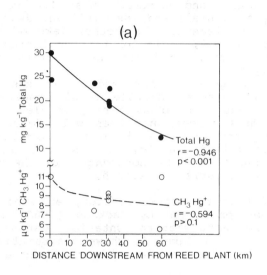

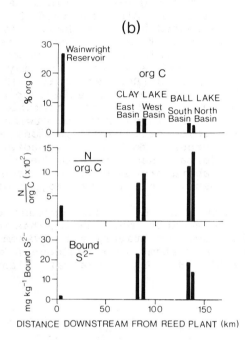

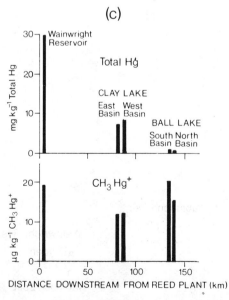

FIGURE VIII.7   Sediment concentration of total and methyl mercury, C and N in the English-Wabigoon River downstream of the Reed chlor-alkali plant at Dryden (after Jackson, 1980)

(ii) increasing pH (range 4.4 to 7.3) reflects a decline in the quantity of wood fragments downstream; (iii) a relatively constant sediment CH_3Hg^+ is due to the combination of high microbial activity and low pH in the upstream sector, and the availability of adsorbed, easily-exchangeable Hg on Fe-Mn oxide surfaces downstream. This was verified by chemical fractionation techniques.

To demonstrate the effects of contamination and uptake by benthic organisms and fish, Jackson (1980) assembled data on pelagic fish (walleye, pike, cisco, whitefish, and sauger) and crayfish. This data, together with water data, is summarized in Figures VIII.8a and VIII.8b. The data was evaluated in terms of "allochthonous" riverborne CH_3Hg^+ and "autochthonous" CH_3Hg^+ generated locally within the lakes, as measured during the study. The mean Hg concentrations in pelagic fish decrease from Clay Lake to Ball Lake, and with a continuing decline as far as Tetu Lake near the Manitoba border; these parallel the trend of "allochthonous" CH_3Hg^+. In contrast, the mean Hg concentrations of bottom-feeding fish (suckers) increase and follow the trends shown by sedimentary CH_3Hg^+ content; however, no significant change was noted in crayfish. The results suggest that Hg contamination of pelagic fish is due primarily to CH_3Hg^+ loadings in the river, while benthic feeding organisms are contaminated to an equal or greater extent by CH_3Hg^+ generated in local bottom sediments.

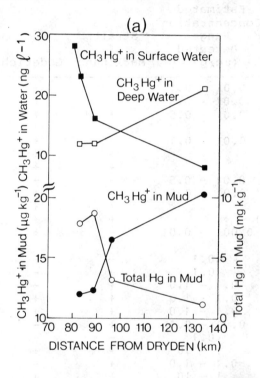 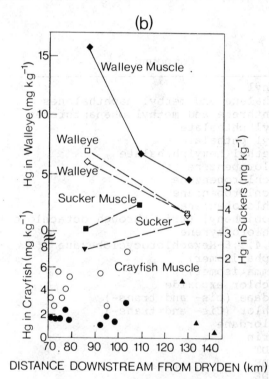

FIGURE VIII.8 Total mercury in mud and fish and crayfish and methyl-mercury concentrations in water and muds downstream from Dryden (after Jackson, 1980)

VIII.3   Organic Contaminants

VIII.3.1   Introduction

In recent years, organic contaminants have become a major concern in aquatic systems in many parts of the world.

The development and use of DDT, and its effectiveness as a means of controlling disease-carrying insects during the Second World War, led to its rapid and widespread use for the control of insects deleterious to agricultural production. Major usage in agriculture started in the early 1950's. During the early 1960's the ecological and direct toxic effects on terrestrial ecosystems were publicized in the book 'Silent Spring' by Rachel Carson (1962). This resulted in an increase of research into the impacts of DDT which led to a ban on its usage in North America in 1970. With the loss of dependence on DDT, and recognizing the ease and efficiency of chemical controls, the chemical industry developed a host of other synthetic organic compounds for the control of insects (insecticides), weeds (herbicides), and fungi (fungicides). Additionally, the post-war evolution in the petro-chemical and chemical industries has produced a burgeoning number of synthetic industrial organic compounds (e.g., plastics, etc.), which continue to substitute for and replace the natural products of an earlier technology.

The increasing agricultural and industrial use of synthetic compounds has resulted in their migration to, and incorporation in, the aquatic ecosystem. As an example, Table VIII.5 provides a summarized list of compounds identified in fish from Lake Huron and reported by the International Joint Commission (1977).

TABLE VIII.5 Organic compounds detected (+) and not detected (-) by combined gas chromatography/mass spectrometry in whole fish samples of burbot from the open waters of Lake Huron (International Joint Commission, 1977)

Compound	Estimated Concentration Range Detected ($\mu g/g$)	Straits of Mackinanc	Goderich
Biphenyl	0.01 - 0.1	-	+
Naphthalene and methyl naphthalenes	0.01 - 0.5	+	+
Phenanthrene and methyl phenanthrenes	0.01 - 0.5	+	+
Diethyl phthalate		+	+
Dibutyl phthalate	0.01 - 0.1	+	+
Di-2-ethyl hexylphthalate		+	+
Trichlorobenzene		+	+
Tetrachlorobenzene	0.01 - 0.5	-	+
Pentachlorobenzene	0.01 - 0.5	-	+
Hexachlorobenzene		+	+
Chlorobiphenyl (tri- through octachloro PCB's)		+	+
Octachlorostyrene	0.001 - 0.01	-	+
1,2,3,4,5,6-Hexachlorocyclohexane			
(alpha isomer)	<0.1	-	-
(gamma isomer)	<0.1	-	-
Heptachlor expoxide	0.1 - 1.0	+	-
Chlordane (cis- and trans-)	0.1 - 1.0	+	+
Nonachlor (Cis- and trans-)	0.1 - 1.0	+	+
Oxychlordane	0.01 - 0.1	+	-
Dieldrin	<0.1	-	-
pp' DDT	1 - 10	+	+
op' DDE	0.1 - 1.0	+	-
pp' DDE	1 - 10	+	+
pp' DDD	0.1 - 1.0	+	+
pp' DDMu	<0.01	-	-
Toxaphene components ($C_{10}H_8Cl_{7,8}$ trans-)	0.1 - 1.0	+	-
Methylbenzothiophene	0.01 - 0.1	-	+

The scope of the subject of organic contaminants in the environment, together with their levels and effects, is far too large for this Guidebook. We have, therefore, restricted our discussions to a few examples or case histories in which we try to emphasize the role of sediment in the environmental cycling of these materials.

VIII.3.2 The role of sediment in the adsorption/desorption of organic chemicals

A number of studies have been carried out on fluvial systems in the Great Lakes drainage basin, which have shed considerable knowledge about the interactive

194

roles of sediment on the adsorption and desorption of insecticides. In particular, we refer to studies in the Big Creek and Holland Marsh watershed (Miles, 1980). Big Creek has a drainage area of 725 km^2 and drains a mainly sandy soil, in a tobacco and vegetable growing area, and flows directly into Lake Erie. Holland Marsh, with an area of 3035 ha, has an artificially drained organic soil under intensive vegetable production, which drains into the southwestern part of Lake Simcoe, north of Lake Ontario. Both areas are under intensive agriculture and are subject to the heavy use of agricultural insecticides. The soil concentrations of a number of insecticides identified in Holland Marsh soils between 1972 and 1975 (Miles, 1980) are shown as an example in Figure VIII.9. During his study of drainage waters, Miles (1980) analyzed both total water samples and the separated suspended solids as a means of evaluating the partitioning of solid to solute phases of selected insecticides. The results are summarized in Table VIII.6

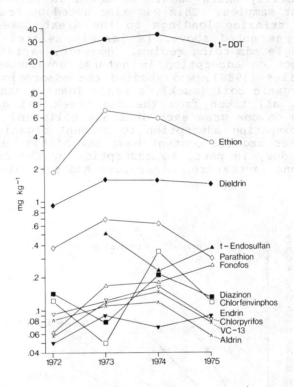

FIGURE VIII.9   Insecticide levels in soils of Holland Marsh
(after Miles, 1980)

TABLE VIII.6   Insecticides on filtered sediment, reported as percent of total water analysis (after Miles, 1980)

		Total DDT	Dieldrin	Diazinon
Holland Marsh	Average	62	12	0
	Range	(31 – 93)	(3 – 42)	
Big Creek	Average	59	18	–
	Range	(30 – 90)	(10 – 29)	
Solubility in water (mg l^{-1})		0.0012	0.186	40

The sediment adsorbed DDT to a greater extent than dieldrin, and no adsorption was detected in the case of the organo-phosphorus compound diazinon. This sequence is inverse to the water solubility of the compounds. This was further examined by Miles (op.cit.) in laboratory adsorption studies, using dieldrin, ethion, lindane, diazinon and carbaryl with sediment from Big Creek as the adsorption medium. Adsorption isotherms developed for these compounds are shown in Figure VIII.10. DDT was also included in the experiment but it is not shown in the graph, since its low solubility resulted in 90 to 100 percent adsorption. From a comparison of the adsorption curves for the insecticides shown in Figure VIII.9, it can be seen that adsorption is inverse to the water solubility of the compounds, as noted in the field data shown in Table VIII.6. Although dieldrin and ethion are represented by the same curve, it should be noted that dieldrin is an organo-chlorine compound whereas ethion is an organo-phosphorus compound. Lindane, the most water-soluble organo-chlorine compound, occurs midway between dieldrin and the insecticides diazinon and carbaryl, which were included to show the much lower adsorption of the more water-soluble organo-phosphorus and carbamate insecticides. Adsorption by sediment is thus clearly a product of water solubility which should be noted in selection of compounds to be analyzed on sediment samples. This was also noted by Frank et al. (1979), in an evaluation of the triazine loadings to the Great Lakes from corn growing regions. Adsorption, as noted above, is largely related to solubility, when assessed against a single adsorbing medium. However, variation in sediment type may also have an effect on adsorption in natural environmental systems. This too was examined by Miles (1980), who studied the adsorption of dieldrin on one gram each of a high organic soil (muck), a sandy loam, a sand (Plainfield sand), and a creek sediment, all taken from the Big Creek and associated watershed. Adsorption of dieldrin on one gram each of these soils and sediment is shown in Figure VIII.11. By comparing adsorption to percent organic matter, it appears that samples with higher organic content have the highest uptake of this insecticide. This may be due, in part, to adsorption by the organic matter but it also reflects variations in texture, mineralogy and particle surface area available for adsorption.

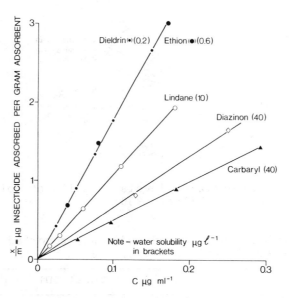

FIGURE VIII.10   Insecticide adsorption isotherms (adsorbent = Big Creek sediment) (after Miles, 1980)

In terms of desorption, Miles (1980) examined six insecticides adsorbed to Big Creek sediment. The Big Creek sediment was treated with 2 mg kg^{-1} of each compound and equilibrated with 200 ml of water. After centrifugation, 190 ml was removed and analyzed. Following this, 190 ml of distilled water was added, allowed to equilibrate, and again analyzed after centrifugation. This procedure was followed twice more, to produce a total of four elutriate tests. Results are shown in Figure VIII.12. Little or no DDT was removed and significant amounts of ethion and dieldrin still remained adsorbed after the fourth elutriation. Only 17 percent of the lindane and less than 10 percent of the more soluble organo-phosphorus and carbamate insecticides (diazinon and carbaryl), remained adsorbed after the first rinse.

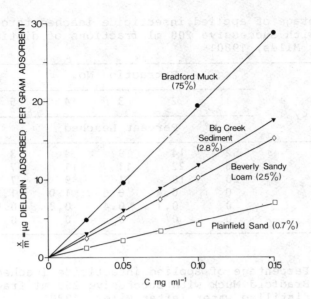

FIGURE VIII.11 Dieldrin adsorption on four adsorbents. Percent organic matter in parenthesis (after Miles, 1980)

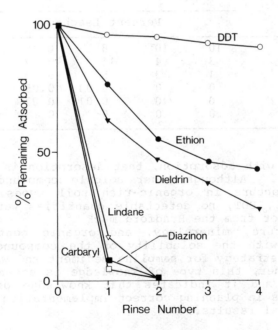

FIGURE VIII.12 Successive desorption of six insecticides from 1 g Big Creek sediment (after Miles, 1980)

Miles (op.cit.) also conducted leaching experiments on two soil types, the Plainfield sand and the Bradford muck. In this experiment, 10 g of each soil were treated separately with 2 and 4 mg kg^{-1} of the insecticides, and placed in a 4.5 cm diameter glass cylinder, inserted 1 cm into 300 g of wet sand in a Buchner funnel. Distilled water was allowed to flow into the cylinder to maintain a 1 cm water depth above the treated soil. Suction was applied to the

197

receiving flask and 200 ml fractions of elutriate were collected in 10 successive extractions and analyzed. The results are summarized in Tables VIII.7 and VIII.8.

TABLE VIII.7 Percentage of applied insecticide leached through Plainfield sand with successive 200 ml fractions of distilled water (after Miles, 1980)

| Insecticide | Solubility mg l^{-1} | Extraction No. | | | | | Total 10 Extractions Percent Leached |
| | | 1 | 2 | 3 | 4 | 5 | |
		Percent Leached					
Carbaryl	40	52	14	9	4	3	86
Diazinon	40	26	22	11	11	7	95
Lindane	10	20	18	11	9	7	93
Ethion	0.6	0	0.4	0.6	1.0	1.5	14
Dieldrin	0.2	0	0.1	0.4	0.8	0.9	10
p,p'-DDT	0.001	0	0	0	0	0	0

TABLE VIII.8 Percentage of applied insecticide leached through Bradford Muck with successive 200 ml fractions of distilled water (after Miles, 1980)

| Insecticide | Solubility mg l^{-1} | Extraction No. | | | | | Total 10 Extractions Percent Leached |
| | | 1 | 2 | 3 | 4 | 5 | |
		Percent Leached					
Carbaryl	40	10	10	8	6	5	53
Diazinon	40	3	4	11	9	7	50
Lindane	10	1	3	5	5	4	34
Ethion	0.6	0	0	0.03	0.09	0.11	1.2
Dieldrin	0.2	0	0	0.01	0.07	0.08	0.8
p,p'-DDT	0.001	0	0	0	0	0	0

These results show, as with adsorption, that desorption is a function of both solubility and substrate. Although other soluble compounds are more easily leached, less leaching occurs in organic-rich soil types. For the highly insoluble compounds, e.g., DDT, no detectable quantities were recovered either from the Plainfield sand or from the Bradford muck.

Clearly, sediment texture, mineralogy, and organic content are extremely important and, together with the solubility of the compounds to be examined, will form the basis of a strategy for sampling sediment and water under environmental conditions. Further, this type of knowledge is essential in the interpretation of field data and it indicates that knowledge of the compound and sediment are prerequisites in planning correct implementation of a field program and interpretation of final results.

VIII.3.3 PCB in Lake Erie sediments

PCB (polychlorinated biphenyl), is an industrial compound whose thermal properties make it an ideal material for high temperature applications; e.g., in transformers, capacitors, and as an additive to hydraulic fluids and high temperature oils. It was first prepared in 1881 and it has been used extensively since 1930, followed by a rapid increase in its use after about 1954. However, since 1971, its use in North America has been severely restricted, mostly to transformers and capacitors, because of the high and widespread levels observed in biological materials and potential hazard to human health. PCB is both persistent and insoluble (0.0095 to 0.062 mg l^{-1}), depending on the isomer (Chiou et al., 1977), and in this respect it is similar to DDT. It is also lipophyllic and subject to bioaccumulation and biomagnification.

Frank et al. (1977) reported levels of PCB in the sediments of Lake Erie from samples collected during 1971.

An analysis of a sediment core, taken from the western basin of Lake Erie (Table VIII.9), showed that the first appearance of PCB occurred at the 10 to 12 cm depth increment, estimated to be equivalent to the time period 1956 to 1958. This is entirely compatible with the known increase in use occurring in 1954. Values increase dramatically at the surface of the core to a level of 340 µg kg^{-1}.

TABLE VIII.9   PCB residues in core U-42, western basin of Lake Erie
(Frank et al., 1977)

Depth cm	Years	PCB Concentration µg kg^{-1}
0 - 2	1969 - 1971	346.0
2 - 4	1966 - 1968	10.0
4 - 6	1963 - 1965	6.0
6 - 8	1961 - 1963	10.0
8 - 10	1958 - 1960	Not Detected
10 - 12	1956 - 1958	1.0
12 - 14	1953 - 1955	Not Detected
14 - 112	1827 - 1952	Not Detected

Frank et al. (1977) also discussed levels of PCB observed in 259 surface sediment samples. These samples covered the entire lake and provide values from an integration of the top 3.0 cm of the sediment column. In order to assess the regional in-lake variations of concentration, the lake had been sub-divided into discrete basins and areas of non-deposition (Figure VIII.13, Thomas et al., 1976), on the basis of known sedimentological properties.

Mean values of PCB, for individual basins and the non-depositional areas, are given in Table VIII.10.

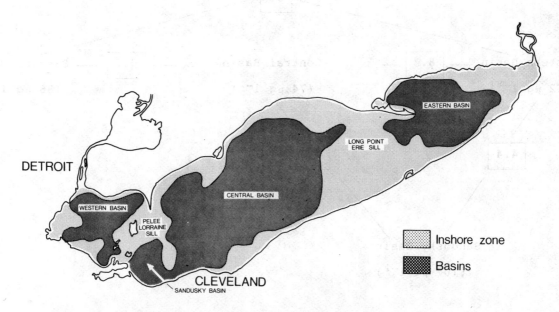

FIGURE VIII.13 Distribution of non-depositional (inshore zone) and depositional basins in Lake Erie (after Thomas et al., 1976)

TABLE VIII.10 PCB residues in Lake Erie sediments, non-depositional and basin non-depositional zones (Frank et al., 1977)

| Zone | Number of Samples | PCB Concentration ($\mu g\ kg^{-1}$) | | | |
		Mean	Standard Deviation	Minimum	Maximum
Total Lake	259	95	114	5	800
Non-Depositional Zone	104	64	105	8	800
Total Basins	153	115	114	4	660
Western Basin	32	252	156	4	660
Central Basin	84	74	56	12	330
Eastern Basin	30	86	85	12	320
Sandusky Basin	7	107	46	50	170

The mean PCB residue for the whole lake was 95 $\mu g\ l^{-1}$ and may be compared to the values of 64 and 115 $\mu g\ l^{-1}$ for the non-depositional zones and basin zones, respectively.

These values indicate, firstly, that concentrations are related to the major textural differences (coarser sediments in the shallower non-depositional zones, in contrast to the finer silty-clays of the depositional basins (Thomas et al., 1976). Secondly, the values in the non-depositional zones indicate the presence of unexpectedly high residues. These may be associated with the movement of fine sediments through such zones, which become incorporated into the existing sedimentary regime of the nearshore, or other areas.

Comparison of the values for individual basins show that there is a considerable variation in mean values, with highest values in the Western and Sandusky Basins. Frank et al. (1977) applied the student's t test, to these means, to test for significant differences btween the mean basin values. The results are summarized in the schematic diagram in Figure VIII.14, in which a mean of 2.6 or greater indicates a significant difference between means at the 0.01 probability level.

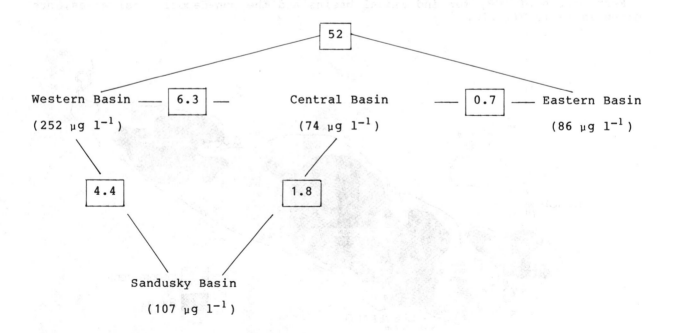

FIGURE VIII.14 Schematic diagram showing Student's t-test values comparing mean values between basins. Mean PCB value in parenthesis (after Frank et al., 1977)

The decrease in total PCB levels, between the Western Basin and all other basins, is statistically significant; whereas no statistically significant difference occurs between the Sandusky, Central and Eastern Basins. This implies that PCB loadings were heaviest to the Western Basin and that, at least until 1971, most of this contaminant had been retained in this basin.

This is confirmed by the distribution of total PCB in the sediments of Lake Erie, shown in Figure VIII.15. Highest values are clearly observed in the Western Basin, where high concentration gradients indicate a major source from the Detroit River. High values on the south shore of the Sandusky and Central Basins are associated with major transportation along the south shore which is supplemented by sources in the Cleveland area.

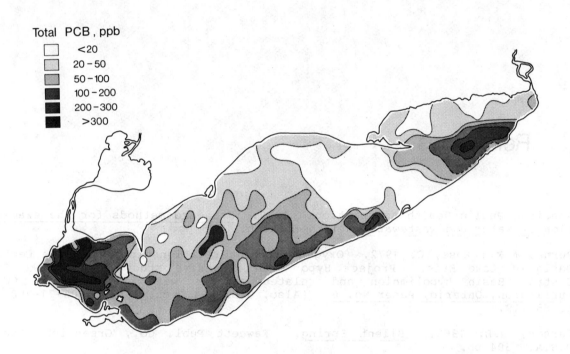

Total PCB, ppb

	<20
	20 - 50
	50 - 100
	100 - 200
	200 - 300
	>300

FIGURE VIII.15 Distribution of PCBs in the surficial 3 cms of sediment in Lake Erie (after Frank et al., 1977)

Frank et al. (1977) tried to determine how the PCB's were incorporated in the sediment, by statistically analyzing the inter-relationships between a number of geochemical variables. Table VIII.12 summarizes these relationships in the form of a correlation matrix.

TABLE VIII.11 Correlation matrix showing degree of linear relationship between selected geochemical variables (Frank et al., 1977)

	Al_2O_3	K_2O	MgO	Org C	Hg	DDE	TDE	PCB
Al_2O_3	1.0							
K_2O	0.837	1.0						
MgO	0.242	0.327	1.0					
Org C	0.571	0.537	0.203	1.0				
Hg	0.365	0.320	0.204	0.547	1.0			
DDE	0.322	0.318	0.225	0.432	0.475	1.0		
TDE	0.316	0.308	0.200	0.459	0.492	0.741	1.0	
PCB	0.227	0.188	0.099	0.394	0.547	0.408	0.445	1.0

On the basis of 259 samples, it was demonstrated that PCB showed the most significant relationship with org C, Hg, DDE, and TDE. This, together with the relationship of org C to Al_2O_3, was interpreted as indicating a primary adsorption of PCB (and indeed the DDT compounds and Hg) to organic matter; this, in turn, is also related to the clay composition and texture of the sediment. Since clear relationships on a lakewide basis would be masked by the influence of point sources, it was felt that a better understanding of the mechanisms of adsorption could be obtained only by separate evaluation of the individual basins.

References

American Public Health Association. 1960. Standard methods for the examination of water and wastewater. 11th Edition. 626 pp.

Burns, N.M.; Ross, C. 1972. Oxygen-nutrient relationship within the Central Basin of Lake Erie. Project Hypo - an intensive study of the Lake Erie Central Basin hypolimnion and related surface water phenomena. CCIW, Burlington, Ontario, Paper No. 6. (Also, U.S. EPA Tech. Rep. TS-05-71-208-24: p. 85-119.)

Carson, R.L. 1962. Silent Spring. Fawcett Publ. Co., Greenwich, Conn., U.S.A. 304 pp.

Chau, Y.K.; Chawla, V.K.; Nicholson, H.F.; Vollenweider, R.A. 1970. Distribution of trace elements and chlorophyll a in Lake Ontario. Proc. 13th Conf. Great Lakes Research. 1970: p. 659-672.

Chiou, C.T.; Freed, V.H.; Schmedeling, D.W; Kohnert, R.L. 1977. Partition coefficient and bioaccumulation of selected organic chemicals. Environm. Sci. Technol., 11: p. 475-478.

Cronan, D.S.; Thomas, R.L. 1972. Geochemistry of ferromanganese concretions and associated deposits in Lake Ontario. Bull. Geol. Soc. Amer., 83: p. 1493-1502.

Förstner, U. 1977a. Metal concentrations in freshwater sediments - natural background and cultural effects. In: Golterman, H.L. (ed.), Interactions between sediments and freshwaters, p. 94-103. Junk/Pudoc, The Hague.

Förstner, U. 1977b. The fluvial transport of sediment-associated nutrients and contaminants. In: Shear, H.; Watson, A.E.D. (eds.), The fluvial transport of sediment-associated nutrients and contaminants, p. 219-233. Internat. Joint Commiss., Great Lakes Regional Off., Windsor, Ontario.

Förstner, U.; Patchineelam, S.R. 1980. Chemical associations of heavy metals in polluted sediments from the lower Rhine River. In: Kavanaugh, M.C.; Leckie, J.O. (eds.), Particulates in water. Amer. Chem. Ser., No. 189, p. 177-193.

Förstner, U. 1982. Accumulative phases of heavy metals in limnic sediments. In: Sly, P.G. (ed.), Proc. 2nd Internat. Symp. Sediment/Freshwater Interaction, Queen's University, Kingston, Ontario. June 15-18, 1982. (In press.) Junk/Pudoc, The Hague.

Frank, R.; Thomas, R.L.; Holdrinet, M.; Kemp, A.L.W.; Braun, H.E. 1977. Organochlorine insecticides and PCB's in sediments of Lake St. Clair (1970 and 1974) and Lake Erie (1971). Sci. Total Environm., 8: p. 205-227.

Frank, R.; Sirons, G.J.; Thomas, R.L.; McMillan, K. 1979. Triazene residues in suspended solids (1974-1976) and water (1977) from the mouths of Canadian streams flowing into the Great Lakes. J. Great Lakes Res., 5: p. 131-138.

Golterman, H.L. 1982. La géochimie du Rhin et du Rhône et l'impact humain. In: Sly, P.G. (ed.), Proc. 2nd Symp. Sediment/Freshwater Interaction, Queen's Univ., Kingston, Ontario, June 15-18. (In press.) Junk/Pudoc, The Hague.

de Groot, A.J. 1966. Mobility of trace elements in deltas. Trans. Internat. Soc. Soil Sci. Aberdeen, 1966, p. 267-279.

de Groot, A.J.; Zschuppe, K.H.; de Bruin, M.; Houtman, J.P.W.; and Singgih, P.A. 1968. Activation analysis applied to sediments from various river deltas. Proc. 1968 Internat. Conf., Modern Trends in Activation Analysis, Gaithersberg (U.S.A.), p. 62-71.

de Groot, A.J.; de Goeij, J.J.M.; Zengers, C. 1971. Contents and behaviour of mercury as compared with other heavy metals in sediments from the Rivers Rhine and Ems. Geol. Mijnb. 50: p. 393-398.

de Groot, A.J.; Allersma, I.E.; Van Driel, W. 1973. Zware Metalen en fluviatiele en mariene ecosystemen. Sympos. Waterloopkunde in dienst van industrie en milieu, Sept. 5,1973. Publ. No. 110 N. 27 pp.

Gunnerson, C.G. 1962. Sacramento River water pollution survey - water quality. Bull. Calif. Dept. Wat. Resources, No. 111, Appendix B. 372 pp.

Gunnerson, C.G.; Morris, J.M. (Jr). 1963. Interrelationships of suspended sediment and water quality. Publ. Internat. Assoc. Sci. Hydrol. 64: p. 25-33.

International Joint Commission. 1977. The waters of Lake Huron and Lake Superior. Volume II. Part B. Lake Huron, Georgian Bay, and the North Channel. Great Lakes Reg. Off., Windsor, Ontario. 743 pp.

Jackson, T. 1980. Mercury speciation and distribution in a polluted river-lake system as related to the problem of lake restoration. Proc. Internat. Symposium for Inland Waters and Lake Restoration. (U.S. EPA/OECD), Sept. 8-12, 1980, Portland Maine, p. 93-101.

Miles, J.R.W. 1980. Adsorption of insecticide residues - importance in environmental sampling and analysis. In: Afghan, B.K.; Mackay, D. (eds), Hydrocarbons and Halogenated Hydrocarbons in the Aquatic Environment, p. 81-90. Plenum Press, New York.

Müller, G.; Förstner, U. 1975. Heavy metals in the Rhine and Elbe estuaries: mobilization or mixing effect. Environm. Geol. 1: p. 33-39.

Reuther, R.; Wright, R.F.; Förstner, U. 1981. Distribution and chemical forms of heavy metals in sediment cores from two Norwegian lakes affected by acid precipitation. Proc. Internat. Symp. Heavy Metals in the Environment, Amsterdam. (In press.).

Thomas, R.L.; Jaquet, J.-M.; Kemp, L.W.; Lewis, C.F.M. 1976. Surficial sediments of Lake Erie. J. Fish. Res. Bd. Can., 33: p. 385-403.

Thomas, R.L.; Mudroch, A. 1979. Small craft harbours - sediment survey. Lakes Ontario, Erie and Lake St. Clair, 1978. Dredging summary and protocol. Rept. from Great Lakes Biolimnol. Lab. to Small Craft Harbours, Ontario Region. 2 vols. 148 pp and appendix.

U.S. Bureau of Reclamation. 1953. (Monthly Rept. of Operations; Region 3, Central Valley Operations Office, Sacramento, California, et seq.)

U.S. Geological Survey. 1962. Suspended sediment in California streams. Quality of Water Branch, Sacramento, California. Unpubl. Records. 64 pp.

Wood, J.M. 1974. Biological cycles for toxic elements in the environment. Science, 183: p. 1049-1052.

IX Case histories (3)
Nutrient contaminants

IX.1   Introduction

The study of nutrients in water systems is extremely complex and does not readily lend itself to presentation in the form of case histories because, to be representative of the many different controlling factors, it would require several lengthy examples. The presence of excess nutrients is considered to be a contaminant problem in both rivers and lakes, although the effects manifest themselves in somewhat different forms.

In rivers and in very shallow lakes, where the euphotic zone may extend to the bed, the presence of excess nutrients usually results in dense weed growth by rooted and attached aquatic plants. However, during periods of highly turbulent flow or in areas of high particulate concentration, plant growth may not respond to the presence of nutrients. Thus, although excess quantities of nutrients may be carried through a river in high flow conditions, productivity may be suppressed by physical controls. Plant growth is generally most extensive in summer, in warm water, and under low flow conditions. Depending on the type of vegetation, nutrients may be utilized directly from the water in soluble form, or by roots which penetrate the sediments of the bed. In some areas not suited for rooted   vegetation and in which water residence times are intermediate between a lake and a river, rafts of floating vegetation may develop on a seasonal basis.

In lakes, the primary productivity and composition of phytoplankton can be used to characterize their trophic state (i.e., conditions of nutrient availability). Deep, cold, clear lakes are termed oligotrophic, when they are characterized by low concentrations of available nutrients in the water. Phosphorus is a limited supply; diatoms can be restricted in yield by a lack of dissolved silica. Silica is not normally a contaminant.

Because nitrogen is widely available from many sources, including atmospheric fixation and agricultural usage, trophic state in increasingly nutrient rich waters is most often controlled by phosphorus. Only when large amounts of phosphorus are available will other nutrients, and or light, become limiting factors in primary productivity. Thus, in hyper-trophic conditions, nitrogen or light may be critical. Although phosphorus is not the only element which may control trophic state, it is the most common cause of undesirable change. It is also the only nutrient element which is subject to management control.

Changes in trophic state can be illustrated by the classical simple relationship (Vollenweider, 1971) between total phosphorus input (loading) and the mean depth of a lake. In Figure IX.1 it can be seen that, while only small increases can shift a lake from oligotrophic to mesotrophic conditions, larger quantities are required to effect change at higher trophic states. With higher trophic state there is a marked increase in primary productivity and biological composition shifts, often towards less desirable forms.

Although values for mean depth are often available or easily obtained, they are of limited use as a predictive characteristic since individual lakes vary enormously in size and form, circulation, stratification, and residence time; similarly, although total phosphorus may be more easily measured than its components, there is no consistent relationship between this value and the quantity of phosphorus available for biological uptake.

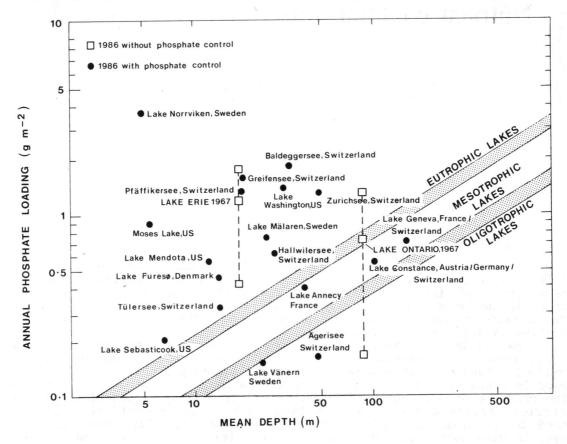

FIGURE IX.1   Total phosphate loadings vs lake mean depth (m), based on Vollenweider (1971); and after Stumm and Baccini (1978).

The empirical relationships expressed in Figure IX.1 provide, however, an excellent means of comparing many lakes on a regional basis and there is good reason to believe that many lakes, which show a significant shift to more eutrophic conditions, are subject to a greater percentage of available phosphorus within increasing loads of total phosphorus. Increasing quantities of biologically available phosphorus are frequently associated with the use of phosphorus in fertilizers and with many other urban and industrial activities.

Due to the importance of phosphorus as stated above, a more detailed description of phosphorus/sediment relationships follows next.

IX.2   Sediments as an Aid to an Understanding of the Phosphate Cycle

IX.2.1   Phosphate cycle and human impact

Waters receive phosphates from natural sources by chemical and mechanical weathering from human wastewaters, and from agricultural run-off. The phosphorus occurs in both soluble and particulate forms from these sources. Different forms of phosphates interchange at different rates in response to various biological and chemical processes, but eventually about 70 percent of all phosphate ends up in the sediments.

Phosphate entering an aquatic system, as shown (later) in Figure IX.8, may become adsorbed by sediments, taken up by algae, or remain in solution and thus increase the existing concentration in the water. During the growing season, orthophosphate is usually taken up rapidly by algae; in most mid-latitude lakes this uptake controls algal growth and the phytoplankton may deplete orthophosphate to very low concentrations (to 0.1 μg l^{-1}, or so). The sizes of phytoplankton populations change rapidly with seasonal conditions, at mid to high latitudes.

After algal death, most cellular phosphates will be mineralized to orthophosphate. This recycling, which may occur as much as 10 to 40 times a year, depends upon many factors such as: irradiance, length of growing season, temperature, and possibly nitrogen supply. Phosphate recycling is often as important as a supply of nutrient for algal growth, as the supply from external sources.

Because of recycling, little algal-phosphate will be lost as refractory material (about one to five percent); but much larger quantities become adsorbed on to inorganic suspended matter and removed by sedimentation (Golterman, 1980a). This process continues throughout the year but it is quantitatively most important during the winter.

The rate at which phosphate is removed by sedimentation, is influenced by turbulence in the water column, flushing of the water body, and by resuspension of bottom material. During the summer season both cellular phosphate and phosphate adsorbed on to silt/clay particles may be lost in the outflow of a lake; whereas, during the winter, phosphate loss is usually in the forms adsorbed on to particulates or as the soluble fraction (there being little significant algal growth during winter). Although winter and spring water flows may be high, the amount of phosphate removed from a lake may be controlled more by thermal stratification than simple volume displacement. Inflowing waters at a temperature significantly different to that of the receiving lake may pass through it as an entrained flow with no major displacement of lake water; thus, the behaviour of many lakes may be modified by local climatic conditions and lake morphology.

Because of recent water use practices there have been massive increases in the amounts of phosphate-loading to many water bodies. The following examples illustrate the trend in (soluble) PO_4-P loadings which are typical of much uncontrolled water use:

Approximate year, loading value in g m^2 y^{-1}

Lake	Pre Control						Post Control	
	1940	1945	1950	1955	1960	1965	1970	
Erie (North American)	0.1	0.2	0.3	0.4	0.5	0.5	0.3	Gilbertson et al., 1972 Fraser and Williams, 1981
Washington (North American)	–	–	0.5	0.6	1.1	1.2	0.2	Edmondson and Lehman, 1981
Mendota (North American)	–	0.2	0.4	–	–	0.5	–	Lee et al., 1966 Vollenweider, 1971

The total-P loading to lakes can be much greater than the (soluble) PO_4-P loading, but since most of the total-P is usually in mineral form (such as apatite), much remains biologically unavailable.

In Lake Erie, apatite-P represents about 50 percent of the composition of the total phosphorus in sediments which were deposited before European settlement and, even now, apatite-P represents 30 to 50 percent of the total-P in most Erie sediments. On the other hand, total-P may be more than an order of magnitude greater than PO_4-P in some alpine lakes (such as the Greifensee, Zürichsee and Bodensee, in Switzerland), although PO_4-P loadings remain generally between 1 and 2 g m^{-2} y^{-1}.

Due to phosphate sedimentation, many lakes show a P-retention which is inversely related to water retention time. Retention, however, is complex and can be influenced by the location of nutrients within the water column, water depth and sediment resuspension, thermal regimes (Kortmann et al., 1982) and the mixing with inflowing waters, the ratio of epi/hypo-limnetic volumes, and many other factors.

As an illustration of some of these factors, Figure IX.2 (Thomas, 1968) shows the distribution of phosphate in the Zürichsee and its increasing content between 1941 and 1964, at the depth intervals of 10 to 136 m. The decrease during the spring and early summer in the 0 to 10 m depth interval was originally attributed to P-sedimentation; Golterman (1973), however, has shown that this decrease can be explained by the seasonal flushing of epilimnion waters and that this effect is dominant.

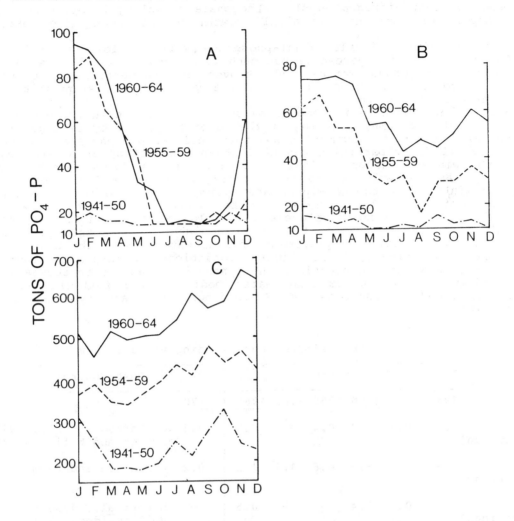

FIGURE IX.2   Phosphate content in waters at different depth layers in
               Lake Zürich (Switzerland), modified after Thomas (1968).
               A is depth layer 0 - 10 m, B is depth layer 10 - 20 m,
               C is depth layer 20 - 136 m. Mean values for different
               year classes, data expressed in tons of PO_4-P per whole lake.

IX.2.2   Mechanisms of phosphate sedimentation

Although P-sedimentation includes settlement of dead algal cells, most is caused by precipitation of phosphorus with hydrated ferric hydroxide, calcium carbonate or apatite, and adsorption on clays, minerals, and other fine particulates. Depending upon the concentrations of adsorbent and reaction rates (in the order of days rather than hours) these mechanisms may be either competitive or supportive.
    In hardwater lakes, especially if receiving sewage water, the calcium carbonate/apatite system seems to be most important (Golterman, 1977a). If hypolimnion waters are more acidic the solubility of apatite may increase, although the dissolution is largely controlled by the rate of this process.
    Iron oxide, which is widely available, is very efficient in precipitating phosphates and plays a major role in retaining phosphates within anoxic

hypolimnia. Under these conditions, both phosphate and soluble iron are released from anoxic sediments and diffuse upwards towards oxygenated zones, where the iron is oxygenated. It then sinks, as $Fe(OH)_3 \cdot xH_2O$, and rapidly adsorbs all available orthophosphates. This process often takes place during or before the seasonal overturn and is particularly important as a means of retaining phosphates in the sediments of many softwater lakes.

Interconversions may take place within sediments and Williams and Mayer (1972) showed that, in the lower parts of Lake Erie cores, much of the phosphate is present as apatite; some of which may have formed by interconversion.

In Lake Kinneret, Serruya (1971) demonstrated a good correlation between Fe and P in sub-surface sediments. In two deeper cores, Serruya found a positive relationship between Fe and P and a negative relationship between Ca and P. (In the deepest core, at a depth of more than 30 cm, the Ca content decreased sharply, but the Fe/P ratio decreased less severely.) Although Serruya explained these effects as being caused by a reduction in primary productivity or by increased rates of mineralization, there may be another reason for these changes.

The correlations (calculated by Golterman, 1973) were found to be:

	Ca/P	Fe/P
Core A	r = -0.62 (significant to 5% level)	r = 0.34 (not significant)
Core B	r = -0.84 (significant to 0.5% level)	r = 0.73 (significant to 1% level)

The correlation between Fe and P is strongly significant in the deepest core (B) and it seems likely that the stronger the positive correlation between Fe/P, the stronger the negative correlation between Ca/P. It seems possible, therefore, that these relationships may reflect processes of selective formation, since the removal of phosphate by iron would decrease the possibility of forming $Ca_5(PO_4)_3 \cdot OH$ precipitates, Golterman (1982b).

Such interactions may differ from lake to lake, and special attention should also be given to the character of allochthonous materials eroded from the surrounding watershed.

IX.2.3   Phosphate in sediment profiles

The total-P content in unpolluted, naturally formed, lake muds normally lies in the range of about 0.5 to 5 mg g^{-1} of dry sediment. (The total-P content in igneous rocks is higher.) Variations in total-P content in sediment cores are usually associated with either layers of different particle size or with changes within the watershed such as increased soil loss or the addition of human sewage wastes, or industrial products. Mackereth (1966) recorded that total-P varied between 1 and 4 mg g^{-1} in sediments from the English Lake District and in Figure IX.3 total-P is plotted from Lakes Washington and Erie (North America) and the Bodensee (Switzerland). In these examples, the background level of total-P is similar in both Lake Erie (about 0.6 mg g^{-1}) and the Bodensee (about 0.5 mg g^{-1}). In Lake Washington the background content of total-P is about 2 mg g^{-1}. In all three examples, there is a well-defined increase in total-P content towards the upper part of each core, illustrating the increased total-P loading as a result of (human) cultural impact. The increase in Lake Washington (Shapiro et al., 1971) is to about 6 mg g^{-1}, in Lake Erie (Williams et al., 1976) to about 1.5 mg g^{-1} and in the Bodensee to about 1 mg g^{-1} (Wagner, 1972).

Usually, the total-P content in sediment increases by little more than a factor of 3, although actual loading values may have increased by substantially greater amounts. This is due both to the complexities of P-retention (discussed previously) and to the fact that P-content in sediments is also controlled by adsorption according to the formula: $A - KC^V$, where A is quantity of metal adsorbed per unit weight of absorbent, K is a constant, C is the equilibrium concentration of metal remaining in solution, and v is a constant. With v about 0.2 to 0.3, a ten-fold increase in C causes only a two-fold increase in A (Golterman, 1980a).

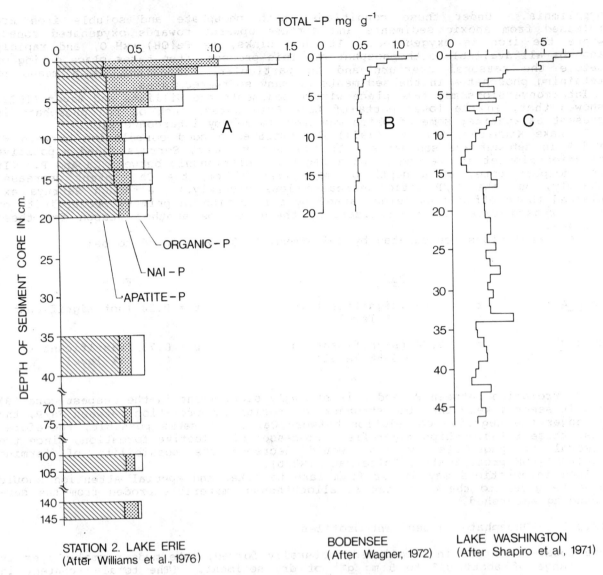

TOTAL -P mg g^{-1}

A — STATION 2. LAKE ERIE
(After Williams et al., 1976)

B — BODENSEE
(After Wagner, 1972)

C — LAKE WASHINGTON
(After Shapiro et al, 1971)

FIGURE IX.3 Total-phosphorus and phosphorus factions
in some lake sediment cores

Although recent increases of total-P content in sediment cores are clearly
related to the general effects of cultural loading, the changes in content of
different P fractions can be used to illustrate even more dramatic changes.

In Figure IX.3A the Lake Erie core (Williams et al., 1976), is shown to be
composed of three fractions, termed apatite-P, NAl-P, and organic-P.   The
apatite-P is in mineral form and is largely derived from the erosion of shoreline and nearshore material; NAl-P is described as non-apatite inorganic phosphorus and represents much of the biologically available phosphorus; the
organic-P is largely associated with dead algal material.   In this core, the
increase of both NAl-P and organic-P fractions is dramatically shown.   The
apparent decrease in apatite-P, towards the top of the core, may be caused by
material dilution, rather than by a decrease in apatite supply.   If the effects
of compaction are removed and P-contents adjusted for rates of sediment accumulation and dilution, all P-fractions increase.

IX.2.4   Equilibria

Since most of the chemical controls on the content of P in sediment are through
equilibria processes, P release may take place as soon as the concentrations of

210

P, Ca, and Fe change. This particularly affects the presence of P in the surface sediments of stratified lakes; in waters overlying these sediments the concentrations of phosphate tend to be relatively high (often up to 0.1 to 0.5 g m^{-3} of PO_4-P). However, the exchange of soluble phosphates between hypolimnion and epilimnion waters is further controlled by turbulent mixing and diffusion processes, as previously discussed.

IX.2.5   Total-P loads and discharge

Much of the phosphorus data, prior to the early 1970's, is of limited use in characterizing the relationships between P-content and discharge or flow, because of a lack of comparable stream flow measurements. Cahill (1977), however, was able to summarize a number of studies based on comparable chemistry and flow data. From these, he determined that:
   - concentration of total-P increased with discharge;
   - there was a strong relationship between total-P and suspended solids;
   - mass transport during storms or spring run-off tends to comprise a very large proportion of the annual P-loading;
   - past methods of estimating long-term loading rates usually underestimated annual mass transport.

It is difficult to generalize the relationship between total-P and water discharge; sometimes a correlation can be found, in some watersheds, but not in others. In some cases, the concentration may increase up to a certain discharge value, and then remain constant (see Figure IX.4). This behaviour is probably caused by the fact that total-P is composed of several different components, each of which may respond differently; thus, for example, PO_4-P usually shows only a limited relationship to discharge whereas particulate-P (which is strongly associated with the suspended solids) shows a close correlation with discharge. A detailed analysis and explanation of these differences is provided in Verhoff et al. (1982a).

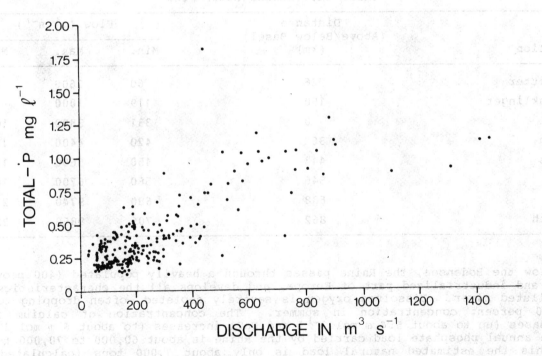

FIGURE IX.4 Relationship between total-P and water discharge (from Lake Erie Water Management Study 1976, and shown in Cahill, 1977).

Two important remobilization processes may also affect the concentration of P in flowing water; erosion of bed material under high flow conditions may resuspend considerable quantities of particulate-P and, under anoxic conditions (low

211

flow) PO_4-P may be released from the bed of organically contaminated streams and rivers (Fillos and Swanson, 1975).

Cahill (1977) found that, for some Lake Erie watersheds, a linear regression could be fitted for the expression:

$$a = 1.32 \ b + 153$$

where a = total-P (mg m^{-3}) and b = suspended solids (g m^{-3}).

The correlation between suspended solids and particulate-P (total-P - PO_4-P) was extremely high.

IX.3   Phosphate in the River Rhine

This discussion continues (from VIII.2.2) with the case study of the River Rhine, as it relates to nutrient contamination.

The source of the River Rhine is in Switzerland, in an area of extensive (mountainous) carbonate rocks, and the water is often supersaturated with $Ca(HCO_3)_2$/$CaCO_3$, with a pH in the range of 7.6 to 8.

The Rhine loses the coarse fraction of its suspended load as it passes through the Bodensee. In the upper Rhine, the clay minerals are characterized by illite and chlorite; in the lower Rhine, montmorillonite and kaolinite are dominant and reflect the difference in mineralogy and the geology of the watershed changes downstream. Table IX.1 provides a summary of the flow characteristics of the Rhine, above and below Basel, on the Bodensee. It is remarkable that the range between minimum and maximum flow conditions remains so constant below Basel (ratio, a little more than 1:10); no doubt reflecting the influence of the Bodensee.

TABLE IX.1   Rhine River Flow

Location	Distance (Above/Below Basel) (km)	Flow ($m^3 \ s^{-1}$)		
		Min.	Max.	Mean
Schmitter	226	60	2600	233
Rheinklinger	150	119	1000	372
Basel	0	331	3890	1079
Maxau	362	420	4400	1310
Worms	443	450	5600	1440
Kaub	546	560	6700	1680
Koln	688	680	9740	2190
Lobith	862	705	9850	2282

Below the Bodensee, the Rhine passes through a heavily populated (400 people/km^2) and industrialized part of Europe, and develops all the characteristics of a polluted river. Dissolved oxygen is severely depleted, often dropping to 25 to 30 percent concentration in summer. The concentration of calcium ions increases (up to about 5.4 m mol l^{-1}) and NaCl increases (to about 6 m mol l^{-1}).

The annual phosphate load carried by the Rhine is about 60,000 to 70,000 tons; of this the estimated natural load is only about 1,000 tons (calculated by reference to silica, PO_4-P:SiO_2 = 1:110 or by erosion in the watershed, Golterman, 1977b). Agricultural run-off accounts for up to 10,000 tons of the annual phosphate load (run-off rates of 5 to 50 kg per hectare y^{-1}), and the remainder of about 50,000 tons per year is derived from urban and industrial wastes (averaging about 1.5 kg y^{-1} per person).

About 50 percent of the phosphate is carried as particulate matter and, since the ionic product of Ca^{+2} and PO_4^{3-} is around the solubility product, the water is probably saturated with respect to apatite.

In the next part of this chapter, the problem of phosphate accumulation is discussed in the delta lakes of the Netherlands, near the mouth of the Rhine.

IX.4   Effects of Phosphorus Additions to Dutch Lakes

IX.4.1   Introduction

The average annual loadings of the Dutch lakes is at least 6 g m^{-2} y^{-1} of PO$_4$-P (Kolenbrander, 1974). The mean depth of most of these lakes is between 2 and 3.5 m, so they do not stratify. Algal densities of up to 100 mg m^{-3} chlorophyll a are regularly recorded in several lakes, and densities of over 300 mg m^{-3} have been recorded, e.g., the Border Lakes between the newly reclaimed polders in the IJsselmeer and the old land (Figure IX.5).

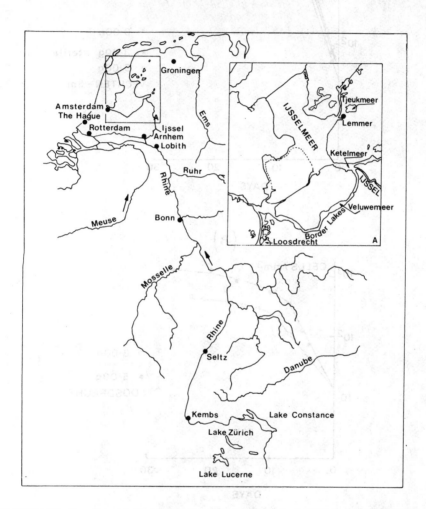

FIGURE IX.5   Course of the River Rhine. Insert: IJsselmeer with border lakes. (Modified after Golterman, 1977b)

In many of these highly eutrophic lakes, phosphate is no longer the factor limiting the density of algal populations; instead they represent cases where nitrogen or irradiance control algal growth. These lakes are typical illustrations of Lund's (1970) argument, that the more eutrophic lakes have a tendency to move away from phosphate limitation. Nitrogen limitation may become more and more important due to the fact that, in eutrophic shallow lakes, the sediments cause nitrogen to be lost from the system by denitrification. In addition, light shading finally becomes the controlling factor.

In earlier work it was shown (Golterman et al., 1969) that sediments are a good source of phosphate for algae (Figure IX.6). The present work with algal cultures, shows that not all sedimentary phosphate is available. It describes a chemical fractionation of the different compounds and the extent to which such sources may be utilized under natural conditions.

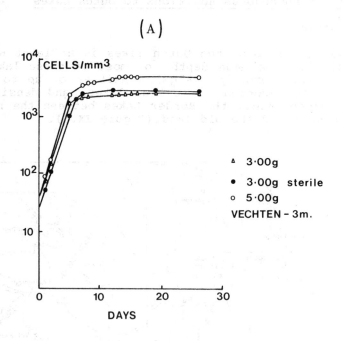

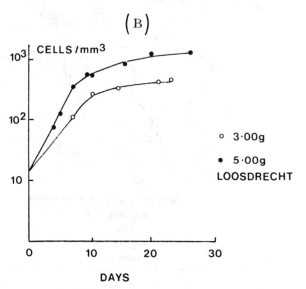

FIGURE IX.6 (A) Growth of _Scenedesmus_ cells on a culture solution with sediments from Lake Vechten. Sediments from 3 m depth. One sample was sterilised with UV radiation. (From Golterman et al., 1969.)

(B) Growth of _Scenedesmus_ cells on a culture solution with Loosdrecht Lake mud as only source of phosphate. (From Golterman et al., 1969.)

IX.4.2   Bio-assays with sediments as phosphate source

Sediments from several Dutch lakes, which differ in chemical or mineral composition (clay, peat or gyttja), were separately added to Rodhe's culture solutions without phosphate. Scenedesmus sp. was inoculated and there was a good growth in all cases, although there was always some unused phosphate, Golterman (1977b). Fitzgerald (1970) found that there was no algal growth if sediments were separated from the algae by dialysis tubes. Golterman et al. (1969) showed that even when inorganic phosphate was added to the sediments in the dialysis tubes, no growth occurred; although there was good growth with dialysis tubes containing inorganic phosphate alone. It is assumed that low concentrations of phosphate in the tube were caused by the adsorption of phosphate on to the sediments. This decreased the diffusion rate; thus reducing the rate of algal growth. This does not mean that 'physical' contact between algal cells and sediment particles is necessary; good growth can be obtained by mixing the sediments with a ten to twenty-fold excess of agar-agar solution (40°C) and cutting the block (after cooling and solidifying) into slices of 0.5 cm. The growth rate in some, but not all, cases was reduced. This technique was used to estimate the different chemical fractions in the sediments after algal growth, which required separation of algae and sediments.

Although all sediments gave good growth, not all the phosphate present could be utilized by Scenedesmus. This fact suggests that certain compounds are, and others are not, available for the growth of this algae. Because chemical fractionation is much quicker and easier for estimating the portion of available phosphate present in a given sediment than a bioassay, Golterman (1977b) tried to establish a chemical fractionation that would measure the same amounts (and presumably, therefore, the same compounds which can be utilized by the algae).

Mild extractants were used to remove the phosphate salts of calcium and iron by chelation of these cations, without disturbing other structures such as clay bound and organically bound phosphate. Considerable quantities of iron, calcium, and phosphate were released, using a 0.01 M solution of NTA (nitrilotriacetic acid), but not all extractable phosphate appeared in the first extraction. Normally, 0.5 to 1.0 g of dry sediment were extracted with three portions of 200 ml, at pH = 7. From the experiments in Table IX.2, it can be shown that the amount of phosphate extracted with 0.01 M NTA was equal to the amount of phosphate used by Scenedesmus, within the expected experimental error (two to five percent). In later work, NTA solutions up to 0.1 M were used with success.

In the second experiment, the agar blocks were separated from the culture and inoculated again. In the fourth extraction, about four to five percent of the previous total (one to three) was extracted. Because these sediments might have a complex mixture of several phosphate binding mechanisms, of which adsorption on clay might be one, Golterman studied phosphate behaviour after adsorption on clay, both with chemical and biological extractants. This experiment used a clay collected from the Kainju River (Uganda) which has never been polluted. At the place where the sediment was collected, the river is swept free of clay in the wet season; so the sediment must have been in position for less than a year. From the information given in Table IX.3, it can be seen that a small fraction (ca. 10 percent) of the total natural phosphate could be extracted by NTA, and a slightly larger proportion could be used by Scenedesmus. By suspending this clay in a phosphate solution, the clay was enriched with freshly adsorbed phosphate. This amount, together with the already present extractable amount, could be extracted for ca. 100 percent while a slightly lower recovery was made with Scenedesmus cells.

An extraction with NTA does not separate between iron bound and calcium bound phosphate ('Fe-PO_4' and 'Ca-PO_4') which, for biological reasons, may be desirable. Therefore, other chelators with larger stability coefficients for calcium and iron (EDTA and DTPA - diethylene-triamino-pentacetate) were used. However, they did not give as good a separation between the calcium and iron bound phosphates, as was expected from their stability coefficients. With normal lake sediments, DTPA extracted more phosphate than Scenedesmus. Adsorbed phosphate on the Kainji River clay appeared to be 95 percent extracted by DTPA, 90 to 100 percent by NTA and only 75 percent by EDTA.

A solution of 0.01 M Ca-NTA (NTA solution with stoichiometric amounts of $CaCO_3$) appears to be a promising method for the separation of iron bound and calcium bound phosphate. This extractant makes only the 'Fe-PO_4' soluble, 'Ca-PO_4' is then extracted with Na-NTA (see also Golterman, 1982a).

No 'final' extraction scheme can yet be suggested, and it has been found that the pH adjustment is critical for different sediments (usually a pH of 6 or 7 is necessary). Furthermore, the Ca-NTA solution must have an excess of 1 meq l^{-1} of Ca^{2+} otherwise some 'Ca-PO_4' may go into solution.

TABLE IX.2 NTA extractions and _Scenedesmus_ growth. (After Golterman, 1977b)

2 g sediment of Lake Vechten (wet weight = 0.58 g dry weight) was solidified with agar-agar and sliced (0.5 cm). The slices were: a) extracted with 200 ml of 0.01 M NTA at pH = 7; b) suspended in Fernbach-flasks and inoculated with _Scenedesmus_ The amount of phosphate utilized by _Scenedesmus_ could be estimated, because 1 mg PO_4-P is equivalent to 10^{10} cells. Results are expressed per g dry weight.

	NTA-Extractable (μg PO_4-P)		_Scenedesmus_ cells ($\times 10^9$)	
	Sediment 1	Sediment 2	Sediment 1	Sediment 2
1)	412	307		
2)	203	265	6.7	6.5
3)	57	83	is equivalent to	
	672	655	670 μg	650 μg

In a second series, a fourth NTA extraction was carried out, while the blocks were recovered from the culture, washed, and used again

	NTA-Extractable (μg PO_4-P)	_Scenedesmus_ cells ($\times 10^9$)
1)	260	
2)	271	6.15
3)	96	is equivalent to
	627	615 μg
4)	re-extraction	re-inoculation
	29	26 μg

TABLE IX.3 Clay from the Kainju River (Uganda) extracted with solutions of NTA, EDTA and DTPA (0.01 M, pH = 7). (After Golterman, 1977b)

The clay was further enriched with phosphate by adsorption. Both samples were used for chemical extractions and _Scenedesmus_ cultures. 650 μg of PO_4-P (± 25; duplicates) could be extracted by fusion with $NaKCO_3$ from the natural clay.

Results in μg PO_4-P g^{-1} dry weight of clay

	NTA-Extractable	_Scenedesmus_ Available
Natural clay	72	90
"Enriched" clay (+ 425 μg)	479	493
	DTPA Extractable	
"Enriched" clay (+ 834 μg)	734 = 88%	800 = 96%

Mean recoveries of freshly adsorbed phosphate with:

DTPA: 88 — 96%
NTA: 90 — 100%
EDTA: 75%

216

In addition to these direct measurements, much can be discovered from the algal growth rate (Golterman et al., 1969). In batch cultures, the relation between growth rate and phosphate concentration followed a monod saturation curve of the type:

$$\beta = \beta_{max} \frac{PO_4}{C_1 + PO_4}$$

in which: β = growth rate
β_{max} = maximum value for β in these experimental conditions
C_1 = half saturation constant.

Comparing the growth rate obtained with almost insoluble compounds such as $FePO_4$ and $Ca_5(PO_4)_3(OH)$, it was possible to define an 'apparent' phosphate concentration; i.e., the (lower) phosphate concentration (as KH_2PO_4) that would give the same growth rate as the insoluble compounds. However, equilibrium growth rates were not always obtained.

In Figure IX.6 there appears to be little difference in the growth rate associated with Lake Vechten mud, irrespective of the sample size; this is strongly suggestive of an equilibrium condition. However, the Lake Loosdrecht muds show a greater variation in growth rates, in relation to sample size; these muds have a high organic content.

Recent work with cultures having very low phosphate concentrations, show that growth rate and saturation constant (C_1) are strongly pH-dependent, as shown in Figure IX.7.

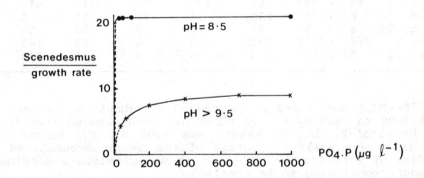

FIGURE IX.7 Relation between growth rate of Scenedesmus (day^{-1}) and phosphate concentration at different pH values (pH = 8.5 from Golterman, 1977b and pH >9.5 from Golterman et al., 1969.)

IX.4.3 Experiments in lake enclosures

These laboratory experiments show a capacity for phosphate uptake from sediments by algae, but they do not show the extent to which this process will occur in nature. It seems likely, that utilization of sediment-phosphate is less important in lakes with a high phosphate loading than in lakes with a low, or decreasing phosphate loading.

To examine this problem an experimental pond (enclosure) was made in the Veluwe Border Lake. A plastic sheet was fixed around a circular floating device (diameter about 40 m, depth 1.5 m) and the lower part was dug into a circular trench of about 20 cm depth; this was filled in again with the sediment, fixing the sheet to the lake bottom. The whole structure was supported by wooden piles pushed into the lake. Although the lake is only 1.5 m deep, the sheet has a potential height of more than 10 m, enabling the outside water level to move

0.5 m up or down without flushing water into or out of the enclosure and to maintain constant volume. The enclosure could be flushed with 'polder water', relatively poor in phosphate.

Kouwe and Golterman (1976) reported that the enclosure was flushed through six times in 1975 (once with 1700 m^3 and five times with 3500 m^3). On every occasion there was enough phosphate available to produce chlorophyll a concentrations equivalent to the surrounding lake water, providing nitrate was added as a nitrogen source. It took about one week to reach equivalent concentrations, except in October when growth rates were less rapid.

The experimental data are summarized in Table IX.4. During the experiment the Ca-NTA extractable iron bound phosphate decreased from 190 (± 10) to 82 μg g^{-1} dry sediment. This happened in the period 18-8 to 1-9, when the largest increase in particulate-P was found. After 1-9, the concentration of 'Fe-PO$_4$' remained constant. In the period 25-9 to 7-10, when the concentration of particulate-P was increasing rapidly again, the amount of 'Ca-PO$_4$' decreased from 163 to 114 (± 10) μg g^{-1} dry sediment. The decrease of the 'Fe-PO$_4$' concentration took place mainly in the 2 to 4 cm layer, where 74 percent disappeared. The average for the 0 to 6 cm layer was 62 percent. The decrease of the 'Ca-PO$_4$' was 37 percent, with a maximum in the 4 to 6 cm layer of 51 percent.

TABLE IX.4 Increase in concentrations of chlorophyll a, PO$_4$-P in the periods after flushing the enclosure in 1975. (After Golterman, 1977b)

Period	Chlorophyll a		PO$_4$-P		Particulate-P		Days After N Supply
	μg l^{-1}	%	μg l^{-1}	%	mg l^{-1}	%	
Jul. 18 - Aug. 18	168 → 206	23	451	278	3	1	–
Aug. 22 - Sept. 1	123 → 193	57	-125	-89	231	513	5
Sept. 3 - Sept. 16	63 → 213	238	-34	-77	11	4	7
Sept. 18 - Sept. 23	68 → 96	41	0	0	20	23	5
Sept. 25 - Oct. 7	42 → 139	231	0	0	95	142	12
Oct. 9 - Oct. 22	54 → 180	233	ca.23	–	145	100	13

The sum of 'Fe-PO$_4$' and 'Ca-PO$_4$' decreased by about 40 percent and it was estimated that 1000 to 1600 mg m^{-2} of PO$_4$-P had been removed from the sediments; the increase in total-P, in the water, was 1200 mg m^{-2} during this period. Although this is a very small percentage of the amount accumulated in the lake (20 years loading of 2 to 4 g m^{-2} y^{-1}), it is nevertheless a considerable fraction of the amount considered to be available.

Two smaller enclosures were built (diameter (6 m), in addition to the large one. The first of these was not flushed and remained green all through summer, leaving the sediment store untouched. The second enclosure was flushed through but it was not supplied with extra nitrate. This pond remained clear for about three months, suggesting that the development of nitrogen-fixing blue green algae takes some time. After three months the pond suddenly became green, with a bloom of (non-nitrogen)-fixing Oscillatoria. Although this strongly suggests that the nitrogen fixers could not compete with the blue greens already present, it is also possible that the unusually warm period (with very little wind) had caused a temporary stratification in the small pond. From this, it is clear that the role of bottom sediment in phosphate metabolism cannot be understood without a better insight into the relationships between nitrogen supply and blue green algae.

IX.4.4   Discussion

The number of publications stating that sediments act as a sink for phosphate is probably about as large as the number describing an opposite effect. Further, it is clear that the role of sediments can be understood, only by evaluating their influence on the whole phosphate metabolism of a lake. This can be represented, as in Figure IX.8. From this figure it can be seen that sediment reaction IIa will be of little or no importance as long as external reactions Ia or Ib provide sufficient phosphate to meet algal demands. It is also clear, that the output reaction (V) will be of only minor importance if the phosphate binding reactions (Ic and IV) are strong. The output of phosphate can be important if the algae are washed away. When establishing phosphate loadings, a distinction must be made between output by algae and that fraction occurring as dissolved inorganic phosphate, particularly in winter. The recycling of phosphate between the algal and dissolved fractions may also control sedimentation, reaction IIIc. In addition, it should be remembered that not all the organic phosphate entering the sediments will remain in organic form. It seemd likely that some of these compounds will be converted into 'Fe-PO_4' or 'Ca-PO_4', which may also undergo further interconversions.

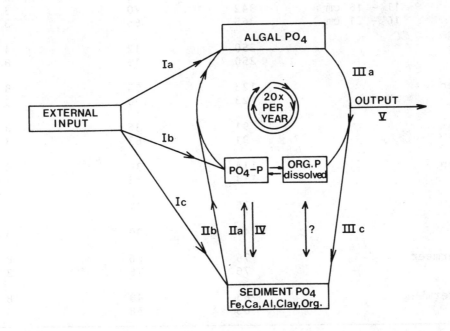

FIGURE IX.8   Schematic representation of the phosphate cycle.
(From Golterman, 1975.) The indicated turnover-time
may vary between 10 and 40 times a year.

Comparisons between laboratory and field experiments suggest that the two may not be exactly comparable. Due to the effects of differing concentrations, chemical gradients, and hydrodynamic controls, it is very difficult to simulate natural conditions in artificial systems.

IX.4.5   Summary

It seems that the phosphate bound into the clay lattice (the natural clay phosphate) is not available to algae, although it is available for agricultural crops (Golterman, 1973). Phosphate, freshly adsorbed on to clay, is available to algal cultures. It was found that NTA extracted an amount of phosphate which was approximately equal to the amount which could be used by algae. Iron bound phosphate is entirely available and the availability of apatite depends on the crystal size. Natural lakes are strongly influenced by the hydrodynamics of their systems.

As a further demonstration of the substantial quantities of P which can be made available from sediments, Golterman (1980b) examined sediment samples from a number of Dutch lakes (Table IX.5). In most of the sediments sampled at least 50 percent of the phosphorus could be considered as being biologically available.

TABLE IX.5   Phosphate content (μg g^{-1} wet weight) and percentage of
available phosphate from bottom samples of Dutch lakes.
(Modified after Golterman, 1980a)

Lake	P-Content	Percentage P Available	Quantity of Sample in Experiment (g)
Veluwemeer			
Near island	101	13;20	4;2
Middle	245	20	3
Middle	203	26	3
Dredged channel)			
sediment depth) 0 - 6 cm	300	93	3
6 - 11 cm	225	56	3
11 - 16 cm	342	70	3
16 - 21 cm	365	65	3
Loosdrecht	250	12	4
	250	19	8
Grote Brekken	123	55	8
	123	100	3
Pilkmeer	91	36	8
	91	63	3
Langw. Wielen	114	36	8
	114	53	3
Braudermeer	25	32	3
Tjeukemeer	242	100	3
South Sneekermeer	76	66	8
	76	78	3
North Sneerkermeer	63	48	8
	63	58	3

IX.5   Nutrients in Tropical Fresh Water Systems

Although the studies on nutrient release in Dutch lakes, cited by Golterman
(1977b), indicate that bottom sediments can be a major source of nutrients to
the overlying waters, these studies are more characteristic of mid to high latitude conditions than tropical conditions. Studies on some African lakes demonstrate that the behaviour of sediments in shallow eutrophic lakes in low latitudes, may be significantly different. As an example of this, the following
summary has been prepared from Viner (1977).

In tropical areas high radiant energy with comparatively little variation
results in more continuous productivity than in comparable mid-latitude conditions. Maximum use is made of available nutrients, and this is characterized by
a high turnover rate; there is little loss of non-utilized available nutrient to
outflow. In shallow lakes (often subject to considerable wind stress and
unstable density stratification, e.g., day/night variation), mixing may be
intense.

In Lake George (Uganda), which has an average depth of about 2.4 m, the gross
metabolized quantities of carbon, nitrogen, and phosphorus nutrients are very
high (Table IX.6), being approximately 20 times the total nutrient loss to sediments and outflow (effluent), calculated on an annual basis. Further, the loss
of nutrients to the sediments represents less than 10 percent of this annual
deficit (effluent loss + sediment). Viner's studies in Lake George have demonstrated that decomposition of organic material in the bottom sediments is not
efficient, even though the bed is well mixed by wave action (to depths of 6 cm

and greater), and that there is little NH_4-N of PO_4-P in the top 6 cm of sediment. The combined effects of diffusion and decomposition release result in a slower rate of nutrient loss than nutrient release from turbulent mixing (wave effects) and, since the main release mechanism is abiotic, sediment contributions appear to be largely influenced by diffusion.

TABLE IX.6 Mass budgets, as metric tons per year (t y^{-1}) for C, N and P in Lake George (Uganda), from seston data. (After Viner, 1977)

		C	N	P
Export	Effluent	25000	3400	220
	Sediment	2500	235	18.7
Total Export		27500	3635	239
Gross metabolized		529250	71325*	4649*
Gross metabolized				
Total export		19.3	19.6	19.5
Gross metabolized				
Sediment		212	303	248

* Potential rates, assuming mean rates of uptake are similar to the mean rate of carbon metabolism, based on C/N = 7 and C/P = 113.

The studies of nutrient release, however, are further complicated by the presence of large quantities of occluded algae within the muds, which continue to metabolize at a low rate even though nutrient uptake and photosynthesis may not be in phase (Viner, 1973). Under these conditions, therefore, nutrient recycling may take place in the upper part of the sediment in the same way that it does in the water column above.

Interestingly, the normal sediment profiles of N and P nutrients indicate that the effective gradient occurs within the muds; suggesting, further, the importance of diffusion within the sediments rather than at the sediment/water interface.

Although Lake George may be considered as an example of an extreme tropical condition, the behaviour of the surface muds is similar to that of the hypolimnion of permanently stratified deep lakes in which bottom sediments contribute little to the nutrient budget of the lake.

A further contrasting regime of sediment/water interaction occurs in tropical flood plains which are characteristic of both fluvial systems and temporary lakes.

'In both these examples the element of time is evident. Because of the very rapid re-establishment of a community that is possible under the tropical conditions, the exposed sediment acquires terrestrial primary producers and consumers which sustain the movement of chemical nutrients throughout the dry stage, and whose organic products provide decomposer substrates upon their subsequent re-inundation. This in turn permits a rapid return of the aquatic community. An analogy is the seasonal draining and fallowing of fish ponds, but in the tropics this cycle need only take a few weeks.' (After Viner, 1977).

References

Cahill, T. 1977. Forms and sediment associations of nutrients (C, N and P), pesticides and metals. Nutrients-P. In: Shear, H.; Watson, A.E.P., (eds). The fluvial transport of sediment-associated nutrients and contaminants. Proc. Internat. Joint Commiss. Workshop, Kitchener, Ontario. p. 163-180.

Edmondson, W.T.; Lehman, J.T. 1981. The effect of changes in the nutrient income on the condition of Lake Washington. Limnol. Oceanogr., 26: p. 1-29.

Fitzgerald, G.P. 1970. Aerobic lake muds for the removal of phosphorus from lake waters. Limnol. Oceanogr., 15: p. 550-555.

Fillos, J.; Swanson, W.R. 1975. The release rate of nutrients from river and lake sediments. J. Wat. Pollut. Contr. Fed., 47: p. 1032-1041.

Fraser, A.S.; Willison, K.E. 1981. Loading estimates to Lake Erie, 1967-1976. Can. Dept. Environm., Inl. Wat. Direct., Sci. Ser., No. 120.

Gilbertson, M.; Dobson, H.H.; Lee, T.R. 1972. Phosphorus and hypolimnial dissolved oxygen in Lake Erie. In: Burns, N.M.; Ross, C. (coord.), Project Hypo, Can. Centre Inl. Wat., Pap. No. 6: p. 141-145. (Also, U.S. Environm. Protect. Agency, Techn. Rept., TS-05-71-208-24.)

Golterman, H.L. 1973. Vertical movement of phosphate in freshwater. In: Griffith, E.J.; Beeton, A.; Spencer, J.M.; Mitchell, D.T. (eds.), Environmental phosphorus handbook: p. 509-538. John Wiley and Sons, New York, London, Sydney, Toronto. 718 pp.

Golterman, H.L. 1975. "Physiological limnology: an approach to the physiology of lake ecosystems." Elsevier Publ., Amsterdam and Oxford. 489 pp.

Golterman, H.L. 1977a. Preface. In: Golterman, H.L. (ed.), Interactions between sediments and freshwater, Junk/Pudoc, The Hague.

Golterman, H.L. 1977b. Sediments as a source of phosphate for algal growth. In: Golterman, H.L. (ed.), Interactions between sediments and freshwater: p. 286-293. Junk/Pudoc, The Hague.

Golterman, H.L. 1980a. Phosphate models, a gap to bridge. Hydrobiologia, 72: p. 61-71.

Golterman, H.L. 1980b Onderzoek in de proefvijvers in het Velvwemeer, H_2O, Tijdschr. Watervoorz. Afvalw., 13: p. 513-515.

Golterman, H.L. 1982a. Differential extraction of sediment phosphate with NTA solutions. In: Sly, P.G. (ed.), Proc. 2nd Symp. Sediment/Freshwater Interaction, Queen's Univ., Kingston, Ontario, June 15-18. (In press.) Junk/Pudoc, The Hague.

Golterman, H.L. 1982b. Loading concentration models for phosphate in shallow lakes. In: Sly, P.G. (ed.), Proc. 2nd Symp. Sediment/Freshwater Interaction, Queen's Univ., Kingston, Ontario, June 15-18. (In press.) Junk/Pudoc, The Hague.

Golterman, H.L.; Bakels, C.C.; Jakobs-Möglin, J. 1969. Availability of mud phosphates for the growth of algae. Verh. Internat. Verein. Limnol., 17: p. 467-479.

Kolenbrander, G.J. 1974. Een schatting van de fosfaataccumulatie in Nederland in 1970. Rapt. Inst. Bodemvruchtbaarheid, No. 10-74.

Kortmann, R.W.; Henry, D.D.; Keuther, A.; Kaufman, S. 1982. Epilimnetic nutrient loading by metalimnetic erosion and resultant algal response in Lake Waramang, Connecticut. In: Sly, P.G. (ed.), Proc. 2nd Symp. Sediment/ Freshwater Interaction, Queen's Univ., Kingston, Ontario, June 15-18. (In press.) Junk/Pudoc, The Hague.

Kouwe, F.A.; Golterman, H.L. 1976. Rol van bodemfosfaten in het eutrofiërings proces. H_2O, Tijdschr. Watervoorz. Afvalw., 9: p. 84-86.

Lee, G.F., et al. 1966. Report on the nutrient sources of Lake Mendota. Rept. Techn. Comm. Lake Mendota Study, Jan. 1966. (Mimeo).

Lund, J.W.G. 1970. Primary production. Wat. Treatm. Exam., 19: p. 332-358.

Mackereth, F.J.H. 1966. Some chemical observations on post-glacial lake sediments. Proc. Roy. Soc. Edinburgh., 250: p. 165-213.

Serruya, C. 1971. Lake Kinneret, the nutrient chemistry of the sediments. Limnol. Oceanogr., 16: p. 510-521.

Shapiro, J.; Edmonson, W.T.; Allison, D.E. 1971. Changes in the chemical composition of sediments of Lake Washington, 1958-1970. Limnol. Oceanogr., 16: p. 437-452.

Stumm, W.; Baccini, P. 1978. Man-made chemical perturbation of lakes". In: Lerman, A. (ed.), Lakes: chemistry, geology, physics, p. 91-126. Springer-Verlag, New York, Heidelberg, Berlin. 363 pp.

Thomas, E.A. 1968. Die Phosphattrophierung des Zürichsees und anderer Schweizer Seen. Mitt. Internat. Verein. Limnol., 14: p. 231-242.

Verhoff, F.H.; Melfi, D.A.; Yaksich, S.M. 1982. An analysis of total phosphorus transport in river systems. In: Sly, P.G. (ed.), Proc. 2nd Symp. Sediment/Freshwater Interaction, Queen's Univ., Kingston, Ontario, June 15-18. (In press.) Junk/Pudoc, The Hague.

Viner, A.B. 1973. Response of a mixed phytoplankton population to enrichments of ammonia and phosphate, and some associated ecological implications. Proc. Roy. Soc. London, B183: p. 351-370.

Viner, .A.B. 1977. The influence of sediments upon nutrient exchanges in tropical lakes. In: Golterman, H.L. (ed.), Interactions between sediments and freshwater, p. 210-215. Junk/Pudoc, The Hague.

Vollenweider, R.A., 1971. Scientific fundamentals of the eutrophication of lakes and flowing waters, with particular reference to nitrogen and phosphorus as factors in eutrophication O.E.C.D., Environm. Direct., Paris. 254 pp.

Wagner, G. 1972. Stratifikation der Sedimente und Sedimentationsrate im Bodensee. Verh. Internat. Verein. Limnol., 18: p. 475-481.

Williams, J.D.H.; Mayer, T. 1972. Effects of sediment diagenesis and regeneration of phosphorus with special reference to Lakes Erie and Ontario. In: Allen, H.E.; Kramer, J.R. (eds). Nutrients in Natural Waters, p. 281-315. Wiley-Interscience, New York.

Williams, J.D.H.; Murphy, T.P.; Mayer, T. 1976. Rates of accumulation of phosphorus forms in Lake Erie sediments. J. Fish. Res. Bd. Can., 33: p. 430-439.

X Contaminant hazard assessment, biotransformation, and availability to higher organisms

X.1   Introduction

Throughout most of the preceding descriptions and discussions, this Guidebook has directed attention to methods for identifying the presence of potential contaminants in sediments and providing methods for tracing their subsequent sediment-associated transport in an aquatic system, and changes with time. No special emphasis has been given to the significance of potential contaminants in terms of their impact on biota or human health.

Although, of course, this latter point is the principal concern which underlies most environmental studies, it encompasses a very broad range of interactive environment processes into which sediment-related studies can only provide partial input. Up to this point, the lack of focus on hazard assessment has been intentional in this Guidebook; even though the topic has more than enough importance to merit separate publication. The authors recognize that it would not be appropriate to complete this text without some further consideration of the biological significance of sediment-associated contaminants. The reader must also recognize, however, that there is no universal 'cook-book' of recipes for demonstrating the acceptability or non-acceptability of different sediment-associated contaminants. Rather, there are certain principles which may be applied through test procedures often on a site selective basis (Ward, 1978).

There are many case histories which could serve as examples of short-term hazard assessment but, of much greater importance, few, if any, long-term assessments may be considered to have yet stood the test of time.

X.2   Hazard Assessment

The authors are indebted to Lee and Jones (1979) from whose work much of the following text is cited.

Environmental hazard assessment should have two basic components: environmental toxicology and environmental chemistry-fate. Environmental toxicology considers the concentrations and durations of exposure to organisms of a chemical compound and its transformation products which can adversely affect aquatic and terrestrial organisms. Environmental chemistry considers the transport pathways and ultimate disposition of the chemical in the environment, the transformations of a chemical which occur and the rates of these transformations, and it provides an estimate of the expected concentrations of a contaminant in various environmental compartments. A hazard assessment is made by proceeding through a series of testing levels or tiers, which develop information on the toxicology of the chemical and its environmental chemistry, until a decision can be made about the environmental risk. The rate and extent of biotransformation of a contaminant is a major factor in considering environmental risk.

In situations where the nature of a chemical contaminant is known (perhaps because of association with a unique source) both forms of assessment may proceed, such as outlined in Table X.1 (after Kimerle et al., 1978). On the

TABLE X.1 An example of the tiered hazard assessment approach. (After Kimerle et al., 1978)

	Screening Studies	Predictive Studies — Expected Exposure Concentration From Laboratory Fate Studies (EEC)			Confirmative Studies	Monitoring Studies
		Additional Acutes	Short-Term Chronic	Long-Term Chronic		
Environmental Fate	Calculated Exposure Concentration Maximum (CEC MAX)	Expected Exposure Concentration From Laboratory Fate Studies (EEC)			Measured Exposure Concentration in Field (MEC)	Verified Exposure Concentration Under Use (VEC)
Aquatic Toxicity	Acute Toxicity	Additional Acutes	Short-Term Chronic	Long-Term Chronic	Field Studies Experimental Conditions	Field Studies Under Use Conditions
Hazard Evaluation Criteria						
Risk Acceptable Continue Testing	CEC $1-1/1000$ LC_{50}	EEC $1-1/500$ LC_{50}	EEC $1-1/50$ Estimated MATC	EEC $1-1/20$ Measured MATC	Minor Impact on Ecosystems	Ecological Monitoring
Risk Acceptable No Further Testing	CEC $<1/1000$ LC_{50}	EEC $<1/500$ LC_{50}	EEC $<1/50$ Estimated MATC	EEC $<1/20$ Measured MATC	No Measurable Impact on Ecosystems	Monitor Environmental Concentration
Risk Unacceptable Stop	CEC $>>LC_{50}$	EEC $>LC_{50}$	EEC $>$Estimated MATC	EEC $>$Measured MATC	Ecosystem Impaired	Restricted Use or No Approval

MATC = Maximum Allowable Toxic Concentration.

other hand, the form and source of contaminant may be unknown and only an adverse environmental impact observed. Under such conditions extensive research may be required before identifying the cause of the problem .... which may not always be due to the presence of a chemical contaminant.

The tiered screening process for hazard assessment generally involves the measurement of toxicological and chemical properties in a series of changing levels of sophistication, with a decision point at the end of each level.

The first tier of testing usually consists of relatively unsophisticated, inexpensive tests. The second and subsequent tiers involve tests having greater degrees of sophistication for environmental toxicity and chemical behaviour. In proceeding through the tiers of hazard assessment it is important to recognize that a fixed rate or extent of biotransformation or other chemical reaction cannot be used to trigger the next tier. The trigger for work in higher tiers must be based on an evaluation of all information including other chemical toxicological (and economic) considerations. As one proceeds through the tiers, the reliability of the estimates of toxicity and environmental concentration and hence the precision of the decision, should be significantly improving. This relationship is depicted in Figure X.1 (after Cairns et al., 1978). The precision of the measurements in any tier should be geared to the sensitivity of the water use requirements.

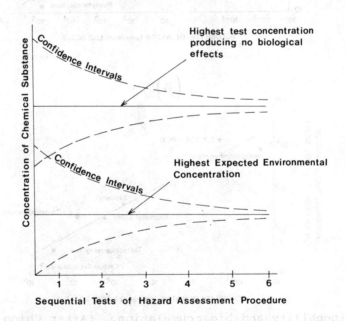

FIGURE X.1 Diagrammatic representation of a sequential hazard assessment procedure demonstrating increasingly narrow confidence limits for estimates of no biological effect concentration and expected environmental concentration. (After Cairns et al., 1978.)

So long as the estimated/observed environmental concentrations are less than the highest test concentrations, producing no biological effects, the risk is termed acceptable. If the estimated/observed environmental concentrations are greater, then there is a risk; and at this point the risk must be weighed against other factors. For example, the presence of DDT in sediments may be considered unavoidable in areas where malaria is endemic, but not in others.

As one example of the initial phases of a screening procedure the potential bioconcentration of various organic contaminants may be considered in relation to their solubility. In Figure X.2a and b (after Chiou et al., 1977, and cited in Stumm and Baccini, 1978), both n-octanol-water partition coefficient and bioconcentration in rainbow trout (a common cold water bioassay test species) are shown to be inversely proportional to aqueous solubility.

Environmental assessments may test contaminants subject to many other reaction processes, such as acid-base precipitation, complexation, oxidation-reduction, sorbtion, hydrolysis, photolysis, gas transfer, and biochemically mediated reactions, termed biotransformation.

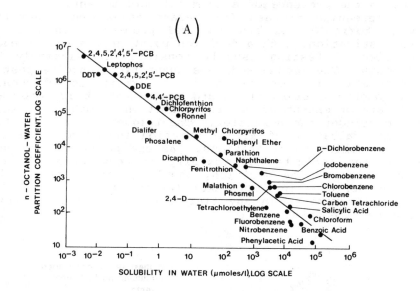

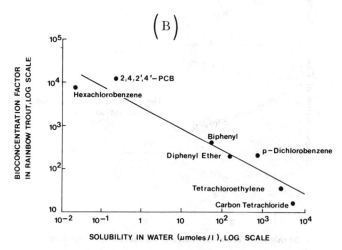

FIGURE X.2   Lipophility and bioaccumulation. (After Chiou et al., 1977.) Both n-octanol-water partition coefficient and bioconcentration factor in rainbow trout are inversely proportional to aqueous solubility.

Most of these (physical-chemical) reactions can be well stimulated by laboratory test procedures but this is not so (at least at the present time) for biotransformation, which is one of the more important and least understood processes. There are major differences between laboratory microcosms and the outside environment, which limit the transposition of experimental results, and this is a particular reflection of the need for a better understanding of the aquatic chemistry of the actual environment.

X.3   Biotransformation

There are several key aspects of the various tiered hazard assessment schemes such as are presented in Table X.1 which are pertinent to the design of procedures to assess the biotransformability of a chemical. Depending on the design of the hazard assessment scheme, the first tier of testing can be as simple as an examination of the structure of the chemical in order to estimate the tendency for biotransformation based on known behaviour of similar chemicals or functional groups within the chemical molecule. For example, certain types of functional groups are known to be readily attacked by aquatic micro-organisms. This type of information can be used to make a preliminary assessment of the potential for microorganisms to cause an alteration in compound structure.

The next tier usually involves one or more laboratory assessments of biotransformation. For materials whose use would result in their being present in domestic wastewaters, laboratory activated sludge, anaerobic digestion, and river die-away, tests would normally be conducted. These tests might be conducted in such a way as to screen for overall biotransformation potential without trying to define the kinetics (rate) of reaction. Detailed kinetic data (the form of the rate expression and the rate constant) are needed only for biotransformations that take place at what are considered moderate rates. Highly labile compounds and highly resistant compounds can be handled in a different way. There is little or no need for accumulating detailed kinetic data for compounds with first order biotransformation half-lives of months to years. If the testing for other transformations show the compound to be highly persistent then, from an environmental hazard assessment point of view, these compounds can be considered essentially conservative and their estimated environmental concentration can be based on dilution-dispersion models.

For highly labile compounds which are biotransformed within a few minutes to a few hours, there is little need for kinetic data on the parent compound since it would not be expected to be present for a sufficient amount of time to have an adverse effect on aquatic organisms, except possibly under spill conditions or for contaminants associated with wastewater discharges or other highly concentrated inputs.

Sometimes a bioassay designed to measure acute toxicity can be a useful substitute for an analytical characterization of transformation products, in a hazard evaluation scheme. Since the primary concern in such a scheme is often toxicity to aquatic organisms, bioassays conducted on an 'environmentally aged' sample can provide valuable information on the potential hazard of transformation products of the chemical.

Consideration should be given in the higher tiers to assessing the potential of biotransformation of chemical transformation products. It is highly conceivable that hydrolysis or photolysis of a biologically persistent chemical could convert it to a form that could be readily attacked by microorganisms.

All biotransformation studies of persistent chemicals should be conducted in such a way as to provide for organism acclimation and co-metabolism. Further, it should be recognized that in some higher organisms, biotransformation may occur within the body organs (independent of, and different from, that associated with aquatic microorganisms). While, generally, emphasis should be given to evaluation of biotransformation under aerobic conditions, anaerobic transformations should be considered for persistent compounds in higher level tiers.

For certain types of compounds, such as chlorinated hydrocarbon pesticides, exposure to anaerobic conditions results in a dehalogenization which permits microbial transformation of the compounds under aerobic conditions. The environmental significance of such a phenomenon is not understood. While known to occur in laboratories, it does not appear that this phenomenon is of particular importance in the environment, otherwise there would not have been the world-wide accumulation of chlorinated hydrocarbon pesticides and PCBs in sediments. While these reactions have not eliminated the environmental contamination by these chemicals, they may have minimized their adverse impacts.

In formulating the rate expression for biotransformation reactions, the typical approach that is used for biochemical oxygen demand (BOD) formulation, involving a first order rate expression, should not be used. The rate of biotransformation of a compound is dependent on the enzyme activity within the system. Therefore, some measure of enzyme activity, such as the concentration of organisms present that can bring about a certain type of transformation, should be part of the rate expression. This means that the typical biotransformation rate expression should involve a second order formulation in which the rate of reaction is dependent not only on the substrate concentration but also on the enzyme activity within the sample.

In this regard it may be useful to have an estimate of overall aquatic microorganism activity levels. Further, there may be a general relationship between the classical oligotrophic-eutrophic classification of waterbodies and the transformation potential of aquatic systems for certain types of compounds. The bacterial populations of aquatic systems are closely correlated with the phyto-plankton production (Lee and Hoadley, 1967). In many waterbodies, there is a correlation between the normalized phosphorus load and the algal biomass (Vollenweider, 1976; Rast and Lee, 1978; Lee et al., 1978). It is possible that a relatively simple parameter such as planktonic algal chlorophyll or, for phos-phorus limited waterbodies, the normalized phosphorus load, could be an indi-cator of overall organism activity. But, since many chemical compounds, which are potentially hazardous to the environment, tend to be strongly sorbed by natural water particulate matter, the rate at which aquatic microorganisms transform the chemical may be greatly influenced. The development of biotrans-formation test procedures should therefore include an evaluation of the poten-tial significance of sorption reactions. This should include the influence of not only large (1 μm diameter) particles, but also colloidal particles.

X.4   Contaminant Availability to Higher Organisms

The following brief summary places the role of sediments, as a source of con-taminants in the aquatic environment, in perspective; but, because of the great range of compounds derived from man's activities and the variations in their distribution, it is not possible to be compound specific. These conclusions are modified after Lee and Jones (1979).

1) Some aquatic sediments, especially those near urban, industrial, mining or intensive agricultural centres, contain sufficient concentrations of various chemical contaminants which, if present in a biologically available form at a sufficient rate and for a long enough time, can represent significant environmental hazards.

2) Because of the small quantities of most toxic contaminants in sediments, even those of greatest environmental concern (such as PCBs, DDT, and heavy metals) usually do not adversely affect beneficial uses of a waterbody. However, in certain types of sediment, and under some conditions, sufficient release of contaminants can occur to adversely affect water quality for aquatic organisms and/or to impair the use of some aquatic organisms as a food for man. The amount and rate of contaminant release is not necessarily related to the total quantity of contaminant present in the sediment.

3) Although particulate phosphorus represents a significant fraction of the total phosphorus load in most aquatic systems, only a part of this fraction is available to support phytoplankton growth; the amount available is influenced by both mineral composition and the size of particulate material. Nitrogen is available from several sources; however, supply may control primary production under highly eutrophic conditions. There is evidence that it may often control primary production in the tropics.

4) The physical, chemical, and biological properties of deposited or suspended sediments, the properties of the overlying water, and the chemical of con-cern, all control the rate and extent of release of available forms of con-taminants from the sediment. One of the main factors governing release of sediment-associated contaminants to the water column is the amount of sedi-ment and interstitial water mixing with the overlying waters. Further, the presence of organics, oil, grease, and iron hydroxides, in combination with certain redox conditions, can control release-sorption reactions with the sediments, for many contaminants; biotransformations are of major importance.

5) The determination of many normally-measured sediment chemical characteris-tics, including the bulk chemical composition, is neither a suitable nor a technically valid basis for predicting the rate and extent to which sediment-associated contaminants may become available to affect water quality.

6) At the present time, a combination of a sediment leaching test (such as an elutriate test) and bioassays should be used to assess the extent of release, and potential significance, of nutrient and toxic contaminants in sediments.

7) The environmental hazard associated with the release of a contaminant from a deposited or suspended sediment must be judged in terms of the presence of biologically active forms (including transformations), their concentrations and duration of biological exposure to the contaminant(s). Worst case water quality criteria have little applicability in judging the significance of sediment-associated contaminants and their impact on water quality and biota.

8) While the use of lethal dose (LD_{50}) and lethal concentration (LC_{50}) bioassay tests are a useful means of assessing the short-term toxicity of sediments and sediment/water mixtures, they are not appropriate as a simulation of long-term exposure to low level concentrations of persistent contaminants. In these situations it will be particularly useful to make comparison with other case histories in which the environmental conditions and the nature of contaminants are similar to those under investigation, and for which sufficiently long periods of observations have been able to demonstrate the nature of biological impact (including human health).

References

* Cairns, J.; Dickson, K.L.; Maki, A.W. (eds.) 1978. Estimating the hazard of chemical substances to aquatic life. Amer. Soc. Testing Materials, Spec. Publ., No. 657. 278 pp.

Chiou, C.T.; Feed, V.H.; Schmedding, D.W.; Kohnert, R.L. 1977. Partition coefficient and bioaccumulation of selected organic chemicals. Environm. Sci. Technol., 11: p. 475-478.

* Kimerle, R.A.; Gledhill, W.E.; Levinskas, G.I. 1978. Environmental safety assessment of new materials. In: Cairns, J.; Dickson, K.L.; Maki, A.W. (eds.). Estimating the hazard of chemical substances to aquatic life. Amer. Soc. Testing Materials, Spec. Publ., No. 657: p. 132-146.

Lee, G.F.; Hoadley, A.F. 1967. Biological activity in relation to the chemical equilibrium composition of natural waters. In: Amer. Chem. Soc., Equilibrium concepts in natural water systems, Advances in Chem. Ser., No. 67: p. 319-338.

Lee. G.F.; Jones, R.A. 1979. Availability of chemical contaminant in sediments to higher oganisms. Unpubl. Rept., Colorado Sate Univ., Fort Collins, Colorado. 6 pp.

Lee, G.F.; Rast, W.; Jones, R.A. 1978. Eutrophication of water bodies: insights for an age-old problem. Environm. Sci. Technol., 12: p. 900-908.

Rast, W.; Lee, G.F. 1978. Summary analysis of the North American (U.S. portion) OECD Eutrophication project; Nutrient loading - lake response relationships and trophic state indices. U.S. Environm. Protect. Agency, EPA 600/3-78-009. 455 pp.

* Stumm, W.; Baccini, P. 1978. Man-made chemical perturbation of lakes. In: Lerman, A. (ed.), Lakes: chemistry, geology and physics, p. 91-126. Springer-Verlag, New York, Heidelberg, Berlin.

Vollenweider, R.A. 1976. Advances in defining critical loading levels for phosphorus in lake eutrophication. Mem. Ist. Ital. Idrobiol., 33: p. 53-83.

Ward, D.V. 1978. Biological environmental impact studies theory and methods. Acad. Press, New York, San Francisco, London. 157 pp.

* Suggested text for further reading.